Sawbones to Keyholes

The Presidents of the Nottingham Medico Chirurgical Society, 1828 - 2002

Researched and Compiled by
Paul Swift

First Published in Great Britain in 2003 by Barny Books
Text © Paul Swift
All rights reserved
Design © TUCANN*design&print*

ISBN N° 1 903172 27 6

Published by Barny Books, Hough on the Hill, Grantham, Lincolnshire
Produced by: TUCANN*design&print*, 19 High Street, Heighington Lincoln LN4 1RG
Tel & Fax: 01522 790009
www.tucann.co.uk

This work is dedicated to all of those
who practice the art of medicine.

CONTENTS

This section contains, reference to members of Nottingham Medical Book Society, the society which predates the Nottingham Medico-Chirurgical Society by eleven years. Part two contains references to all the presidents of the Nottingham Medico-Chirurgical Society from 1828 to 2002.

Included as well are the appendices. This section includes the titles of presidential addresses from 1885 to 1977, plus a text of some of the above mentioned addresses.

Finally, included in the appendices is a section entitled:- "Biographies of those within the medical profession whose names are mentioned within the texts of this research."

Acknowledgements

It is difficult to know where to start when thanking people who have been so generous with their time in helping me with my research. I shall start with thanking the President of the Society for 1997-98, Mr. John Bruce, for allowing me access to the society's archives. As my interest was initially drawn to the copies of photographs that form part of the society's archives, I would like to thank the staff of the Information Services, Resource Centre who were so generous with their time in helping me when I started by scanning the photographs on to floppy disks. It would also be appropriate to thank the staff of the Audio Visual Departments, both at the Queen's Medical Centre, Nottingham and at the Nottingham City Hospital, who have all been of great assistance in helping me put together an extensive archive of the past presidents of the society.

I would like to thank the staff of the Professor Greenfield Library at the Medical School, Queen's Medical Centre, Nottingham for their assistance.

This research not only involved me in taking frequent trips to the Medical School Library, but on two separate occasions to the Royal College of Surgeons of England in London. To have the chance to be able to work in such historical surrounds is something I shall look back on with great pride. The generosity of the library staff there with their time, help and research knowledge was for me a great privilege. I must also thank the Royal College of Physicians for passing on information about certain past presidents who were fellows of that Royal College.

I would like to thank the staff of the Local Studies Library on Angel Row, Nottingham.

The staff on the reception desk and the library staff at the Post Graduate Medical Centre, Nottingham City Hospital deserve a special mention.

There are two more people who deserve a very special mention. That is the Administrator for the Society, Ann Booth, and my friend David MacLean.

No writer can do without a friend and proof reader like David MacLean.

To both of you, thank you all very much for you assistance.

Finally, if there is anyone who hasn't been mentioned please accept my apologies. It is not that I've forgotten you, more that I've had so much advice and help from so many people, that to have to write down the names of each and every one of you would take, unfortunately, far too long for my readers' patience.

However, to you all, thank you very much.

Paul Swift,
Hon. Archivist.
Nottingham City Hospital,
January 2001.

PREFACE

For nearly two hundred years the Nottingham Medico-Chirurgical Society, the second oldest medical society in the country, has been at the hub of medical life in the City. Over this period it has been the chief meeting place for members of the medical profession, providing a centre for discussion, fellowship and, most importantly, continuing education. Under the guidance of successive Presidents, each usually serving for one year and drawn from various branches of the profession, the Society has organised educational and social programmes for its members. Indeed, until the 1960s and 70s, when formal postgraduate education became more generally available, local Medical Societies, such as the Nottingham Medico-Chirurgical Society, had a crucial role in ensuring that doctors "kept up to date."

With establishment of the new Medical School in Nottingham in the late 1960s, it was clear the Medico-Chirurgical Society would become an important link between "town and gown." This link was strengthened by the move to the Post Graduate Centre at the Nottingham City Hospital in 1972 and the sale of the Society's previous premises at 64, St. James's Street in 1973 which gave the Society financial security. This enabled a visionary President, Dr. James MacFie, to encourage the establishment of a Charitable Trust, which has subsequently enabled the Society to extend its educational activities with travelling scholarships, prizes and grants.

The early years of this new millennium sees the Society thriving as one of the most vigorous and successful in the United Kingdom and this account of the lives of its Presidents brings together many strands, not only of Nottingham medicine, but also much of Nottingham Life too. We learn much about the social and medical conditions of Victorian and Edwardian England. We learn of the scientific achievements of those physician-scientists such as William Henry Ransom FRS, who combined basic physiological research with the everyday care of patients. And, in more recent years, in the life of Tony Mitchell, Foundation Professor of Medicine, we are able to follow the development of the new Nottingham Medical School into one of the most prestigious in Europe.

The Nottingham Medico-Chirurgical Society is delighted that Paul Swift, as Honorary Archivist to the Nottingham City Hospital, has catalogued the lives of our Presidents. It is particularly gratifying to see the interest, skill and enthusiasm that he has brought to the task. It all began, he tells me, whilst moving chairs in the Council Room! He began to wonder what lay behind those photographs of the Presidents, which glared down so sternly on him from the walls. I have to say that some of the early faces do look so fierce and forebidding that they would surely have deterred weaker men!

Although the book "has been designed more as a reference book," it achieves much more than that. It is a window into every aspect of Nottingham Medical life. Paul Swift is to be congratulated on his efforts.

Peter Toghill.
President, Nottingham Medico-Chirurgical Society 1987-88.
Physician Emeritus, Queens Medical Centre

Introduction

***The Presidents of the Nottingham Medico
Chirurgical Society, 1828 - 2002.***

***Also with reference to members of the
Nottingham Medical Book Society, 1817.***

Finding the right way to put into words an introduction about the Presidents of one of Nottingham's Premier Medical Societies is somewhat difficult, especially when the person writing the introduction is not a member of the medical profession. I therefore feel the best way of starting this introduction is to say this is not a book about medicine but more about those who were figureheads in the development of medicine in Nottingham. The figureheads to whom I'm referring are, of course, the Presidents of the Nottingham Medico-Chirurgical Society.

This book is based on a collection of obituaries from two of medicine's premier medical journals, the Lancet and the British Medical Journal. Both these two journals give full and frank details of the educational and working lives of many individual Presidents. As all obituaries talk of individuals in the past tense I've adapted them so they appear as biographies. However, when a personal reminiscence is written by one of that person's former colleagues, I refer to the individual as *"in an obituary."* Not all Presidents had obituaries or notices of death published in the Lancet or the B.M.J., so it was necessary to research several other forms of written material. One source was death notices published in local papers such as the Nottingham Evening Post and other local papers which are now out of circulation. I decided to transcribe the text as it was written in the original publication at the time of their death. Also included in this work are biographies of Presidents adapted from the *"Contemporary Biographies"* which are held at the Local History Library, Nottingham. If a President were a fellow of either the Royal College of Physicians, London or the Royal College of Surgeons of England they would have a biography published in either the *"Lives of the Fellows of the Royal College of Surgeons"* or *"Munks Role - The Lives of the Fellows of the Royal College of Physicians."*

One of the former Presidents was a playing member of Nottinghamshire County Cricket Club. Not only was I able to write about that former President but also show his batting and bowling averages! In some cases the only available evidence was the entry from the *"Medical Directory"* which I used as primary source information in the early days of the project

My final sources of information were two books. The first, written by Frank Harwood Jacob (himself a President on two separate occasions) is entitled *"A History of the General Hospital, Nottingham."* The second was by another former President, Robert George Hogarth, entitled *"The Trent and I go wandering by."* This last source of information was useful as apart from it being an autobiography it also contained the full text of his inaugural address when he was made President of the British Medical Association in 1926. It has been designed more as a reference book.

This is about the people who were figureheads in the development of medicine in Nottingham;, showing a measure of the kind of person each was. For example when clinical trials were still being carried out on the tuberculin vaccine by the German Scientist Dr. Robert Koch . William Bramwell Ransom, President for the year 1896 travelled to Berlin to obtain phials of this new vaccine to treat his patients back home in Nottingham.

William Bramwell Ransom was not the first President to introduce new methods of treatment. The first significant introduction was established by the society's founder member, Dr. John Attenburrow. He was a keen follower of Edward Jenner, the discoverer of the smallpox vaccine in 1798, Dr Attenburrow established a "Vaccine Institution" for the sole purpose of paying for a surgeon for inoculating the children of the poor in 1805.

Another medical development was the introduction of Radiotherapy in 1901 by Robert George Hogarth (President, 1913). Hogarth was a forward-thinking man. In his inaugural address as President of the British Medical Association in 1926 he endorsed the idea of a National Health

Service, an idea that was to see him ostracised by his medical colleagues for a time. The formal establishment of the National Health Service took place on 5th July 1948.

This book is not just about individuals' efforts to establish medicine in Nottingham, there is also evidence of efforts to overcome the forces of prejudice. An excellent example of this was none other than the first lady President Dr. Sarah Gray, President for 1921 to 1922. In 1899 she was elected to her first public appointment at the Nottingham Womens' Hospital, where she was given the post of assistant surgeon in charge of outpatients or, as it was then called, the chloroformist. Her appointment was viewed by most of her colleagues with distrust. For a whole year one of them insisted on being present whenever she administered an anaesthetic. It could be said that the appointment of Dr. Sarah Gray as the Society's President in 1921 was living proof that women had become accepted in medicine.

It can be said that the establishment of the Nottingham Medico-Chirurgical Society in 1828 has not only been of great benefit to the people of Nottingham but has also been influential in establishing Nottingham as one of the world's leading centres of medical research and technology. These advancements in medical technology are still very much in progress. The story of the Nottingham Medico-Chirurgical Society goes on and with it a new generation to whom we turn to bear the torch that was lit 175 years ago.

This book, their story, continues.

Paul R. Swift,
Hon. Archivist,
Nottingham City Hospital.

A brief history of
The Nottingham Medico-Chirurgical Society

The Nottingham Medico-Chirurgical Society was founded on the 30th October, 1828. It was conceived from The Nottingham Medical Book Society, a society that was formed in 1817. Its original title was the Nottingham Medico-Chirurgical Book Society. The more familiar title of the Nottingham Medico-Chirurgical Society was adopted in 1884. It was not until May 20th, 1853 that the Society's founding principles were established.

This object was:- *"The cultivation and promotion of medicine and surgery and the auxiliary sciences: and the establishment of a library of works on the same subjects,"* to which was subsequently added:- *"the discussion of questions of medical policy and medical ethics."*

The establishment in 1828 of the Society brought the various disciplines of medical practice together. It wasn't until 1832 and the establishment of the Provincial Medical and Surgical Association, which in 1856 became the British Medical Association, that medicine in the provinces was taken seriously by the Royal Colleges. Without medical societies like the Nottingham Medico-Chirurgical Society and other similar societies, there would probably be no British Medical Association. The provincial medical societies were the grass roots of medicine in the UK.

The Society's first premises 64, St. James Street, Nottingham, were opened on 28th June, 1910 which was to be the Society's home for sixty-three years.

The Nottingham Medico-Chirurgical Society has been a society of considerable local influence in the advancement of medical practice. It has been in the vanguard of development of hospital and clinical based practice and teaching. Its proudest achievement is to have been involved in the development of the Medical School at the Queens Medical Centre in Nottingham from its conception in 1965 through to its opening in 1970. Professor Tony Mitchell, the Medical School's Foundation Professor of Medicine was the first academic to become president of the Society

The Society's involvement in establishing a faculty of medicine in Nottingham came as part of the Pickering report of 1965. Sir George Pickering, Regius Professor of Medicine at Oxford University, was selected to chair the Medical School Advisory Committee which published its report in 1965 recommending a Teaching Hospital and Medical School adjacent to the University Campus in Nottingham.

Travelling scholarships are awarded by the Society, not just to medical students to advance their medical knowledge, but also to those who are already qualified.

The Society has attracted many influential people involved in pioneering work within the field of medicine as guest speakers.

The Nottingham Medico- Chirurgical Society, to this day continues to go from strength to strength with ever increasing applications for membership. Its influence goes ever far and wide. It would be appropriate to end this brief history with a quote from the book written in 1978 to celebrate the Society's 175 years. It goes as follows:-

> *May all future members enjoy the same*
> *affection and regard for the Society as*
> *we who trod the narrow street and fusty*
> *corridors and may the Society remain an*
> *independent benevolent symbol of*
> *stability and competence.*

CONTENTS

APPENDICES

Biographies of those within the medical profession whose names are mentioned within the texts of this research.

JOHN STORER, M.D., F.R.S.

"Member of the Nottingham Medical Book Club"

The first Physician to the Nottingham General Hospital

John Storer was born at Kinross in 1747, the son of a minister of the church. He was educated in Scotland and studied theology at Glasgow University. His interests turned to the healing of the sick and he finally emerged from Glasgow with a Degree of Doctor of Medicine. His next ten years were spent in the Army Medical Service as a surgeon, much of the time with a Scottish regiment serving in Holland. Returning to civilian practice, he moved to Grantham in 1777. He finally settled in Nottingham. In 1781 where he quickly established himself as the leading medical practitioner in the town. He took an active part in the foundation of the General Hospital and became the institute's first physician in 1782. After 20 years of unstinting service he was appointed Consulting Physician Extraordinary for Life upon his retirement from the hospital in 1802. Besides his work for the hospital, John Storer helped to found and operate the Sneinton Lunatic Asylum and the Vaccination Institution. He became the first President of the Bromley House Subscription Library.

He carried on his practice at Thurland Hall, where he lived until his retirement in 1828. He died, aged 90, on 17th September 1837 and was buried in the village churchyard at Hawksworth, Nottinghamshire.

ALEXANDER MANSON M.D.

"Member of the Nottingham Medical Book Club"

Physician at the Nottingham General Hospital from 1813 to 1832.

Born in Scotland in 1774, Alexander Manson served in the Royal Navy for 13 years before settling in Nottingham to practice medicine. He became a physician at the Nottingham General Hospital in 1813, and carried out similar duties for the St. Mary's Workhouse Dispensary, which was situated on Mansfield Road below York Street. Manson pioneered the use of iodine as a cure for certain medical conditions. His surviving note books carry records of the many cases treated by him. In 1825 he published a reference book about his medical researches into the "effects of Iodine in Bronchocele, Paralysis, Chorea, Schropula, Fistula, Lachrymalis, Deafness, Dysphagia, White Swelling, and Distortions of the Spine."

On the 21st September 1813, during the disturbances of the Reform Riots, Dr. Manson, who was thought to be a supporter of the anti-Reformists, was stoned by an angry crowd of demonstrators as he drove his carriage along Pelham Street. Later that same evening his home in Stoney Street was attacked and the windows broken by a gang of marauding youths.

He resigned his appointments in the early 1830s and went to live at Darley Dale, Derbyshire, where he died in 1840 at the age of 66.

MARSHALL HALL
M.D., F.R.S., F.R.C.P.

Member of the
"Nottingham Medical Book Society"

Born, 18th February, 1790.   Died, 11th May, 1857.
M.D., Edinburgh, F.R.S., Edinburgh, F.R.C.P. (1841), F.R.S.

Born in Basford, Nottingham, Marshall Hall was the fourth son of Robert Hall, the first cotton manufacturer to use chlorine for bleaching on an extensive scale, and the brother of Samuel Hall, the inventor. His introduction to science took place through his apprenticeship to a Newark Chemist at the age of fourteen. At Edinburgh University, which he entered in 1809, he distinguished himself by becoming senior president of the Royal Medical Society. As a student he showed a penetrating curiosity in matters outside his syllabus - particularly in the laws governing chemical affinities. The Edinburgh Royal Infirmary gave him the coveted post of resident house physician when he qualified in 1812. A year later he delivered a course of lectures on diagnosis which formed the framework of his publication on this subject in 1817. On leaving Edinburgh in 1814 he spent a year visiting continental medical schools including those at Paris, Gottingen and Berlin.

Hall's first experience of general practice was at Bridgewater. He returned to Nottingham in 1817. He built up both a fine reputation and a large practice on the success resulting from his disapproval of general blood-letting. His conclusions, set forth in *The Effects of Loss of Blood* (1824), were influential in revolutionising the professional attitude to blood-letting. In 1825 he was appointed physician to the Nottingham General Hospital but in the following year he moved to London. It was in the field of research that Hall achieved worldwide fame. Papers on blood-letting and a work on the *Diseases of Females* appeared before 1830. In 1832, observation of the muscular movements of a dead newt led him to a discovery of the first magnitude - that of reflex action. His words on this subject roused much controversy: The Royal Society refused to publish two of his papers and no London hospital would give him a physician's appointment. For some years he was more highly regarded abroad than in his own country. His books, which included *Principles and Practice of Medicine* (1837) and *Practical Observations in Medicine* (1845-46) were widely translated. After his election to F.R.C.P., however, he became Goulstonian Lecturer (1842) and Croonian Lecturer (1850-52) and, from 1842 to 1846, he lectured at St. Thomas's Hospital. Active and versatile, Hall devised a method of artificial respiration and campaigned against slavery, the flogging of soldiers and open railway carriages. Though a stout fighter for his views, he was a man of great simplicity of character and genuine humility. He married Charlotte, daughter of Valentine Green of Normanton-le-Heath, Leicestershire. They had one son.

JOHN HIGGINBOTTOM F.R.S., F.R.C.S.

Member of the Nottingham Book Club
and the
Nottingham Medico-Chirurgical Society

John Higginbottom (1788-1876) was born at Ashton-under-Lyne on the 14th June. His father was known as "the honest lawyer." John also had very independent views which prevented his election to the staff of the General Hospital. He campaigned most vigorously against the medicinal use of alcohol and compared it with indiscriminate venesection which his brother-in-law, Marshall Hall, did much to abolish. In a letter to the Nottingham Free Press in 1860 he complained of £430 spent on wines, spirits and ales during the past year by the Nottingham Board of Guardians. He said that "the old system of blood letting had destroyed hundreds of valuable lives and that the present plan of alcoholizing patients is destroying thousands." In March 1855, he read a paper before the Nottingham Medico-Chirurgical Society on the treatment of fevers, uterine haemorrhage, and delirium tremens without the use of alcohol stimulants. This led to animated discussion. He was challenging authority. Though never president of the Nottingham Medico-Chirurgical Society himself, his son Marshall Hall Higginbottom held this office in 1856.

John Higginbottom practised in Nottingham from 1810. A man of high character and great energy, he remained active in his profession to within a few years of his death on 7th April, 1876, aged 86.

PRESIDENTS OF THE NOTTINGHAM MEDICO-CHIRURGICAL SOCIETY

WITHOUT BIOGRAPHIES OR PHOTOGRAPHS

1. **John Caunt:-** "President of the Nottingham Medico-Chirurgical Society," **1852.** Wheeler Gate, Nottingham: M.R.C.S., and L.S.A., 1825

2. **John Charles Long Marsh:-** President, **1854.** Nottingham, M.R.C.S., England, 1845; L.S.A., 1846.

3. **William Phillimore Stiff:-** President, **1858.** Resident Physician, County Asylum, Nottingham. M.B., London, 1845; M.R.C.S., England and L.S.A., 1842. Contributor "On the Nature and Treatment of Scabies," Medical Times. 'On the Scurvy Endemic at Nottingham," Medical Times, 1847.

4. **Thomas Wilson:-** President, **1859.** Derby Road, Nottingham; M.D., St. Andrews, 1848; M.R.C.S., England, and L.S.A., 1836. Formerly, Resident Surgeon, Nottingham General Hospital.

5. **John Ellam:-** President, **1862.** Sneinton Place, Nottingham. L.R.C.P., London, 1861; M.R.C.S., England, 1842, L.S.A., 1843.

6. **J. Issac Massey:-** President, **1868-9 and 1872/5.** Wellington Circus, Nottingham. M.D., St. Andrew's , 1846; M, 1831; L.S.A., 1831. (University College and Paris). Surgeon, Nottingham County Gaol; Senior Consulting Surgeon, Nottingham Dispensary; Surgeon, South Nott's Hussars Regiment.

   Late Consulting Surgeon, Nottingham Union Hospital. Contributor "Case of Successful Application of a Ligature on Femoral Artery, for a Wound of Anterior Tiberal Artery." Lancet, 1849; "Ivory Exotosis of Fibula, and removal of 8 + inches in length of bone," "On Fluid in Thyroid Body," Guy's Hospital.

Information from the Medical Directories,
1849, 1850, 1854, 1858, 1862 and 1868.

JOHN ATTENBURROW
**Founder Member of the
Nottingham Medico-Chirurgical Society**

JOHN ATTENBURROW

(1756-1843)
Founder member of the Nottingham Medico-Chirurgical Society

Freedom of the City of Nottingham

March 25th, 1799:

"The great mortality that has prevailed amongst the children of the poor from smallpox in the town of Nottingham this winter, has induced the Medical Gentlemen to give their consent to a plan proposed for the inoculation of the children of the town and the neighbourhood. Notice is therefore given that such poor who wish to avail themselves of the opportunity now offered must apply at the Hospital on Tuesday mornings of April and September of the year."

(Nottingham Date Book)

John Attenburrow, a keen follower of Edward Jenner, was senior surgeon to the General Hospital for sixty-one years from 1782 to 1843. He undertook to vaccinate his fellow-townsmen against smallpox in the year 1800. When Attenburrow began his period of inoculation he had to overcome the prejudices from women of all ages. To overcome this prejudice he vaccinated his own son twice and the son of Mr. Charles Baxter, who kept the Cordwainer's Arms public-house on Tollhouse Hill. In both cases the results were successful. Mothers began to flock to John Attenburrow's Surgery on Beastmarket Hill for their children to be inoculated. Instead of making a charge, Attenborrow thanked them for their attendance.

If a child became inflicted with smallpox, its mother was "branded an enemy to her own child, under the impression that its affliction was the consequence of her own obstinacy or neglect."

As a result of John Attenburrow's influence, in 1805 a 'Vaccine Institution' was set up for the purpose of paying a surgeon for inoculating the children of the poor. In 1813 this institution was brought to a close for want of subscriptions to carry it on. At the same time a medical establishment was formed at St. Mary's workhouse by the overseers of the parish where the children of the poor were vaccinated.

"In 1872, the fever block was filled with smallpox and there were 500 cases in the town, most of them housed in a temporary hospital which was built over what is now the tunnel on the Great Central Railway. All cases coming into the General wards, were vaccinated at once and every member of the staff was re-vaccinated on joining up. The result was that no single case occurred in the hospital. I had come from Bath, where there was no smallpox, having previously worked in South Wales, where they had some 50 deaths a week."

(From the Reminiscences by Dr. Lewis Marshall, Resident Surgeon at the General Hospital from 1871 to 1877.)

GODFREY HOWITT, M.D., Edinburgh
The First President of the Nottingham
Medico-Chirurgical Society 1829 - 1839

Godfrey Howitt, (1800-1873), was the first president of the Nottingham Medico Chirurgical Society from 1828 to 1839. When, with his brother Richard, a druggist and a poet, he migrated to Australia on 30th August 1839.

Godfrey Howitt was one of the six sons of Thomas Howitt of Heanor in Derbyshire who resuscitated the fortunes of an old but generously spend-thrift county family by marrying Phoebe Tantum, an heiress of the Society of Friends. As required by the regulations he became a Quaker. Another brother was William (1795-1879) also a druggist and a poet.

Godfrey Howitt was physician to the Nottingham General Hospital from 1829 to 1839 and was keenly interested in science and literature. He wrote the standard work, The Flora of Nottinghamshire, and discovered a new species of catchfly which grew on the Castle Rock. Professor John Wilson described him as "Ane o' the best botanists in England an' a desperate beetle hunter." His ardent love for collecting accompanied him to Australia and he bequeathed his natural history collection and library to the Melbourne Museum (The Howitt Collection). He also gave £1,000 to found scholarships in Natural History in the University. In 1847 he became one of the first physicians to the Melbourne Hospital and had the experience of being paid his fees in gold dust by miners who consulted him professionally.

JOHN CALTHORPE WILLIAMS
"1801 to 1856"

President of the Nottingham Medico-Chirurgical Society
1851

John CALTHORPE Williams:- Nottingham. Fellow of the Royal College of Surgeons, Edinburgh. Graduate of the University of Edinburgh, 1824 Physician to the Nottingham General Hospital and Visiting Physician to the Nottingham Lunatic Asylum. Author of "Practical Observations on Nervous and Sympathetic Palpitations of the Heart."

Medical Directory, 1849.

John Calthorpe Williams was born in Nottingham in 1801 and died 1856. He was the second surviving son of William Williams, M.D. and a member of the Royal College of Surgeons, who practised in Nottingham. Nottinghamshire Directories of 1814, 1818, and 1825 mention W. Williams Surgeon, at Rose Place, Bridlesmith Gate.

J. C. Williams was educated at Repton School under the Reverend Boulthee Sleath, M.D. In his book on palpitations of the heart, Williams states that he was a pupil of Dr. Marsden at the Nottingham General Hospital "sixteen years ago." That would appear to be 1819 or 1820. In his preface Williams says that he was at Edinburgh in 1818. He took his degree at Edinburgh in August, 1824. He practised in Sheffield. On the death of Dr. Pennington, he moved to Nottingham where he lived until his death.

He published a pamphlet in 1827 (which is now in the possession of the Public Library) entitled *A letter to the governors of the Hospital, ie. the* General Hospital, *being a brief collection of medical evidence, proving the safety and propriety of Establishing Fever Wards in connection with general infirmaries.* In a list of physicians in the Nottinghamshire directory for 1829, his address is given as Pelham Street. His name is spelt Calthrop. On the cover of the pamphlet, Williams is described as "Extraordinary member of the Royal Medical Society, Edinburgh."

About 1833-5 a medical school was established in Nottingham with premises in St. James's Street and, in his book on the palpitation of the heart, Williams states that the material in the book was originally a course of lectures that he gave there. He describes himself as "lecturer on the principles and practice of physic." Despite such a distinguished patron as the Duke of Newcastle, the idea of a Nottingham Medical School fell through.

Williams married Anne, eldest daughter of Reverend George Sanders, rector of Wollaton. They had five children - two sons and three daughters. Both sons went to Merchant Taylors School. The Merchant Taylors School register give the following information: "William Rhys Williams, born 7th March, 1839, was admitted to the school in December 1848. He had an Exhibition to St. Thomas's Hospital, 1855. M.D. St. Andrews 1862; L.K.Q.C.P. Ireland, 1865; M.R.C.P. Edinburgh, 1866, Commissioner in Lunacy, 1878." The register states that George was "elected to St. John's Oxford, 1857; elected to Ceylon Civil Service, 1861; Assistant Government Agent at Badulla, 1873."

In the Directory for the City of Nottingham of 1840 it says that John Calthorp Williams of Rose Place, Bridlesmith Gate was "Honorary Physician to Nottingham Dispensary, the General Hospital and the Union Workhouse." The Dispensary was built in 1831 but the Workhouse, begun in 1840, was not completed until 1843.

John Williams M.D. appears as physician to the Hospital, 1843 onwards. Presumably the position was held until 1856 - his death.

> 1856: July 30th. Death of Dr. J. C. Williams, physician of Nottingham through a fall from his carriage near the top of Derby Road the previous evening.

> Condensed from *Nottingham Reviews* of July 25 and August 1st 1856 is the following information:

> Dr. Williams was returning from Wollaton Hall, the home of Lord Middleton whose physician he was when, probably as a result of the behaviour of the horse, he tried to step out of the carriage. He slipped and fell, hitting his head and becoming unconscious. This occurred on Sunday, 20th July. He was buried on Friday, July 25th, in the family vault on the south side of St. Peter's Churchyard.

Dr. Williams was appointed Honorary Physician to the Nottingham General Hospital in 1840; in succession to Godfrey Howitt who had gone to Australia four years after he had written his book.

BOOTH EDDISON

**President of the Nottingham Medico-Chirurgical Society
1853**

Booth Eddison:- High Pavement, Nottingham M.R.C.S., 1835; F.R.C.S. (by exam), 1844; L.S.A., 1829. L.R.C.S., Edinburgh, 1829, Formerly House Surgeon, Nottingham General Hospital.

Booth Eddison, F.R.C.S.

Mr. Booth Eddison, who had been an apprentice 1822-7, held the post now called Resident Surgeon and Apothecary, from 1829 till 1832. He afterwards procured by examination his qualification as member of the Royal College of Surgeons in 1835 and Fellow in 1844. He was elected Honorary surgeon to the Nottingham General Hospital, 1851-9. He was also visiting Surgeon and proprietor of Broom House Private Asylum, Mansfield, Nottinghamshire, and was a member of the Botanical Society. He was President of the British Medical Association, 1857.

In 1851 he showed his foresight and did good service to the General Hospital by securing the site of the old reservoir for £150 and afterwards selling it to the Hospital for the same price, thus securing for the Hospital this very valuable site for its extension in 1875.

A History of the General Hospital near Nottingham,
By Frank Jacob.
Page 123.

WILLIAM HENRY RANSOM F.R.S.
President of the Nottingham
Medico-Chirurgical Society 1855, 1965 & 1887

Born, 19th November, 1823. Died, 16th April, 1907.
M.D. London, F.R.C.P. (1869), F.R.S.

William Henry Ransom was born in Cromer in 1823 and educated at a private school at Norwich. At the age of 16 Dr. Ransom was apprenticed to a doctor at King's Lynn. His father was the captain and owner of a ship. His mother was the daughter of a clergyman. In 1834 he became a student at University College, London, where he graduated in 1848, taking the degree of M.D. Huxley was a fellow student

During 1848 and 1849 Dr. Ransom pursued his studies on the continent, first in Germany and then in France, obtaining a competent knowledge of the language of each country which enabled him to follow the medical and scientific literature of the continent. He also made the acquaintance of many leading figures.

He settled in Nottingham in 1850 and took the house in Low Pavement. He did a good deal of laboratory work and had a couple of rooms fitted up for chemical and physiological study. Amongst the subjects he studied was the early development of ova of fish, the result of his investigations being published in the *Royal Society's Proceedings* of 1867 and in 1870 he was elected Fellow of the Society. Dr. Ransom took a prominent part in the first meeting of the British Association in Nottingham in 1866.

In 1869 Dr. Ransom was elected a Fellow of the Royal College of Physicians of London and subsequently became a Fellow of the

Royal Medical and Chirurgical Society and of University College.

In 1892, when the British Medical Association held its Annual Meeting in Nottingham, Dr. Ransom was President of the Section of Medicine. In his address he alluded to the subject of vegetable morbid growths and their relation to human pathology - a subject he developed much more widely during the last few years of his life. In the course of a strenuous life Dr. Ransom helped to explore the caves of Nottinghamshire and Derbyshire. In the course of his investigations he discovered the jawbone of the lynx believed to be the only one found in England and this probably unique specimen is now in the Nottingham Natural History Museum.

In 1854 he was elected physician to the General Hospital in succession to Dr. Gill, a position he retained up to 1890 when he retired and was appointed an honorary consulting physician, being succeeded by his son, Dr. W. B. Ransom.

It is as a successful consulting physician of more than forty years that Dr. Ransom will be best remembered both by his patients and the numerous members of the medical profession who sought his advice in Nottingham, Nottinghamshire, and the neighbouring counties. Pre-eminent in diagnosis, his self reliance and confidence gave confidence to his patients. Sometimes impatient and occasionally brusque, especially in his early years, he was one of the kindest and most genial of men. Always attracted by the scientific side of medicine. Full use was made of the aids to diagnosis afforded by the collateral sciences. Like most men of unbounded energy combined with unusual mental powers, he naturally took the lead in whatever position he was placed. The enlargement and remodelling of the General Hospital in the late 1870s was mainly directed by his wide knowledge and experience and resulted in a building in which ornament was subordinated to the principles of hospital hygiene. It is a credit to his foresight and to his appreciation of the importance of keeping in the vanguard of sanitary progress that the wards he designed remain well abreast of modern requirements. He remained the leading and moving spirit in all matters connected with the General Hospital for many years.

He became sceptical about the truth of the opinion that cold was the general cause of many diseases. In 1887 he published a paper on "Cold as the Cause of Disease," in which he pointed out that such a doctrine was a gross exaggeration. In recent years the part played by bacteria in the cause of pneumonia and the success of open air treatment of consumption have done much to bring round the profession to his point of view.

The death from scarlet fever of two of his children in 1870 was a severe blow. It stimulated him to study the subject of infection and led him to devise a hot-air disinfecting stove, heated by gas, which was widely used in this country until superseded by steam.

Dr. Ransom was one of the first to join the Robin Hood Rifles in 1859, and he continued as a private in the regiment for fifteen years. Side by side with him on that first parade was the late Right Honorable A. J. Mundella. In the early 1860s Dr. Ransom became a keen politician throwing his whole hearted energies on the side of Liberalism. He appeared on the hustings in the market place to nominate Viscount Amberley, and made a speech in support of reform.

Dr. Ransom was interested in education and was involved in the foundation of the Nottingham Literary and Philosophic Society. He took an active part in the founding the Nottingham University College and was on the governing body of that institution and of the High School.

In an obituary to Dr. Ransom it was said:- "No account of Dr. Ransom could be complete which failed to record the remarkable happiness of his disposition - he was always bright, cheerful and contented. In 1860 he married Miss Elizabeth Bramwell, sister of an old college friend. Mrs. Ransom died eighteen years before Dr. Ransom. Three sons survived - Dr. W. B. Ransom, Senior Physician to the General Hospital; Mr. D'Oyley Ransom, solicitor of Nottingham; and Mr. Herbert Ransom, who is an engineer in London.

MARSHALL HALL HIGGINBOTTOM
(1822 - 1895)
President of the
Nottingham Medico-Chirurgical Society 1856

*This information is from an obituary which appeared
in the Nottingham Evening Post, 25th February, 1895*

The death of Mr. Marshall Hall Higginbottom, surgeon, at his residence, 56, Shakespeare Street, at the age of 72, will remind many of the older residents of one who was highly esteemed as a local practitioner. He was, one of the eldest members of the profession in Nottingham. He had been ailing for some years. His death yesterday was the result of a second attack of pneumonia. The late Mr. Higginbottom was born in 1822, and was a son of John Higginbottom, F.R.S.. Mr. Higginbottom studied at Guy's and St. Thomas's Hospitals, and commenced practice in Nottingham with his father. He travelled for some time, going to Madeira, Constantinople, and various places in the East. He married Harriet Gregory the youngest daughter of Mr. John Hall, surgeon, of Sheffield, who was brother to Dr. Marshall Hall. Mr. Higginbottom outlived most of his old friends and those who knew him during his professional career, but he was always spoken of with the greatest esteem. He leaves a widow and one daughter, who married the Rev. E. B. Braithwaite, Vicar of Bardsey, near Leeds.

TOM WRIGHT
President of the
Nottingham Medico-Chirurgical Society 1857

"The Wrights"

Tom Wright, President of the Nottingham Medico-Chirurgical Society, 1857.

William Wright, President of the Nottingham Medico-Chirurgical Society, 1867.

No less than four members of the Wright family were surgeons to the Nottingham General Hospital: Thomas from 1782 to 1819, his brother John from 1795 to 1819, William (1794-1868) from 1819 to 1866, and his son Thomas from 1851 to 1905; so that from a period of 123 years there was a Wright surgeon to the Hospital. William Wright used to disappear from Nottingham for a week at a time, riding off on his rounds to Southwell, Newark, and elsewhere, and home by Mansfield.

Centenary of the Nottingham Medico-Chirurgical Society

Dr Tom Wright threw himself into the volunteer movement when it sprang into birth at the period of a threatened national peril in 1859. He joined the Robin Hood Rifles upon the formation of the battalion, attaching himself as a private to the Doctors' Company. He was appointed Honorary Surgeon to the battalion in 1860, rising gradually to the rank of Surgeon Lt-Colonel. He retired in 1893.

Dr. Wright was well known in volunteer circles as a skilful marksman. He won a number of prizes at Wimbledon. In 1865 he shot with the English team for the National trophy. He was a member of each of the teams that won the Belgian Challenge Cup in 1877 and 1879. He won the Bronze Medal of the National Rifle Association and was the first winner of the Locksley Cup.

He was interested in the development of the Ambulance and Hospital departments.

In 1892 Queen Victoria conferred on him the Volunteer Officers decoration.

On Thursday, February 23rd, 1893, the officers of the Robin Hood Rifles entertained Colonel Wright at Mess and afterwards presented him with a handsome token of their regard, on the occasion of his retirement from the ranks of the regiment in which he had held a commission for 33 years. The gathering was presided over by Colonel Cantrell-Hubersty.

A true sportsman, Dr. Wright was devoted to fishing, a pastime which he followed until quite a recent period before his death. Indeed only in September, 1910 he was out with the rod. Salmon fishing appealed to him greatly and he also took keen enjoyment in deer-stalking. He participated in some of the best shooting in the neighbourhood.

He was the President of the old Nottingham Club. His character and genial disposition gained him respect of all that knew him.

A venerable figure was Tom Wright. I once *(the author, F. Jacob)* had the honour of seeing him. What an opportunity I missed of learning about the practice of surgery and the history of our hospital (General Hospital) from the day of its opening in 1782: but I was not much interested in the past at that time. He was then some 80 years of age, a finely built, tall, erect man.

A great fisherman and still made his yearly trip to Blagdon reservoir near Bristol, where he fished for big trout.

In 1910 the Monthly Board expressed its appreciation of the Wright brothers saying that: "They discharged their duties in a manner that gained them the respect and esteem of everyone connected with the City and County."

Tom Wright was appointed Honorary Consulting Surgeon to the Hospital when he retired in March, 1891.

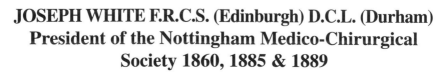

**JOSEPH WHITE F.R.C.S. (Edinburgh) D.C.L. (Durham)
President of the Nottingham Medico-Chirurgical
Society 1860, 1885 & 1889**

Joseph White, Oxford Street, Nottingham Fellow of the Royal College of Surgeons, Edinburgh, 1866, Licentiate, 1847; Licentiate of the Society of Apothecaries, 1847 Honorary Doctor of Civil Law, Durham, 1893; Former President of the British Medical Association. Consulting Surgeon to the Nottingham General Hospital. Author of *"Heredity in Disease."* Contributor to "Medical Topography of Nottingham," *Transcripts Provided by the Medical Association* "Statistics of Amputations." *Medical Times Gazette,"* 1855; *"Action of Chloroform,"* British Medical Journal, 1857.

The Medical Directory, 1894.

Joseph White, 6, Southwell Gardens, Queens Gate, Kensington, S.W. Former Consulting Surgeon to the Nottingham General Hospital.

The Medical Directory, 1899.

The death is announced as having taken place on Sunday last at Eastbourne, in the seventy-seventh year of his age of Mr. Joseph White, D.L.C. Durham , F.R.C.S., Edinburgh, and former President of the British Medical Association and Consulting Surgeon to the Nottingham General Hospital.

The Lancet, September 30th, 1899.
Page 903.
Also reported in the British Medical Journal,
September 30th, 1899, page 890.

SIR WILLIAM TINDAL ROBERTSON F.R.C.P, M.P.
President of the
Nottingham Medico-Chirurgical Society 1861

Born 1825, Died 6th October, 1889.
M.D., Edinburgh, M.R.C.S., L.S.A., F.R.C.P. (1874), J.P., M.P.

William Tindal Robertson:- Wheeler Gate, Nottingham. M.D., London, 1853; External L.R.C.P., London (exam) M.R.C.S., England, 1850; L.S.A., 1848; (University College, London and Edinburgh) Physician, Nottingham General Hospital; Consultant Physician, Dispensary and Union Hospital; Honorary Physician, Midland Blind Asylum. Medical Referee to several Assurance Societies. Formerly:- Resident Medical Officer, Royal Free Hospital, London; and Junior Resident Medical Officer, Middlesex Hospital. Author:- "Sanitary Science," being the Address in Medicine delivered before the British Medical Association, 1857. Contributor:- "On a case of Diffused Aneurysm," Lancet, 1851; "Reports on Epidemic Diseases in Nottingham," Journal of Public Health, 1855-6.

Medical Directory 1861

William Tindal Robertson was born at Bath, the eldest son of Frederick Fowler Robertson and his wife Anne Tindal. He was educated at King Edward VI's Grammer School, Grantham, and University College, London. He qualified in 1848 and served in junior appointments at the Middlesex and Royal Free Hospitals. He then completed his medical training with visits to Paris and Edinburgh proceeding to his M.D. degree in 1853. In the following year he settled in Nottingham, where for nearly twenty years he acted as physician to the General Hospital. He took a leading part in local affairs: he was a member of the town council, promoted the formation of the Robin Hood Rifles and helped to found the Nottingham Literary and Philosophical Society. He retired to Brighton on account of failing eyesight in 1873, but continued to concern himself with municipal and political matters, although he eventually became blind. He was chosen as chairman of the Brighton Conservative Association in 1880 and six years later was returned unopposed to Parliament as representative of the borough. He was knighted in 1888. Robertson married in 1855 Elizabeth Ann, daughter of John Leavers of Nottingham, by whom he had four sons.

**THOMAS APPLEBY STEPHENSON M.D.
(1832 - 1908)
(Edinburgh) M.R.C.S. President of the Nottingham
Medico-Chirurgical Society 1863, 1881 & 1883**

Thomas Appleby Stephenson:- George Street, Nottingham M.R.C.S., England and L.S.A., 1855. (St. Bartholomew's and University of Edinburgh), Surgeon, Nottingham Eye Dispensary; Surgeon Nottingham Provincial Medical Aid Institute. Medical Referee, British Nation, Star, Albert and Medical and Mutual Provident Alliance Assurance Companies. President of the Nottingham Medico-Chirurgical Society.

Medical Directory, 1862

This information is from an obituary that appeared in the Nottingham Evening News, 11th September, 1908.

We regret to announce the death of Dr. Thomas Appleby Stephenson, at the age of 76, at his house in Midway Park, London, N.

The deceased gentleman was at one time a very familiar figure in Nottingham social circles, being amongst other things a prominent member of the Mechanics Committee and of the Liberal Club. He was also connected with the Literary Club when the institution was in existence.

For some 45 years Dr. Stephenson practiced in Nottingham, and quit the city for the Metropolis about six years ago. He was twice married, firstly to Miss Manlove and then to Miss Walsh, of Bristol, both of whom he survived.

His son, Mr. Sydney Stephenson, practices as a surgeon in North London.

Local Studies Library, Angel Row, Nottingham.

E.C. BUCKOLL M.A C.S., L.S.A.
President of the
Nottingham Medico-Chirurgical Society 1864

Edward Charles Buckoll: Sneiton Road, Nottingham
M.R.C.S., England, 1851; L.S.A. 1853, (Kings College).
Surgeon, Nottingham Provincial Medical Aid Institute; Medical Officer, Radford Union. Late Resident Surgeon, Nottingham General Dispensary. Vice President o the Nottingham Medico-Vhirurgical Society.

Medical Directory, 1862

JAMES BEDDARD M.B., F.R.C.S.
President of the Nottingham
Medico-Chirurgical Society 1866, 1879, 1880

James Beddard was born in 1840 at Dudley, West Midlands, and was apprenticed to Drs Fereday and Timmins in that town, then with Webster at Towyn in North Wales. He entered Guy's Hospital Medical School in 1856, where he graduated in 1863, taking the scholarship in surgery at the time that his contemporary and friend Philip Henry Pye-Smith (1840-1914) took the gold medal in medicine and in surgery. His son, Arthur Philip Beddard later senior physician to Guy's Hospital, was Pye-Smith's godchild and named after him. James Beddard was elected surgical registrar at Guy's, but resigned and settled down in Nottingham where an old friend of his Dudley days, the Reverend Francis Morse, had recently been appointed Vicar of St Mary's. He was President of the Nottingham Medico-Chirurgical Society in 1866, 1879 and 1880, surgeon to the General Hospital, consulting surgeon to the Children's Hospital, and at one time President of the Literary and Philosophical Society.

He was taken ill after a shooting holiday in Scotland with symptoms diagnosed as appendicitis. He died at his home on the 21st June 1889.

James Beddard:- MRCS, April 30th, 1861: FRCS, June 9th, 1864: LSA, 1863; MB, London (Scholar in Surgery and 1st Class Honours in Medicine), 1863

Received his professional training at Guy's Hospital, London. He was at one time Medical Tutor at Sydenham College, Birmingham, and afterwards practised at Nottingham (39 Derby Road, and later Park Row), where he was Surgeon to the General Hospital and Consulting Surgeon to the Children's Hospital. He died in 1889.

From
Plarr's Lives of the Fellows of the
Royal College of Surgeons of England

WILLIAM WRIGHT F.R.C.S.
**President of the
Nottingham Medico-Chirurgical Society 1867**

William Wright (1794-1868). M.R.C.S., December 2nd, 1814; F.R.C.S., December 11th, 1843, one of the original 300 Fellows.

Practiced in Nottingham, where he was Surgeon to the General Hospital, becoming Consulting Surgeon, his opinion continued to be highly and deservedly valued throughout the Midland Counties. He died at 40, Pelham Street, Nottingham, on January 7th, 1888.

**From
Plaar's Lives of the Fellows
of the
Royal College of Surgeons of England**

GEORGE EATON STANGER

President of the Nottingham Medico-Chirurgical Society
1870/1-1876/8.

George Eaton Stanger:- M.R.C.S., England and L.S.A. 1840; (Guy's); Consultant Surgeon Nottingham Dispensary.

*****

George Eaton Stanger:- North Circus Street, Nottingham. M.R.C.S., England and L.S.A. (Guy's); Senior Consultant Surgeon, Nottingham Dispensary.

Medical Directories for 1868 & 1881

*****

George Eaton Stanger was born and baptized at the Fleet Baptist Chapel N.C. on the 15th of April 1816. He was one of ten children, five brothers and five sisters.

George Eaton Stanger studied medicine in London. In 1844 his address in Nottingham was Carlton Street. In 1846 he was on the list of members for the Nottingham Medico-Chirurgical Society.

In 1844 he married Mary Hurst, the eldest daughter of Nathan and Sarah Hurst, a very prominent family in Nottingham. Her father was a hosier and Baptist preacher. Her brothers, Nathan and John followed in their father's profession in the hosiery trade and were both aldermen. John, was also a member of the Nottingham Board of Guardians and on the Committee for the Nottingham Racecourse, which at that time was sited at what is now the Forest Recreation Ground. In 1845/6 Nathan was one of the Sheriffs of Nottingham. Mary was one of nine children who all married people with influence in public life.

In the 1851 census returns the Stanger family were registered as living in St. James Street, Nottingham. By then they had, three sons, William, George Hurst and Henry York. They employed three female servants, and a dispensary was attached to their residence.

By 1861 they had moved to North Circus Street mainly due to an addition of five children in the family. They were Margaret Ann, Mary Elizabeth, Charles Edward, Walter and Harriet.

George Eaton Stanger was elected president of the Nottingham-Medico Chirurgical Society twice. Once, 1870/71 and again between 1876/8. In 1881 he was elected vice-president and honorary treasurer. He held this post until the announcement of his retirement in 1888. His practice address was then 67, Gregory Boulevard, and came under the title of Stanger and Son, the son being Charles Edward.

After his retirement he and his wife went to live in London.

It is recorded that at the time of his death in 1892 he was possibly on a visit to his son William. All his estate was left to his wife Mary for her lifetime. Trust funds were made out to Margaret Ann, and Harriet. These were valid under one stipulation, they were to never marry.

From information provided by Mrs. Maureen Hurst, East Leake, Loughborough

cal Society, Edinburgh. Late:- Tutor, Queen's College, Birmingham.

October 15th, 1915 was a very sad day for Dr. Handford.

The 8th Battalion Sherwood Foresters (Territorial) were mobilized at the onset of war. On February 25th, 1915 they went to France and were in the thick of fighting until the end of the war.

On October 15th they took part in the disastrous attack on the Hohenzollern Redoubt. On that day, Dr. Handford's two sons, Captain Basil Handford and Lieutenant Everard Handford were killed. "Two of the most promising young officers in the Battalion."

October 15th was a sad day for many Nottinghamshire homes. Life was never the same for Dr. Handford after this deadly blow.

Dr. Handford's son-in-law, Major John Becher, was mortally wounded and died on January 1st, 1916 - "In John Becher the Battalion lost one beloved of us all, who throughout ever had at heart the welfare of his men, whether in or out of the trenches, at work or at play."

(History of the 1/8th Battalion Sherwood Foresters, 1914 - 1919,
by Captain W. C. C. Weetman.)

[1] Sir Humphrey Rolleston wrote about Henry Handford:-

He was very active at the old Pathological Society of London, and in March, 1884, read a paper to the Nottingham Medico-Chirurgical Society on "Bacteria" which was followed by much discussion. The Hospital Report under the date of April, 1906, contain the following memorandum:-

The Board deeply regrets to report that owing to his having received an appointment under the Nottinghamshire County Council, Dr. Handford has found it necessary to resign his position as an Honorary Physician of the Hospital, which he held with such distinction for upwards of twenty years. While he upheld the dignity of his office by his constant kindness and courtesy he endeared himself to his patients and won the respect and appreciation of all who had the privilege to work with or under him.

Dr. Handford carried on his work as Medical Officer of Health to the County of Nottingham until old age and ill health brought his resignation. At this time his wife became ill with a long and sad illness.

Dr. Handford's character stood the test for he never complained: but accepted the troubles that had come upon him with a sound philosophy.

In 1929 he died and here is the tribute of the Medical Committee:-

March, 1929.

"It is with great regret that we have to put on record the death of Dr. Henry Handford. Those who knew him well admired him equally for his excellence as a physician and for his qualities as a man. No one could be more kind and courteous than he was at all times and under all circumstances; there was about him a sort of refined dignity of bearing which compelled respect. A love of literature and music, and a great hatred of any approach toward untruthfulness completed the picture of a truly cultured gentleman."

A History of the General Hospital near Nottingham
By Frank H. Jacob.
Pages 232, 233.

1See Appendices.

C HAYDON WHITE M.R.C.S., L.R.C.P.
President of the
Nottingham Medico-Chirurgical Society 1890

Charles Haydon White:- 4, East Circus
Street, Park Row, Nottingham. L.R.C.P.,
London, 1877; 1878; Member of the
Pathological Socicty. Latc:- Clinical Assistant, Bethlam Royal Hospital & Assistant Clinical Consultant, St. Thomas's Hospital.

Medical Directory 1890

ALEXANDER RICHARD ANDERSON
(1855 - 1933)
President of the
Nottingham Medico-Chirurgical Society 1891

C.B.E. 1919; M.R.C.S. 24th January 1877; F.R.C.S. 11th December 1884;

Alexander Richard Anderson:- 5, East Circus Street, Nottingham. F.R.C.S. England (exam) 1884, M. 1877, L.S.A., 1867 (St. Bartholomew's) Fellow of the Royal Medical Chirurgical Society; Member of the Pathological Society, London, B.M.A., and the Nottingham Medico-Chirurgical Society. Surgeon (late Resident Surgeon) Nottingham General Hospital.

Born at Plymouth, 12th April 1855, eldest son of Colonel Richard Anderson, of the 56th Essex Regiment afterwards of the K.L.I., and his wife Eliza Harriet Outerbridge. He received his medical education at St. Bartholomew's Hospital and, as soon as he qualified, was appointed resident surgeon on 31st January 1877 at the Nottingham General Hospital. He remained in his post for thirteen years until he was appointed surgeon in 1889. At the time of his death he was senior surgeon to the General Hospital, senior surgeon to the 'Bagthorpe Military Hospital', and an ex-president of the Nottingham Medico-Chirurgical Society. He retired from practice in August 1923 and moved to Boscombe, where he died on 28th July 1933 and was buried in Boscombe cemetery. He is described as an excellent surgeon, a sincere friend, and a bad enemy.

Anderson Married in 1890 Edith (died 1928), daughter of C.E. Tuck of St.Giles, Norwich. His only child was killed in the war of 1914-18.

Publications:
Actinomycosis of the face and neck cured by operation. Med-chir. Trans, 1892, 75, 103.
Cases of perforated gastric ulcer treated by operation. Nott's. medico-chir.soc. 1897.
Some remarks on the radical cure of hernia; 190 cases of operation for the cure of oblique inguinal heria. Brit. med. J. 1901 1, 263.
Twenty-six consecutive cases of gastroenterostomy. Lancet, 1905, 2, 944.

"The Retirement of Mr. Alexander Richard Anderson"

As reported in the Nottingham General Hospital's Monthly Board's Minutes.
Dated October, 1923.

It is with great and sincere regret that the Board have to report the resignation of Mr. A. R. Anderson, C.B.E., F.R.C.S., who has held office as an Honorary Surgeon to the Institution for the past 34 years. During that long period Mr. Anderson has carried out the important duties of his office with the highest professional ability and success, and by kind personal interest which he took to his patients, and the confidence which he inspired by his gentle and sympathetic manner, earned the gratitude of many thousands who were placed under his care.

During no part of his exceptional, zealous services was Mr. Anderson more acceptable and appreciated than during the Great War, when he was deservedly much beloved by the soldiers who came under his care, and in constant attention on whom by day and night he devoted himself more assiduously.

It was resolved at this same meeting that ward 5, which was situated in the [1] *Jubilee Wing of the Hospital should be known as Anderson Ward*

******

In a celebration to the work of Mr. Anderson, at the time of his retirement in 1923 members of the medical profession from both the City and County of Nottingham held a banquet in his honour where a colleague paid this tribute:-

We have on this memorable occasion assembled here together to do honour to the work and personality of Mr. Anderson, as one who has been the pioneer and leader in the surgical branch of our profession for a whole generation and who has ever held high those professional ideals of which we are all justly proud. The ideal of patient before doctor, the welfare of patient before all personal advantage, the ideal of progress in the healing art, ever striving to make good better.

Alexander Anderson earned his position by sheer ability and personality. He lived through revolution in the art of surgery. He has seen Lister's discoveries and sepsis disappear. He was one of the finest surgeons of his age. He was devoted to his profession and became renowned for his after treatment of fracture and other accidents, his insistence on cleanliness and the power of his judgement. He was devoted to his profession. During the Great War, he virtually lived in the surgical wards of Nottingham Hospital.

He had the instinct developed from long experience which learned the respect of all who worked with him. He was a great man and brought repute to the art of surgery.

In reply to his colleagues tribute Mr. Anderson said the following:-

From boyhood I had a desire to become a Surgeon. My hospital work has been one of my chief interests in life, and now that it is over, I can say that I have enjoyed every day of it. It is not a difficult matter to perform work in which one is keenly interested but the wrench is harder when it comes to an end and it has been a difficult task to sever my connection with the Hospital and City in which I have practiced so many years. But there is a limit to the Professional life of an operating Surgeon, and I decided to end mine before apparent failure set in, which it must have done before long with the inexorable flight of time.

At the close of any man's career the sweetest recollections are those associated with the thought of having done his duty to the best of his ability, and of having obtained the good opinion of those among whom he has worked.

---

[1] The Jubilee Wing was opened in 1900. Its Architect was Alfred Waterhouse. A fund of £29,820 was raised so that the building work commence, of which the foundation stone was laid in 1899 by the Duke of Portland.

R.C. CHICKEN F.R.C.S. (England)
President of the
Nottingham Medico-Chirurgical Society 1892

Rupert Cecil Chicken:-Forest Road West, Nottingham. (1850-1925). M.R.C.S., April 30th, 1872; F.R.C.S., June 10th, 1875; L.R.C.P., 1873; L.S.A., 1877. Surgeon, Nottingham General Hospital.Late:- Resident Obstetric Assistant, Guy's Hospital. Registrar Evelina Hospital for Children & Demonstrator of Anatomy, Royal College of Surgeons, England.

Medical Directory, 1892

Born in Nottingham he was educated at Guy's Hospital where he was House Surgeon and Resident Obstetric Assistant. He was afterwards Registrar at the Everlina Hospital for Children and acted as Prosector at the Royal College of Surgeons. He then entered into partnership in Nottingham with Isaac Watchorn, who, died in the early 1880s, leaving Rupert Chicken in charge of a large and varied general practice. Much surgery came his way and he was able to keep up his operative skill, for he was essentially a surgeon. He was elected to the staff of the Nottingham General Hospital in October, 1891. For ten to fifteen years he became a very active surgeon. He was elected President of the Nottingham Medico Chirurgical Society in 1892 and contributed a long succession of papers which demonstrate the wide range of his surgical interests. He was appointed Consulting Surgeon to Nottingham General Hospital in December, 1907. He retired from practice because of long continued ill health.

After leaving Nottingham he acted as a ship's surgeon for a year or more in the hope of regaining his health. During the war (1914-1918) he was Surgeon to the Whipps Cross War Hospital at Leystone. He died on October 3rd, 1925 and was survived by his wife, one son, and two daughters.

Chicken was a sound and careful surgeon, well abreast of the knowledge and technique of his day. He did not adopt new methods without careful consideration and conviction of their utility. He lived to see the day when some leading surgeons were advocating a return to older methods. He was a man of wide culture and reading, a collector of oak and silver. He took much interest in local history and archaeology, as is witnessed by his published *Index to Deering's History of Nottingham* (1899), and by his booklet entitled, *Excavations at the Nottingham General Hospital during the Building of the New Wing* (1899).

W HUNTER M.D. (Glasow)
President of the
Nottingham Medico-Chirurgical Society 1893

Walter Hunter:- Bridgeway House, Arkwright Street, Nottingham. M.D., Glasgow, 1893, M.B., C.M. (Commended) 1874 (University of Glasgow). J.P., Medical Officer of Health, West Bridgford U.D.C. Ex-President of the Nottingham Medico-Chirurgical Society, Member of the British Medical Association. Late:- Assistant Medical Officer, Barony Parish Hospital and Asylum, Glasgow.

Medical Directory 1915

Walter Hunter, M.D. was the son of the late James Hunter, of Broombank, Newton-Mearns, Renfrewshire.

He was educated at Mearns Parish School, Anderson's College, Glasgow, and Glasgow University, where he graduated with a M.B., C.M. in 1874, and an M.D. in 1893. He sailed as a ship's surgeon on the Allan Line of steamers to Canada during the summer of 1874. Afterwards he was appointed to the post of Assistant Surgeon to the Barony Hospital and Asylum, Glasgow.

In 1880 he opened his practice in Nottingham where at the same time he was appointed as Surgeon to the Nottingham Branch of the Midland Railway. He was also examiner for the Mutual Life Insurance Company of New York. His other appointments were Medical Officer of Health to the West Bridgford Urban District Council, member and later President in 1893 of the Nottingham Medico-Chirurgical Society.

He contributed many papers to the various learned Medical Journals. During the time of his practice in Nottingham he was, for twenty years, a conservative member of the Nottingham City Council, and was also the Chairman of Henry Barker, Ltd.

Walter Hunter married Annie Pollock, the youngest daughter of the late William Blackwood, of Glasgow, and niece of the late Dr. John Pollock, J.P., of Springbank, who practiced at Newton-Mearns for fifty-four years. They had four children, one daughter and three sons.

Dr J.S. TEW M.D. (Durham) M.R.C.S., D.P.H.
President of the
Nottingham Medico-Chirurgical Society 1894

Jas. Scott Tew:- 22, Birns Street, Nottingham M.D.,Durham, 1891; M.B., and B.S., 1899; M.R.C.S., England, 1881; L.S.A., 1880; D.P.H., Cambridge, 1887 (University College, London and University of Durham) Prize winner in Hygiene, University College, London; Fellow of the Society of Medical Officers of Health. Medical Officer of Health, Basford R.D.C. Late:- Assistant Demonstrator of Anatomy, University of Durham, College of Medicine.

Medical Directory, 1894

Jas. Scott Tew:- Brook House, Tunbridge Wells, Kent. Doctor of Medicine 1891; Bachelor of Medicine, Bachelor of Surgery, 1889; M.R.C.S. England 1891; Licentiate of the Society of Apothecaries 1880 Diploma in Public Health, Cambridge (University College, London, and University of Durham): Barrister-at-Law, Inner Temple; Medical Officer of Health at the West Kent Combined Districts; Ex-President of the Nottingham Medico-Chirurgical Society; Fellow of the Society of Medical Health Officers. Formerly:- Medical Officer of Health, Basford Rural District and Assistant Demonstrator of Anatomy, University of Durham College of Medicine.

Medical Directory 1915.

Dr F.R. MUTCH M.D. (Aberdeen)
President of the
Nottingham Medico-Chirurgical Society 1895

Forbes Robertson Mutch:- 2, West Street, Sneinton Road, Nottingham. M.D., Aberdeen, 1886, M.B., and C.M., 1879 (University of Aberdeen). Fellow of the British Gynaecological Society; Member of the British Medical Association. Surgeon, Provident Medical Aid Institute; Nottingham Medical Referee, London and Manchester Assurance Company.

Medical Directory 1890;

Obituary
"The British Medical Journal, December 18, 1909"

William Bramwell Ransom M.A., M.D., (Cambridge) B.Sc. (London) F.R.C.P.
(Senior Physician to the Nottingham General Hospital; Physician to the Sherwood Forest Sanatorium)

The name Ransom, father and son, is widely known in the medical world. Dr. William Bramwell Ransom commenced practice in the city in 1890 and shortly afterwards was appointed Physician to the Nottingham General Hospital on the resignation of his father.

He was educated at Cheltenham College. At the age of 17 he proceeded to his father's old school, University College, London. In 1882, he headed the list of physiology honours at the final B.Sc. London, carrying off the university scholarship and medal in 1880. He had already entered Trinity College, Cambridge, and in 1883 graduated B.A., first Class in the Natural Science Tripos. On account of his interest in physiology he was sent by the University to do original work at the Zoological Station at Naples, and at a similar institution at Roscoff in Brittany. As a result of this he published articles on the "Cardiac Rhythm of Invertebrata;" "The Influence of Glycerine on the Liver" *(Journal of Physiology, volumes 5 and 7);* "The Spinal and Visceral Nerves of Cyclostomata," and other subjects.

In 1886 he was elected Fellow of Trinity College and having returned to University College to study medicine, he gained two Fellows medals for clinical medicine, the Liston Medal for pathology and graduated M.B. in 1889. In the following year he became a member of the Royal College of Physicians. The same college recognized his eminent abilities by electing him to the Fellowship in 1898.

No sooner had Ransom settled in Nottingham than the medical profession, recognised his new power. On the boards of charities and other committies he showed an insight into difficult problems which astonished men of years and experience. Whenever he spoke he was listened to and his words were always delivered with grace of style and a fund of ready humour. He speedily became the leading medical consultant in the city and county.

Shortly after he commenced practice Dr. Koch announced the discovery of tuberculin. Ransom made a special journey to Berlin to obtain first hand a supply of the new specific. Its effects were demonstrated to the medical profession in the wards of the General Hospital. Until he was finally struck down by illness, he worked devotedly for the institution. For years he spent the whole of his Sunday mornings in the wards, besides numerous visits on week days. Add to this five or more long hours for out patients on Friday afternoons and some conception can be formed of the work he forced himself to do. The amount of work he got through was a continual triumph of mind over matter. On his Sunday morning visits he was frequently accompanied by a small band of men who wanted to learn from his experience. No matter what the occasion, he always gave his best. His relations with his honorary colleagues and with the resident medical and nursing staff were always cordial. He was a member of the honorary staff of the Nottingham and Notts. Convalescent Homes, to which he rendered valuable service.

In 1892 when the British Medical Association met in Nottingham, W. B. Ransom was Secretary of the Section of Medicine, his father being President. He also took part in the Leicester meeting in 1905. When the British Association for the Advancement of Science met in Nottingham in 1893, Ransom was one of the Secretaries. He was Governor of the Nottingham High School, and a member of the Council of the Nottingham University College. He was President of the Nottingham Medico-Chirurgical Society during the session 1896-7, and delivered a masterly address on "Immunity" afterwards published in a small volume. He was a frequent contributor of valuable clinical and pathological material to the society. Year after year he delivered set addresses and however long these might be, he had the happy art of keeping his audience interested to the end.

Ransom threw himself heart and soul into the question of open air treatment for Phthisis. By his untiring labours and his great enthusiasm a Society for the Prevention of Consumption was formed. A lasting monument to those labours remains in the form of the Sherwood Forest Sanatorium *(Ransom Sanatorium)*. By his own generous and self-sacrificing efforts a building fund of over £5,000 was collected, a site having been provided by the Generosity of the Duke of Portland. It is no easy matter in these days to start a new medical charity and it is not too much to say that this Sanatorium owes its existence to the unstinted efforts of Dr. Ransom in arousing the necessary enthusiasm. The sanatorium was opened in 1901 for 14 patients, all of the poorer class.

By a strange irony of fate Dr. Ransom fell victim to the disease - consumption - which he had done so much to relieve. During the later years of his life he contracted several severe attacks of influenza. Definite symptoms of phthisis showed themselves in the summer of 1907, and the disease proved fatal two and a quarter years later.

CHARLES HENRY CATTLE (1856-1943)
(1856 - 1943)
President of the
Nottingham Medico-Chirurgical Society 1897

Charles Henry Cattle 2, East Circus Street, Nottingham. M.D., London, 1880, M.B., 1877; M.R.C.P. London, 1890, M.R.C.S., England, 1876 (Leeds & University College). Member of the B.M.A. & Honorary President of the Nottingham Medico-Chirurgical Society. Surgical Clinical Prize, Leeds School of Medicine. Honorary Physician Nottingham and Nott's Convalescence Homes. Late Senior Assistant Resident Medical Officer, Leeds General Infirmary, and Senior Resident Medical Officer, Leeds Public Dispensary.

Medical Directory 1897

The son of a Wesleyan Clergyman, Charles Henry Cattle was educated at a Wesleyan college and began his medical education at the Leeds Medical School, afterwards incorporated in the Leeds University. It was here that he became aquainted with Sir Clifford Allbutt, and a friendship arose which lasted throughout their lives. Cattle took his Membership of the Royal College of Surgeons of England exams in 1876 and then graduated M.B., London, and M.D., in 1880. He was in general practice in Nottingham for some years and was greatly helped by Dr. William Henry Ransom F.R.S., who was then his senior physician at the Nottingham General Hospital. In 1908 he was elected Fellow of the Royal College of Surgeons. In 1901 he was appointed honorary assistant physician to the General Hospital, Nottingham. He then became a consulting physician, which had always been his ambition. He followed as full physician in 1906, and he was also physician to the Ransom Sanatorium for Tuberculosis. The whole of his professional life was spent in Nottingham, where he soon gained a high place in the esteem of his fellows.

Cattle made many contributions to medical literature, especially on infections of the heart and lungs. He took an active part in the discussions of the Nottingham Medico-Chirurgical Society, of which he was secretary for many years and later president. Deeply interested in the affairs of his profession, he was a member of the British Medical Association for 63 years. A keen cyclist, he wandered over the greater part of England, Wales, and Scotland. He cycled up to the age of 74. He was also a great walker. He had a retiring, simple, and sympathetic nature, and no desire for publicity. It was said in his obituary:- "The high esteem and affection in which he was held was manifested by the large number, including many colleagues, who attended his memorial service."

T. DAVIS PRYCE M.R.C.S.
President of the
Nottingham Medico-Chirurgical Society 1898

Thomas Davis Pryce:- 64, Claredon Street, Nottingham. M.R.C.S., England and L.S.A., 1882, (St. Bartholomew's) Consultant Surgeon, Nottingham General Dispensary. Late:- Senior Registrar Surgeon, Nottingham General Dispensary. President and Honorary Secretary of the Nottingham Medico-Chirurgical Society.

Medical Directory, 1915.

A well known antiquarian, Dr. Thomas Davis Pryce, formally of Nottingham, has died at Woking, Surrey.

Dr. Pryce practiced in Clarendon Street, Nottingham, until his retirement about 15 years ago.

He was president of the Nottingham Medico-Chirurgical Society in 1898. He was connected with the Nottingham General Dispensary, holding for a time the position of senior resident surgeon.

A Fellow of the Society of Antiquarians Dr. Pryce was associated with important excavation work on various Roman sites in England and Wales.

He collaborated with Dr. Felix Oswald, F.S.A., in the publication of "An Introduction to the Study of Terra Sigillata," a standard work of reference on pottery of the period. He was instrumental in carrying through most successful excavation work on the site of Margidunum, at East Bridgford with Dr. Oswald and others.

Dr. Pryce was the author of a number of medical works as well as a contributor to various antiquarian and historical journals.

Local Studies Library,
Angel Row, Nottingham.

H MICHIE M.B., C.M. (Aberdeen)
President of the
Nottingham Medico-Chirurgical Society 1899

Harry Michie:- 27, Regent Street, Nottingham M.B., C.M., Aberdeen, 1881. Fellow of the Obstetric and British Gynaecological Societies. Surgeon:- Samaritan Hospital for Women, Nottingham*.

Medical Directory 1898

*12th January, 1886, The Samaritan Hospital for Women was opened by Lady John Manvers.

C.B. WRAY M.R.C.S. (England) D.P.H. (London)
President of the
Nottingham Medico-Chirurgical Society 1900

George Bury Wray:- 115, Waterloo Crescent, Nottingham. M.R.C.S., England and L.S.A., 1879, D.P.H., R.C.P.S. London, 1893, University College. Medical Officer of Health, Basford Rural District Council. Member of the Royal Sanitary Institute and the British Medical Association. Past President of the Nottingham Medico-Chirurgical Society.

Medical Directory 1915.

J MACKIE L.R.C.P. (Edinburgh)
President of the
Nottingham Medico-Chirurgical Society 1902

John Mackie:- 14, Regent Street, Nottingham. L.R.C.P., Edinburgh, L.F.P.S., Glasgow.

Medical Directory 1915

DR T BURNIE L.R.C.P., L.R.C.S. (Edinburgh)
President of the
Nottingham Medico-Chirurgical Society 1884 &1903

Thomas Burnie:- 389, Mansfield Road, Carrington, Nottingham. (Burnie & Scott): L.R.C.P., L.R.C.S. (Edinburgh) 1862; (University of Edinburgh and Queens College, Birmingham) Formerly:- Resident Surgeon, General Dispensary, Birmingham and House Surgeon, Birmingham and Midlands Free Hospital for Sick Children.

Medical Directory 1915

H J NEILSON M.D. (Glasgow)
President of the
Nottingham Medico-Chirurgical Society 1904

81

Henry J. Neilson:- Bulwell, Nottingham. M.D., Glasgow (with commendation) 1887, M.B., C.M. 1885 (University of Glasgow, Vienna and Berlin). Medical Officer and Public Vaccination Officer 7th District, Nottingham Union. Medical Officer, Workhouse, Basford Union and Rushcliffe Isolation Hospital. Medical Officer, Infectious Diseases Hospital, Basford Rural District Council. Certified Factory Surgeon. Ex-President of the Nottingham Medico-Chirurgical Society. Late:- House Surgeon and House Physician, Glasgow Royal Infirmary.

Medical Directory 1915

E. POWELL M.R.C.S. (England)
President of the
Nottingham Medico-Chirurgical Society 1906

Evan Powell, City Asylum, Mapperley Hill, Nottingham M.R.C.S. (England) L.S.A., 1873 (University College) Medical Superintendant, City Asylum, Mapperley Hill, Nottingham. Member,Medical Psychology Association, and the Nottingham Medico-Chirurgical Society. Late, Assistant Medical Officer, Kent County Lunatic Asylum, Barming Health. Assistant Medical Officer, Essex County Asylum, and Assistant Medical Officer, North Wales Asylum.

Medical Directory 1915

PHILIP BOOBBYER M.D., M.R.C.S., L.S.A.
(1857 - 1930)
President of the
Nottingham Medico-Chirurgical Society 1908

Philip Boobbyer:- Uphill House, Park Side, Derby Road, and Guildhall, Nottingham. M.D. Durham 1902; M.B., M.S., 1885; M.R.C.S., England, 1881; L.S.A., 1883 (King's College & University College of Durham); Association of King's College, London; Fellow of the Society of the Medical Officers of Health; Fellow and Member of the Council and Examiner of the Royal Sanitary Institute; Medical Officer of Health, Nottingham; Medical Superintendent, City Isolation Hospital.

Late:- Medical Officer of Health, Basford Rural District. Resident Medical Officer for Women and Children, King's College Hospital & Assistant Demonstrator of Anatomy, University of Durham, College of Medicine.

Author of Official Health Reports, Basford, 1885-89, Nottingham Borough & City 1889-1906; "Compulsory Notification & Hospital Isolation," 1891; reports on "Conservancy & Water Carriage in Great Towns," 1894, "Enteric Fever in Houses with Different Types of Closets," 1895, "Knackery & Abattoir Plant in Germany," 1897; "Smallpox Attenuated by Vaccination," 1903; "Special Report to the Home Office on Health of Lace Dressers," 1907; Contributor to "Smallpox Secondaries," *Quarterly Medical Journal, 1893;* "Smallpox Outbreak traced to and by Infected Lace," *Society of Medical Officers of Health,* 1894; "Return Cases of Scarlet Fever," 1895-96; "Ten Years Experience of Enteric Fever," *Transcript, Epidemiological Society* 1899; "Open air treatment of Smallpox," *British Medical Journal,* 1904; "Tramps and Smallpox," *Lancet,* 1904; "Dust Problems," *Congress of the Royal Sanitary Institute.* 1906.

Medical Directory 1908

Philip Boobbyer was the son of Mr. Joseph Hurst Boobbyer, descended from an old Hugenot family. He was a native of Brighton and was educated at Brighton College. Before commencing his medical studies at King's College and later King's College Hospital, London, he spent two years in an engineer's office. After qualifying as a Member of the Royal College of Surgeons he became resident medical officer at King's College Hospital. It was during this period he was to serve for twelve months as demonstrator of anatomy at Durham University, eventually obtaining his University degrees in both medicine and surgery, and the Licentiate of the Society of Apothecaries in London.

While still studying for his degrees in 1884 the position of assistant medical officer of health to the Basford Rural Sanitary Authority became vacant. Dr. Boobbyer was appointed. Within five years he succeeded to the post of medical officer. He was 31 years old. He went on to hold the post, serving with distinction, for a period of 40 years, retiring on the 9th of January 1929.

During those 40 years the health services in Nottingham expanded out of all recognition. When Dr. Boobbyer took over the reins there were only 40 employees under the direct control of the medical officer. By the time of his retirement in 1929 the staff numbers had risen to 220. In the early days there was no pathological laboratory, no maternity and child welfare department, no tuberculosis or venereal disease department, no sanatorium for adults or children, no hostels for mothers, sun-ray clinic, medical service or other departments which were developed during his time.

In many ways Dr. Boobbyer was a pioneer. He fought for many years to induce what appeared to be a lethargic health authority to abolish the 'pail closet' system. Had his advice been adopted at that time it would have saved the ratepayers over £100,000 in conversion costs. Dr. Boobbyer was able to demonstrate by incontrovertible figures that enteric fever, infantile diarrhoea, and other epidemic diseases were largely due to this insanitary system. In 1899 there were 613 cases of enteric fever in the city. By the time of his retirement in 1929 Nottingham was practically free from the disease. Also, in the last five years of the 19th century the death rate from enteric fever stood at 18.9 per 1,000. By 1928 that figure was to stand at 12 per 1,000. With the abolition of the pail closet system and a much improved public sanitary system cases of enteric fever began to show a dramatic decline.

Dr Boobbyer lived to see many of his advocated health reforms receive general recognition. He was once criticised as being an "open-air-crank" because of his belief in pure air as a healing agent. Even by the time the Health Committee's institutions like Bagthorpe Isolation Hospital (Heathfield Hospital, now part of the Nottingham City Hospital) had adopted the open-air treatment, it was still looked on with a great deal of suspicion by certain members of the committee.

However, his belief in pure air as a treatment for enteric fever received international acclaim. At the Dresden Exhibition in 1911 he was awarded a diploma of honour and a medal for his achievements.

The number and variety of tributes paid to him for his campaign for the health of children in Nottingham afforded eloquent testimony to the value of his life's work. Originality, freshness of outlook and freedom from convention were of his outstanding features.

At the time of Dr. Boobbyer's appointment to the post of medical officer the annual expenditure was £8,000. By the time of his retirement the annual expenditure had risen to £121,000. Also, at the time of his appointment infant mortality stood at a rate of 84 per 1,000. By the time of his retirement this figure had dropped to 18.2.

Dr. Philip Boobbyer lived one year into retirement. He died on the 21st January 1930, at the age of 72 after his daily "cold bath," before breakfast.

Dr. Boobbyer was married to the sister of the Architect, Watson Fothergill. She survived him with two sons and two daughters.

His annual reports were able and instructive, and it was unfortuate that zeal for economy led his committee to stop printing them during the [first] war. When he retired, however he was permitted to issue a final account of his work for the city.

Accounts from the Nottingham Evening Post and Obituary Notices, B.M.J., February 1st, 1930, page 221.

A FULTON B.A., M.B., B.Ch., R.U.I.
President of the
Nottingham Medico-Chirurgical Society 1909

Adam Fulton:- 418, Nottingham Road, Old Basford, Nottingham. (Neilson & Fulton). B.A.R.U.I., 1888, M.B., B.Ch., B.A.O., 1893 (Queen's College Belfast and Dublin). Association in Arts, Senior School, in Natural History, Queen's College, Belfast and Dublin, Member of the Advisory Committee, National Health Insurance Commission. Member of the Council of the British Medical Association. Chairman of the Nottingham Medical Committee. Member of the Nottingham Local Insurance Committee. Ex President of the Nottingham Medico-Chirurgical Society. Late:- Resident Clinical Assistant, Belfast Royal Infirmary.

Medical Directory 1915

(1876 - 1943)

Adam Fulton qualified as M.B., B.Ch., B.O.A., and settled near Nottingham, where he built up a large colliery and industrial practice. He joined the British Medical Association in 1904, and in 1910 came to the Annual Meeting in London as Representative of Nottingham. He continued as a Representative until 1914, was a member of the Council from 1913 to 1920, and a very active member of many committees. In 1920 he accepted an invitation to become a Divisional Medical Officer of the Ministry of Health.

A former colleague wrote:- Fulton was a general practitioner of a very fine type, who secured himself the confidence and affection not only of his patients but of his colleagues. Both made heavy demands on his energies which were cheerfully accepted. He was very prominent in the struggle over the 1911 National Health Insurance Bill, and took part in the discussions. He was a man of strong moral courage and never concealed his opinion - that if the main demands of the profession were met, the new health service would be a boon to the public and to the profession. He was vice-chairman for some years of the Notts Insurance Committee, and made his influence so felt that it was no surprise when he was invited to go to the Ministry of Health. I know that his advice was greatly valued by Smith Walker, then the chief medical adviser to the Ministry of Health and by Sir Robert Morant, its secretary. Fulton's official duties, were carried out with his usual tact and sound judgement. The quality of the man was best shown during the First World war when on his Local Medical War Committee and in cooperation with headquarters he organized the doctors in his district in a way which was not surpassed in any other area. The Notts area was exceptionally heavily depleted of doctors, but Fulton and his colleagues met the situation with great ingenuity and courage.

It was a privilege to know and work with a man who had such a great fund of common sense and good humour. He was always listened to with great respect.

B.M.J., October 9th, 1943, pages 467/8

FRANK HARWOOD JACOB
President of the
Nottingham Medico-Chirurgical Society 1911

Born, 4th October, 1872. Died, 25th November, 1952.

President of the Nottingham Medico-Chirurgical Society
1911 & 1927 - 1928
(Centenary year)

Frank Harwood Jacob:- 32, Regent Street, Nottingham.
M.D., London, 1901; M.B., 1898; M.R.C.P. London, 1903,
M.R.C.S., L.R.C.P., London, 1895 *(Kings College Hospital)*
Warenford Entrance Scholarship; Sambrooke, Rabbneth,
Cloth Workers Society; Junior and 2nd year Scholar. Honorary Physician (Late House Physician) General Hospital, Nottingham; Bacteriologist, City of Nottingham. Fellow of the
Royal Society of Medicine; Nottingham Medico-Chirurgical
Society & Rontgen Society, London. Late House Surgeon &
House Physician, Kings College Hospital & Physician, Nottingham Hospital for Sick Children

Medical Directory 1915

Frank Harwood Jacob was born on October 4, 1872, the son of a Naval
chaplain. He attended King's School, Ely. He gained the Warenford entrance scholarship to King's College, London, where he won a remarkable
series of scholarships and prizes during his pre-clinical and clinical studies. He qualified M.R.C.S., L.R.C.P. in 1895. After holding the posts of
house-physician and house surgeon at King's College Hospital, he became house-physician to the Nottingham General Hospital.

He graduated M.B. in 1898 and proceeded M.D. three years later. In 1903
he took the M.R.C.P., becoming a Fellow in 1921. When the honorary
staff of the Nottingham General Hospital was expanded in 1901 Dr. Jacob
became the first assistant physician. Four years later he was promoted to
the full staff, and he continued to serve the hospital faithfully until his
retirement, on reaching the age limit, in 1937. In recognition of his won-

derful service to the hospital, a medical ward, the newest in the hospital at the time, was named after him in 1947. He built up a large consulting practice covering Nottinghamshire, Lincolnshire, Rutland, Derbyshire, and parts of Leicestershire.

A member of the British Medical Association for over 50 years, Dr. Jacob was elected as the representative of his division to attend the first Annual Representative Meeting of the Association, which was held at Swansea in 1903. In 1905 he acted as one of the honorary secretaries of the Section of Medicine at the Annual Meeting in Leicester. He was president of the Section of Medicine at the Nottingham Meeting in 1926, serving also on the Arrangements Committee in that session. He was a staunch supporter of the Nottingham Medico-Chirurgical Society and was twice elected its president.

Many of his juniors have had great cause to be thankful for kindly counsel, given always with a paternal smile of encouragement. It is not to be wondered at that he was affectionately known as "Uncle Frank." The mere accumulation of money meant nothing to him-in secret he was exceedingly generous and probably never refused a request for help, often paying for the treatment of a patient himself. In private life he was a man of simple tastes, taking little interest in food and drink, and, although fastidiously clean, was quite indifferent to the age of his clothes. He was fond of good music, and especially fond of the countryside, particularly Derbyshire. To him no music was lovelier than the wild whistle of the curlew or the low sweet song of a dipper.

When the Second World War came Dr. Jacob helped the local practitioners at Malvern, where only a short time before he had gone to live in retirement. During his retirement, he wrote *A History of the General Hospital near Nottingham*, which was published in 1951.

Dr. J. Wilkie Scott wrote:- By the death of Dr. Frank H. Jacob, a distinguished and very lovable personality of Nottinghamshire has passed away. He preceded me as house-physician at the Nottingham General Hospital, and we were close colleagues for nearly 40 years. On starting practice in 1901, he was given a slender piece of bread and butter by the Nottingham Health Committee to undertake routine bacteriology. Up until that time nearly all pathological material, from both the city and the hospital, had been sent to London for investigation. His laboratory, thus opened, developed, still under his guidance, to become a full pathological service for the hospital, the county, and the East Midlands, being finally taken over by the hospital about 1920. He had also had installed the first private Xray plant in Nottingham, and this also developed into a service supplying the needs of practitioners in the city and county which he continued until after the First World War. All this is evidence of the profound influence he wielded in medical developments in the district. In many other ways he was responsible for improvements, nowhere more than in planning for the betterment of conditions at the hospital, his main objective and consideration always being the good of the patient. He was possessed of a tenacity of purpose and capacity for unremitting work without which his many varied projects could not have materialized. His *History of the General Hospital near Nottingham,* written in a philosophical strain, and interspersed with descriptions of contemporary advances in medical knowledge and practice, make delightful reading, and shows from the references the deep and abiding stimulus he derived from the life and works of Louis Pasteur. Jacob had a first class brain, and, as was to be expected, became a most able, wise, and trusted physician. Although not attracted by social functions he was a fluent and attractive speaker and could grace the big occasion, for which he was much in demand. He was as indifferent to material advantage and worldly honours as he was to the cut and style of his apparel. Cheery and friendly in nature, the soul of candour, nothing aroused his indignation more than any hint of prevarication or insincerity. He was not pre-eminent in games, but in his younger days would show a tough and vigorous side in rugby football, hockey, with the gloves, or in an early morning swim in the Trent. He had deep religious convictions, without parading them, and for years had a class of young fellows on Sunday mornings, whose interest he would hold with talks on nature and science and religion. In his busiest days he would find time to take most devoted care of his mother, over 90 years of age, and during the last few years he gave himself to the nursing and care of a very severely crippled sister, resolutely refusing to leave her even for a day. So he died, looking after others to the end.

B.M.J., December 13th, 1952, page 1312.

WILLIAM GEORGE LAWS (1862-1936)
(1862 - 1936)
President of the
Nottingham Medico-Chirurgical Society 1912

M.R.C.S. and F.R.C.S. 9th June 1892; M.B., C.M. Edinburgh 1888.

William George Laws:- 3, East Circus Street, Nottingham. M.B., C.M., (Honours) 1888; F.R.C.S., England, 1892 (University of Edinburgh & St. Thomas's Hospital); Associate in Science and Scholar; and Exhibitor, University of Durham; Member of the Ophthalmic Society: Senior Surgeon, Nottingham and Midland Eye Infirmary; Late Assistant Editor, Ophthalmic Review; Ophthalmic House Surgeon, St. Thomas's Hospital and Clinical Assistant, Royal London Ophthalmic Hospital.

Medical Directory, 1915.

Born at the Manor House, Barrasford, near Chollerton, Northumberland, 14th June 1862, the second child and second son of William George Laws, civil engineer, and Ellinor Shields, his wife. He was educated at the Newcastle Grammar School and at the University of Durham, where he was an associate in science, scholar, and exhibitioner. He received his medical education at Edinburgh and at St. Thomas's Hospital, London, acting as ophthalmic house surgeon and afterwards becoming a clinical assistant at the Royal London Ophthalmic Hospital, Moorfields. Deciding to specialise in eye work he settled at Nottingham, where he soon became popular and was appointed surgeon to the Nottingham and Midland Eye Infirmary. He gave up practice in 1929 and retired to King's Langley, Hertfordshire, where he died 26th May, 1936.

Laws was a member of the council of the Ophthalmological Society 1909-11, president of the section of ophthalmology at the Nottingham meeting of the British Medical Association 1926, and assistant editor of the *Ophthalmic Review,* **18-28,** 1899-1909.

From the Lives
of the
Fellows of the Royal College of Surgeons.

ROBERT GEORGE HOGARTH
(1868 - 1953)
President of the
Nottingham Medico-Chirurgical Society 1913

Robert George Hogarth:- 60, The Ropewalk, Nottingham.
F.R.C.S. England; 1894 M. 1891; L.R.C.P., London, 1891
(St. Bartholomew's); Surgeon, Children's Hospital, Notting-
ham; Surgeon, General Hospital, Nottingham; Consultant
Surgeon, Grindley Convalescent Home; Surgeon, Notting-
ham and Nott's Sanatorium; Medical Referee Workmen's
Compensations Act; President of the Nottingham Medico-
Chirurgical Society. Member of the British Medical Associa-
tion. Late, Surgeon Samaritan Hospital for Women. Senior
Resident Medical Officer, General Hospital, Nottingham &
House Surgeon, St. Bartholomew's Hospital.

Medical Directory 1915

**Robert George Hogarth (1868 - 1953). C.B.E. 1918; M.R.C.S. 30 July
1891; F.R.C.S. 14 June 1894; Hon. LL.D., Edinburgh 1927; J.P., D.L.
Co Nottingham 1948.**

Robert George Hogarth was a Scotsman, from Berwickshire. He was born
on May 15th, 1868 and was educated at Felstead School. His medical
training was at St. Bartholomew's Hospital, London. He qualified in 1891.
After holding various resident appointments at St. Bartholomew's and a
post as house-surgeon in Wolverhampton, he went to Nottingham as senior resident medical officer at the Nottingham General Hospital in 1894.
In the same year he became a Fellow of the Royal College of Surgeons of
England. He quickly won recognition in the East Midlands as a cultured
and skilful surgeon. He started private practice at a house in the Ropewalk, Nottingham, and throughout his career he continued to serve the
General Hospital as assistant surgeon, then senior surgeon. His interest in
the hospital was not only in its medical service but in its administration.
He was also the B.M.A's vice-chairman and the moving spirit in the building and equipment of the Nottingham General Hospital's Pay-Bed Wing.

He advocated the setting up of such a department in all large hospitals. He was honorary surgeon to the Samaritan Hospital for Women and the Children's Hospital, and consulting surgeon to the Gringley Convalescent Home. He was associated with the British Empire Cancer Campaign, a member of its Grand Council, and chairman of the Nottingham Branch. It was largely due to his efforts that a Radiotherapy Department was established in Nottingham which, today is regarded as one of the best in the country. In 1948 the centre was renamed "The Hogarth Radiotheraputic Centre" by the Duke of Portland in recognition of his services. Finally he was a member of the Council and of the disciplinary committee of the Royal College of Surgeons.

Before he came to the presidency of the British Medical Association he was chairman of the Nottingham Division and in the same year president of the Midland Branch. He served for three years on the Central Council, and in recognition of his services was elected a Vice President. After his tenure of office he rendered some valuable assistance to the Association concerning patients. He was a past president of the Nottingham Medico-Chirurgical Society and a Fellow of the Royal Society of Medicine and of the Association of Surgeons of Great Britain. He contributed papers to the medical journals, his first, being a paper in the Journal on *"The Treatment of Cut Throat,"* written at the time when he was resident medical officer at the Nottingham General Hospital. In 1948 he published a book of memories entitled *The Trent and I Go Wandering By.* For his work as consulting surgeon to the military hospitals in the Nottingham district in the 1914-18 war the C.B.E. was conferred upon him in 1918. In 1927 he was made Hon. LL.D. of the University of Edinburgh, being presented as one who had "long held a very high place in the realms of surgery." He was appointed a Deputy Lieutenant for the county of Nottingham in 1948.

In his younger days Hogarth was a great sportsman. He played football with some famous teams, including the Corinthians and the London Caledonians and occasionally played for Wolverhampton Wanderers. He was also a noted sprinter and jumper, winning the amateur long-jump championship of Britain in 1890. His interest in football and cricket continued until the end of his life. He had been president of the Nottingham Forest Football Club and of the Nottinghamshire Cricket Club.

In 1897 he married Miss Mabel Winifred Lynam, by whom he had one son who died on active service in Italy as a Major in the Grenadier Guards on the 19th July, 1944.

In the opening of the same obituary in the British Medical Journal for July of that year it said:- Mr. R. G. Hogarth, was the oldest of the British Medical Association's Past Presidents. When the Association, after more than a third of a century, returned to Nottingham for its Annual Meeting in 1926 Mr. Hogarth was nominated unanimously by his colleagues in the Nottingham Division for the presidential office. In a personal tribute to Mr. R. G. Hogarth, Dr. J. Wilkie Scott said of him:- Mr. R. G. Hogarth at the time of his death was the doyen of the medical profession in Nottingham.

His career in Nottinghamshire was an outstanding one. He was accustomed to say that he owed his appointments not as house physician and house surgeon at St. Bartholomew's but to his prowess for the hospital at football, cricket, and athletics. He had a brilliant record as an athlete. In his last year at Felsted he won the 100 and 220 yard, the quarter mile, and the long and high jumps. At Bart's he was captain of the cricket and football teams. He played for various first class football clubs. The trophy he prized the most was the medal awarded him for the open amateur long jump in 1890. During a boyhood spent in the Border Country he enjoyed fishing and shooting, and he retained a love of these throughout his life.

Despite his love of and skill at sports Hogarth was never deflected from his ambition to attain success in life and in surgery. His appointments as surgeon to the Nottingham Forest and Notts County Football Clubs led him to take an increasing interest in the treatment of injuries, fractures and joint affections. His services were often required for accidents in the hunting field. He was concerned with the inauguration of the Cripples' Guild. Harlow Wood Orthopaedic Hospital was part of this guild.

Success came to him quickly. . In his presidential address to the British Medical Association in 1926 on "The Medical Practitioner and the Public" he showed remarkable foresight of the shape of things to come. He took the opportunity to advocate such measures as the provision of wards for paying patients and the extension of contributory schemes to meet the rising costs of hospitals. It was only after the lapse of some years and in the face of opposition that these projects were achieved in the county. He had the rare honour for a provincial surgeon not attached to a teaching hospital of being elected to the Council of the Royal College of Surgeons of England. Other distinctions came his way. In his book he looks back upon a life of very varied interests.

Hogarth - Bob to his friends - was a very human, genial person, with much charm of manner. There was nothing in the least degree thrustful in his demeanour. In conversation he was deprecatory of himself - and he was usually the centre of attention in any gathering, even in the presence of more celebrated people. He appeared frequently in the law courts, where he was much in demand in cases arising under the Workmen's Compensation Acts, and was a very able and wily witness. He had a disarming way of belittling his own knowledge and seeming to agree with the opposition, except, perhaps over just one point, which was often a crucial one. He had always been rather occupied with his health, and for years before this really did decline he was a confirmed and self confessed valetudinarian, but, as his complaints were interspersed with his natural drolleries he was never a bore. His final illness was a protracted and a trying one. He was bedridden for over 18 months and it was a relief when the release, for which he longed, came peacefully at the end.

B.M.J., July 14th, 1953, page 47/8 & July 25th, 1953, page 228.

PRESIDENTIAL ADDRESS
BY

ROBERT GEORGE HOGARTH
AS PRESIDENT OF THE BRITISH MEDICAL ASSOCIATION,
AT THEIR 94th ANNUAL MEETING IN NOTTINGHAM,
"JULY 1926"

The Medical Practitioner and the Public

My first duty tonight is strictly personal. It is to express my heartfelt appreciation of the great honour conferred on me. To be President of the British Medical Association is - I hope I speak without bias - to be President of the finest professional association in the world. I can truthfully add that no one in the fast lengthening line of my predecessors in office has entered upon the duties of the Presidency with a greater realization of his own inadequacy to fulfill them as they might be fulfilled, or with a more earnest desire to bring to such fulfillment the very utmost of which he is capable

The Nottingham Meeting of 1892.
May I next remind you of the Association's last visit to Nottingham in 1892 - more than thirty years ago? That was before I came to Nottingham, and certainly had no visions or premonitions that the next time the Association met here I should occupy this exalted position. What made that Nottingham meeting memorable was then, for the first time, the Association, by its vote , admitted women to its full membership. I will not rake over the cold ashes of that dead controversy except to say that no one, as far as I know, regrets that decision today, or if he regrets it, deems it expedient to say so, or wishes that it had been postponed. The wonder now is rather that the prejudice - for time has proved that it was only prejudice - lasted so long.

There is now no degree or diploma, no office, no honour, no post in the medical profession (at any rate on the civil side) which is not open equally to women as to men, and I shall be well satisfied if, in the years to come, the present Nottingham meeting of the Association has as good cause to be remembered with honour and with gratitude, either for some signal reform or some wise and judicious decision, as was the earlier meeting in 1892

Nottingham and its Surroundings.

The abundant literature about [3] Nottingham which all of you have doubtless received makes it quite unnecessary for me to sing the praise of a city which has a glorious past, both in fact and legend, a prosperous present, and a future bright with hope. You will be able to judge for yourselves whether the report speaks in terms too flattering or in terms not flattering enough of Nottingham's varied charms. All I wish to say is that the local members of the Association are immensely proud of the visit of their colleagues from all parts of the Empire, and are deeply grateful to the civic authorities, and indeed to all who have collaborated so generously in the preparatory work necessary to make the visit a success

We who practice our profession in this yet modern city by the Trent invariably find all classes of the population singularly responsive to the many and recurrent humanitarian claims of her medical institutions. You will see the evidence of that in many a fine building, and in none displayed more nobly than in the magnificent Home to Nurses [4], which is built on the very spot where Charles I raised his standard at the opening of the Civil War. The city which chose that home for a war memorial will be proud to show her famed hospitality to those who practice medicine.

The March of Medical Science.

The decrease in the general rate of mortality is one of the most striking proofs of the rapid forward march of medical science. It has fallen by nearly one half in fifty years. Had the birth rate been maintained the Malthusian doctrine would have enjoyed a new lease of life, and we should now be talking in awed tones of the 'hungry generations' treading us down. But it has fallen by a larger proportion in the same period, and the net increase is because of the longer life.

It is a great triumph that a large percentage of humanity can now so far outrange the Psalmist's three score years and ten, and, instead of the added years entailing heaviness and sorrow, can still enjoy the pleasures of a discreetly ordered table and the beneficent exercise of the veteran's game at golf. By taking thought and following advice we can lengthen out the measure of our days and look forward with some confidence to a green old age. This prolongation of life - active of course I mean, though the pace may slacken - is, I say, a great achievement in itself, especially if we agree with Scipio's reason for regretting that so few attained old age - namely, that if more attained it life would be lived in better and in wiser fashion.

Yet is there not a real danger of attaching too much importance to the triumphant statistics of mortality without due consideration of their actual content? Mere prolongation of life is of little good in itself, either to the individual or the nation, unless there is a real capacity to enjoy it. All medical men meet with cases where the efforts made to prolong the life of a patient who is far past effective help hardly seems a kindness to the sufferer and often bring those about him to the breaking point. Far more desirable than to make a brave show in the statistical tables and increase the number of nonagenarians and centenarians is to raise the general standard of health among all ages of the community.

The Practitioner's Duty to the State

Let us look at this question from the point of view of the State, since our duty to the State, according to some people, seems to be reckoned higher than our duty to ourselves. During the war public opinion was shocked to discover that the C3 category was so large in comparison not with A1, but with the B's and even with the C's. But it did not surprise the doctors, who knew the long catalogue of disabling ailments which afflict the general mass of the people.

The first sets of figures published by those who medically examined school children in the elementary schools had already given clear warning. If such distressing percentages prevailed among the children between the ages of 5 and 15, what was to be expected when they grew to manhood? Moreover, a swollen C3 category of men between 18 and 45 necessarily means a still larger percentage of the same category between 45 and 65, after which year, presumably, very few of these damaged people contrive to earn a livelihood. What is true of the men applies no less to the women, and so we have throughout the country an enormous mass of bruised and damaged humanity which never enjoys robust health, which is continually ailing, which provides a multitude of victims for every epidemic, and which, regarded from the purely economic standpoint, never approaches full industrial efficiency, because it is never fit and alert.

I would not paint the picture in too sombre colours. Most of the world's work is routine work, which can be got through more or less satisfactorily at ordinary times, whether for the purpose of the military category, a man is classed C3 or B2. Nevertheless, the C3 man will be oftener on the sick list; he will make more mistakes; he will produce less; he will lose his job sooner; and at any moment of emergency he will be less trustworthy and reliable. His physical deficiencies will increase with the passing years; he will be less able to protect himself and his family; he is more likely to seek support or stimulant from alcohol and then begin to suffer from its cumulative effect. Would it not therefore be better for the State if we took pride, not in rewriting the tables of mortality, but in raising the C3 people to a higher category - not in view of distant military contingencies, but for the immediate purpose of rendering them more efficient citizens, more valuable producers of wealth, parents of a healthier stock, and themselves more contented with their lot?

If we regard the great pool of ill-health and the infinite variety of debilitating ailments, deep-seated and chronic, we are driven to the conclusion that physical inefficiency is at once the most permanent and fruitful cause of individual unhappiness and social discontent. [5] Walt Whitman's lines are worth recalling in this connection:-

> I think I could turn and live with animals,
>   They are so placid and self-contained;
>   I stand and look at them, long and long;
>   They do not sweat and whine about their condition,
>   They do not lie awake in the dark and cry for their sins,
> Not one is dissatisfied, not one is demented with the mania of owing,
>   Not one is respectable or unhappy over the whole earth.

Humans are like animals at least in this, that if they are to be happy and contented they must either keep fit or be kept fit; and the honour of being considered the greatest benefactor to mankind belongs not, as is so often said, to him that can make two blades of grass grow where only one grew before, but to him who can add most to the science of health and raise the standard of fitness throughout the whole community. Surely that would be of more instant value to the State that the preservation of infant life in the first year of existence and the indefinite prolongation of what used to be called the allotted span. If there be any who dislike such a comparison of human values, they may be reassured by the reflection that whatever measures are taken to raise the general standard of life can hardly fail to benefit the infant in the cradle and the aged patient in the Poor Law Infirmary.

The State and the Nation's Health

It must be one of the paramount duties of the State to concern itself more and more intimately with the health of the nation. It can do that by solicitude for those who are sick, and by taking whatever measures are possible to keep them from becoming sick. Its action, in a word, must be both curative and preventative. While the science of medicine was mainly empirical and the causes of disease were either unknown or wrongly attributed, preventative measures by the State were little thought of. Today a long series of Public Health Acts and the still recent creation of a [6] Ministry of Healthattest the full recognition that acceptance by the State and of the public authority to invade this particular domain is no longer challenged. It is seen to be for the common good that the sanitary and the factory inspector are armed with the sanction of the public authority; and as the ameliorative possibilities, latent in preventative measures, are better understood, there will be a growing impatience with the obstacles placed in the way of their effective exercise by selfish or interested parties.

The establishment of the Ministry of Health bore witness, not to the sudden discovery of a new truth, but to the proved results of much admirable work which had been done in the previous half century and the need of its more resolute prosecution. We are now accustomed to the blessings of a pure water supply and efficient systems of drainage and sewerage; we have grown intolerant of the most offensive features of a slum; we have a clearly defined standard of, say, the minimum hygienic requirements of a new house. Throughout the wide field of industrial hygiene we know what conditions are desirable and what are dangerous to health. Our knowledge is fairly complete; the practical difficulties are connected with administration - how to deal with the borderline cases, and how to make the best use of the money at disposal, for improvements are always costly and public expenditure can only be met either out of rates or out of taxes.

Public opinion has to be educated continuously all the time. For example, the compulsory notification of diseases is now extended far beyond its original scope to as many as twenty two notifiable diseases, and will probably be extended much further within the near future. The agitation when the [7] National Health Insurance Act was being passed is now remembered with a smile for the broken vows that were registered never to lick Mr. Lloyd George's new fangled stamps. But even the greatest changes are very soon accepted as if they had always been, provided that on the whole the new institution functions well and promotes, in spite of whatever defects, the general well being.

Preventative Legislation

The scope of preventative legislation is almost limitless, and we are likely to see the State interfering - or shall I say intervening? - more and more in the interests of public health. For example, all the Licensing Acts of the last half century are based in the last instance on the argument that stricter regulation is necessary for the general public health and safety, and it is obvious that that particular field of controversial legislation is by no means exhausted.

Moreover, the State is beginning to assert its regulative powers in departments of social and even of family life from which hitherto it has held aloof, and its justification will always be that the interests of public health override the personal interest of the individual, who, as a member of the community, does not and cannot act to himself alone. We may expect sharp controversy, for example, if and when the State concerns itself directly with eugenics, and asserts its solicitude for a generation not yet born, not by the provision of cradles and nurseries, but even by the very determination of parentage itself. This might have seemed fantastic a few years ago. But now that the idol of state socialism has been set up for our worship we may be sure that sooner or later the theorists will attempt to invest the Ministry of Health with increasingly autocratic powers, and will seek to transform the whole medical service of this country into a State service, with State hospitals, State examinations for degrees, and the state payment of doctors. This would be a perfectly logical development in a socialist State, nor can it be pretended that such a system could not be worked. But whether it would be as efficient as our present system, whether it would be as acceptable to the general body of the people, and whether the vastly increased cost would be repaid by equivalent advancement of a medical knowledge or improvement in the public health, there is room for the very greatest doubts.

Doctor and Patient.

The patient's right to choose his medical advisor - which right is indispensable to the creation of the perfect relationship between them - has contributed largely to the smooth working of the National Health Insurance Act. There are roughly thirteen million insured persons rather than thirteen million medical practitioners on the panels. These are not, as some ill-informed critics of the service would seem to assume, a separate and inferior class of men. They are in every sense of the word general practitioners, and the service they give is a general practitioner's service.

To each patient on his list the insurance practitioner accepts the relationship of a family doctor, just as he would do if he were called in by a private patient. He gives to each the skill and attention within his power, and he gives them, as a rule, cheerfully and willingly, as he has contracted to do. One sometimes hears general complaints of too rapid and casual diagnosis; but when the waiting room is full the same complaints are not wholly unheard even in the most august thoroughfares of the London specialists. The true test of value of the service given is to be found in the fact that in 1924 only 404 complaints were received by Insurance Companies and investigated by their expert sub-committees, and in only four cases did the more serious charges result in the removal of the practitioners' names from the Medical List.

It is likely that a better service would be provided if each insurance practitioner were selected for inclusion in the list by some official of the Ministry of Health, and if he were required to give even more detailed and minute account of his practice and submit still more voluminous reports. The panel would still be composed of exactly the same people, and even if the allotted quota of patients were reduced, is it at all certain that the individual patient would receive a greater share of the doctors attention?

We know what happens in all State services. The red tape machine would soon be started; more and more reports would be called for; the doctor might see fewer patients but the volume of his activities would be in no wise lessened; and the cost of the service to the taxpayer would be enormously increased. You will not make the panel doctor a better doctor by making him more of a civil servant and less of a doctor; nor will you make the thirteen million patients more contented with their treatment.

The reform that is most required in connection with the insurance service is one which shall link up the insurance practitioner with the consultant physician and the consultant surgeon, and give the insured patient the benefit of the profession's specialized, as well as of its general knowledge.

The Voluntary Hospitals

Nowhere is the principle of voluntaryism so well worth maintaining as in connection with the hospitals; nowhere has it been so triumphantly maintained. It is sometimes suggested that the chief virtue of voluntary agencies is to do the rough pioneer work in difficult and intractable places, to create a favourable public opinion, and then, in due process of time, to hand control to some department of State which will carry on the work upon an altogether larger scale. Indeed, I have seen it stated that voluntaryists ought to be proud to merge their small individualities into the larger being of a public department and lose themselves like rivers in the sea. But the enthusiastic friends of the voluntary hospitals are human beings, not mere charitable machines which function altruistically because their well disciplined hearts happen to be set that way. They are proud of their work. They love it. They see results which encourage and inspire them. They do not want to sink themselves, but to express themselves. The gratitude of those who are healed is sweet to their ears. Voluntaryism is the very life and soul of the whole hospital movement.

It is not suggested that the hospitals would wither if the voluntary principle were abandoned. They would still multiply and prosper. Their orderly routines might well show an even more brilliant imposing efficiency. But the rules and regulations would lengthen. The spirit of institution would suffer change and lose something - I fear much - of its geniality and kindliness. Why is it that such a difference exists today between the voluntary hospital and the Poor Law Infirmary, which is often better constructed and much better equipped? If you ask a patient to which he would rather be sent, why does he always say the hospital? To some extent the old hard, unforgettable associations and traditions of the Poor Law still chill the heart. But that is not the whole truth. There is something inherent in officialdom which freezes the genial application of whatever new principles of kindliness and mercy it can never be thawed right out.

Hospitals and the State

Other countries have their State hospitals services. Some of you may remember that certain British delegates who visited the show hospital of the Medical State Services of Soviet Russia were enormously impressed by the freshwater tank in which they saw the live fish whether so much as the heads and tails reached the patients in the wards, and whether even this agreeable luxury was much compensation for the complete inadequacy of that particular State medical service to cope with a hundredth part of a 1 per cent of the disease and suffering in Russia.

Let us stand by the principle of voluntaryism in the hospitals at whatever cost of energy and patience required for their adequate provision and efficient maintenance. I need not remind this audience that it will take a vast and sustained effort to provide 10,000 additional beds which the Voluntary Hospitals Commission has declared to be necessary. For that effort the friends of the hospitals will soon have to brace themselves, There is to be no financial assistance from the State. The Minister of Health last February very reluctantly came to the conclusion that no subvention was possible, at any rate at the moment, and so the hope that the Government might repeat its unconditional grant of half a million to the hospitals after the war, in recognition of their invaluable war work and of the utter impossibility during the war period of keeping abreast of their requirements, has been cast to the ground.

Unless this second grant had been as unconditional as the first, I do not know that I am altogether sorry at the Government's decision. If the Ministry had begun to impose conditions of control it might well have marked the beginning of the end of the voluntary system. I contend that the work done by the hospitals is of such inestimable value, and the confidence placed in them by the public is so well justified, that the State, if it makes any subvention at all should do so without restrictions, knowing that the money will be judiciously expended. The hospitals should beware of even the mildest beginnings of State control and the relentless, however friendly, grip of any State department.

However, as there is to be no grant, these particular anxieties do not arise, and the supporters of the hospitals must shoulder their burden. So large a sum as four or five millions for new capital expenditure will take a very considerable time to raise for, over and above all this, the maintenance cost has to be found for each new bed provided, and this means an additional recurrent annual cost of £148 per bed. Many of us were disappointed that once again the Chancellor of the Exchequer in the last Budget failed to exempt bequests to hospitals from liability to legacy duty. That is claimed as an act rather of justice than of grace. The toll taken by the State is an interception of charity which is repugnant to good feeling and a sense of fair play to the suffering.

The hospitals, of course, in their turn, owe to their generous supporters the duty of sound economic management, which in turn depends primarily upon the choice of governors. Those which show the best financial balance sheets usually have upon their board of management some outstanding figure of marked ability who has made the local hospital his hobby, his interest, his care, and his pride. However that may be, there must be the undoubted assurance of economic and prudent management if the full support of the public is to be continued. It may well be that a closer co-operation between hospitals - large and small, general and special - is possible and desirable, and that considerable economies might be effected without infringing the real autonomy of each institution, which is so properly and jealously guarded. Charitable effort in this country has always been specially subject to the besetting sin of overlapping and wasteful management. Voluntaryists must be ready to face a searching criticism of their accounts by business men whom, if they are wise, they will invite and welcome to their councils.

CHANGING TYPE OF HOSPITAL PATIENT.

Again, we must not shut our eyes to the rapidly changing character of the personnel of hospital patients. The hospital is no longer the lazar-house of the destitute, the place to which homeless and plague-stricken outcasts crawled to die, or into which they were herded if they seemed too noisome and dangerous to be tolerated at large. Such it was in medieval times; then came the period, which lasted more or less down to our own day, when the hospital was still exclusively used by such as were too poor to pay for the ministrations of a doctor. Some people still hold that this should be the fundamental function of any hospital which is supported by public sub-scriptions, and I agree that this primary purpose for which hospitals exist - namely that of taking in and caring for the indigent poor must in no way be shelved or neglected. But we have advanced far beyond that simple conception in these days, and we shall advance much further still, if only because the hospitals, from being mere infirmaries, have become the cen-tres of the best medical and surgical skill in the areas they serve. The best nursing, the latest scientific apparatus, all are concentrated there for the service of the poor, and while the rich and the well-to-do can look after themselves, there remain large intermediary classes of the population who are cut off from the best skill because, on the one hand, they cannot afford the fees, and, on the other, they are not of the class for which the hospitals were intended. If that were pressed it would indeed be intolerable, espe-cially in view of the increasing expansiveness of any serious operation or illness, the cost of nursing homes, and the palpable unfairness of leaving out in the cold the great body of the middle classes, whose financial bet-terment has by no means kept pace with that of the superior artisan class, and who have been in the past, according to their means, good and loyal friends of the hospitals.

WARDS FOR PAYING PATIENTS.

It is certain, therefore, in my opinion, that we shall see a steady extension of the principle of the paying ward, and even of the paying hospital, for the use of the patient who pays in accordance with his means. In many hospitals today all but the very poorest patients are expected to contribute to the cost of their healing, and there is little need to lament the disappear-ance of the old principle that the hospitals were absolutely free - a princi-ple which, in fact, was often grossly abused. The interests of the middle classes deserve attention no less than those of any other class. May we not, therefore, look forward to a time when every general hospital will be well equipped with paying wards, or will have a paying hospital in asso-ciation with it, served by the same staff and the same nurses? A middle-class patient who is a suitable hospital case could be seen by the almoner of the hospital, and, after stating his income and position, terms could be arranged according to means. Naturally that will open up the question of fees for the surgeon or the physician, and some obvious and possibly difficult adjustments would have to be made but no vital principle that I can see would be endangered by the payment of these special fees, or even by the hospital itself making a substantial profit on such cases which would help towards the maintenance of more beds in the non-paying wards. Such changes are likely to be gradual; we can carefully note what effect, if any, they have upon the flow of subscriptions. Personally, I do not think that the charitable donor is likely to object to a middle-class paying patient receiving a share of the fruits of his bounty. He had a much more valid grievance against those who abused the freedom of the hospital and never contributed a penny to its funds.

The medical profession is generous in accommodating its fees according to the patient's income. But every medical man knows cases where the serious illness of the breadwinner or the wife or child has exhausted the savings of a middle-class home or crippled it with a load of debt. The middle-class patient, moreover, is the principal sufferer from the high fees of the nursing home, another institution which has a necessary place in our existing system for dealing with the cure of disease, but which is by no means immune from well justified criticism. Is it, indeed, too much to say that the extreme expensiveness of nursing homes - I speak, of course, in purely general terms - is contributing as much as anything else to the extension of the system of paying wards in hospitals and the call for its rapid development?

WORKING CLASS CONTRIBUTIONS TO HOSPITALS.

There is also another important development in process with regard to the hospitals. More and more in the large cities and industrial areas the hospitals are coming to rely upon the subscriptions of the working classes, contributing through a general Hospital Sunday collection or through a direct trade union levy. In this district, for example, the Hospital Saturday Committee are very good friends of the hospitals, contributing willingly, cheerfully, and without condition or stipulation as to the hospital service for their members they will receive in return. This trust is not misplaced. They lose nothing by not dealing in terms of contract and demanding the strict recognition of a right.

Many county hospitals are stimulating interest in their work by forming a collecting committee in every village and persuading the cottages to subscribe to its funds, almost in the same way that they subscribe to a sick or benefit club. This will necessarily lead to a great extension of the hospitals, for those who pay will expect to receive hospital treatment as a *right* in case of serious illness. When the small contributor begins to talk about 'our hospital,' the vitalizing spirit of voluntaryism is at work. Open the door to State direction and control and the cold east wind of officialism will contrive an entrance too.

THE GENERAL MEDICAL COUNCIL.

Another aspect of the relationship of the medical profession to the public has been much discussed of late in connection with certain punitive actions taken by the General Medical Council. This discussion has removed many misconceptions as to the specific purposes for which the Council was created by the legislature - not, as was too often supposed, to serve as the executive of a powerful professional organization protecting the interests of its members, but as a body entrusted with powers, clearly defined first by Parliament and later by the judges, for the protection of the public against the incompetence and the imposture of unqualified medical prac titioners. Practically the only criticism directed against the Council arises from the fidelity with which, in these days of growing laxity, it has maintained its jealous regard for the purity of its register of membership. There are really two main questions in which the lay public is interested. The first is: Is it or is it not to the public advantage that the General Medical Council should set its face like flint against professional self-advertisement? The second is: Is it or is it not to the public advantage that the Council should show a less uncompromising attitude towards the unqualified practitioner and a greater leniency towards those who transgress its stringent rule against covering?

The rule against professional self-advertisement is unquestionably in the public interest. The publicity agents of the commercial world may sound their slogan as they will about ' Truth in advertising.' But, as Dr. Johnson once shrewdly observed, the secret of advertising is' large promise; ' and large, limitless, boundless promise is wholly out of place in the practice of the medical art. Inseparable from quackery, it is the sign manual of the unqualified nostrum-monger. In my view, this most salutary rule against professional self-advertisement needs to be observed more than ever now that the old reticences are being broken down in so many directions, and in view of the growing disposition to discuss all medical subjects freely in the public press.

Whether we like it or not, that school of thought is prevailing which holds that the open forum is the best of all popular educators, that ignorance is the greatest of all dangers, and that publicity alone can create the new public opinion out of which it is hoped there may issue a higher moral sense and a stronger self-control. The public press will devote more and more space to the problems of public health, and it is obviously desirable that what is written should be written with authority. No anonymous article on a technical or professional subject carries the weight of the signed contribution, and if doctors write for the lay press, as they will be urged to do with an ever-increasing insistence, the opportunities of professional self-advertisement will greatly multiply.

Nevertheless, it is to the common interest of the profession and of the public that these temptations - not, indeed, to inform the public of what is for its good, but to inform it in such a way as to advertise and glorify the writer and conduce to his personal gain - shall be resisted, and that the Medical Council shall still continue to exercise its powerful restraints In other countries a different practice may be followed, but till it is shown that their method is more conducive than ours, either to the dignity and character of the profession or to the protection of the public from the charlatan and the quack, these restraints should not be weakened. Many borderline cases are bound to occur as they do at present, but I assume that the Council will continue to act with that judicial discretion which has on several occasions received the acknowledgment of the highest legal authorities.

UNQUALIFIED PRACTITIONERS

As for the unqualified practitioner, I say without hesitation that the Medical Council cannot and must not recognize him, and therefore cannot and must not abate its strong reprobation of covering. To do so would be to stultify itself and the Register, which is its special creation and instrument. It cannot, to borrow an expression from another profession, recognize any orders but its own. I do not mean that it should seek to induce the State, to make unqualified practice illegal as is done in some countries. Even if that were desirable, the public would not permit it. Public opinion has a sporting fancy for the outsider, and outsiders, even the rankest, do sometimes win. But, though rare and exceptional cases may arise, the Council cannot extend either the bow of friendship or the nod of recognition to any unqualified practitioner without placing itself in a false position. If an unqualified practitioner really discovers a new cure or treatment for one of the ills of humanity, his consulting room will not long remain empty of patients. If his method is genuine it will endure, and, soon or late, it will win general recognition. But no one can reasonably expect admission to the *Medical Register* - or to any appendix thereto - by any except the approved channels.

Admission is not a question of initiation and secret rite. It is a plain question whether the entrant has gone through certain courses of medical training and passed the presented examinations. How can either be abandoned with safety to the public interest? The unqualified practitioner may or may not have sufficient general medical knowledge to enable him to make a diagnosis. A few may have gone through some sort of a medical course; the majority have not. It takes the ordinary medical man five years or more to complete his course; the unqualified man often does not give as many months. He professes to be a specialist without even elementary grounding in the essential rudiments of medical knowledge. I say nothing against the science of osteopathy or these uses of the manipulative treatment. I only say that those who practice these arts should have the medical knowledge without which they may do their patients infinite harm.

The champions of the unqualified practitioner fall into two main classes. One consists of those good people, invincibly credulous and optimistic by nature, who chatter about cures and treatment as others chatter about politics, and on whose ears well-syllabled words like ''osteopathy' and 'manipulation' fall with a sweetly modulated cadence of solace and hope. The other class consists of the ingenious rebels against all authority but their own, the sophists of the day, who deride professional etiquette and grimace at professional tradition. Perhaps here and there certain solemn pomposities do linger even yet in our profession and an occasional grin at these may do no harm; but the health of the public is no grinning matter.

The plain truth remains that behind the rare - the very rare - unqualified practitioners of whose success so much is made, but whose failures pass is unrecorded, there are scores of other practitioners of technique ancient and modern, who are eager to take advantage of any momentary opening of the door, which it is the declared policy of the General Medical Council to keep tightly shut.

A selfish obscurantist policy would he totally contrary to the free spirit of Inquiry which animates the medical science of today. But this is neither selfish nor obscurantist. Whatever in any modern technique is tested and proved good is sure of eventual adoption and not even the gates of the General Medical Council will prevail against it. But the tests and the proofs must be such as are recognized by that universal medical science which talks a common language throughout the world and which alone can securely judge.

The public mind was perhaps never more impatient of authority than it is today. Unable to distinguish with certainty where the trained expert alone has any claim to be heard, multitudes of people are still prepared to accept offhand the morning and the evening stunt of their favourite newspapers, which are then forgotten as soon as read. So many romantic impossibilities of yesterday have become the casual scientific commonplaces of today that the very word 'miracle ' itself has shrunk back to its original connotation, and even the wisest have still no effective retort to Hamlet's gibe as to the inadequacy of their philosophy to embrace the content of heaven and earth. Nevertheless Authority remains unshaken on her intellectual throne, though the gusts of change may a little disorder her raiment and Authority herself acquires a riper wisdom and a larger experience with the passage of the years.

The medical profession is a living profession. It is forever breaking new ground, mapping and charting as it goes, and the necessary correction of a too hasty observation or faulty induction, as well as the need to include new knowledge, requires us from time to time to revise our atlases. And though we may be fairly confident that the older continents are now accurately charted, there is always the need to be prepared for the crash of old-established notions and for restless movements of insurgence along boundaries which once appeared to have been fixed for all time.

It is a sobering reflection that, but for the violent wrench out of its true direction which medical science suffered two thousand years ago, some of our most recent discoveries might well have been among the oldest blessings to suffering humanity. With the abandonment of the one true scientific method of patient observation and careful induction there was also unhappily discarded that sagest of all the medical maxims of ancient Hellas, that the physician is the servant of Nature.

The human race has suffered sorely because medical art and science took so tragically wrong a turning, after making so brilliant a start. Probably the perversity of the patient was largely responsible. Popular demand has always been insistent for the bottle of medicine and the charm. Science, under the lead of Aristotle, had sought to exorcise the potion-monger and the thaumaturgist, but back they came with a rush and when the ancient scientist candidly admitted that he was uncertain as to the nature or the cure of the complaint the patient soon betook himself to one who promised a safe, quick and pleasant cure.

The great truth that the supernatural and the scientific do not run well in double harness need, I believe, a resonant restatement today. The profession is often blamed for its instinctive repugnance to the introduction of the supernatural into the art of healing. This is attributed to that professional jealousy which is supposed to seize every doctor when an unregistered hand assumes the gold-headed cane which is the symbol of his craft. I do not know that there is more professional jealousy among doctors than there is among lawyers; I doubt if there is as much as among plumbers and bricklayers.

No professional body loves an outsider who usurps its own particular functions, and long experience has shown that the unqualified practitioner of medicine is in double measure an unqualified danger to the public. And yet clients troop to his door or rain in upon him a shower of post-office orders if he is a shrewd exploiter at once of the foibles and the earnest longings of mankind. So it has ever been; so it will ever be. As the cynic long ago said: "If the public want to be deceived, let them." But the obvious fact is that the public want not to be deceived but to be cured and that is why, if an authorized prescription in our cryptic Latin fails to bring

between them. The public expect much of the doctor and take much for granted. I like that old story of the woman of Selkirk who, observing her doctor ride by, said to the neighbour with whom she was gossiping, "Aye, there goes the doctor - honest man! He's brought all my ten bairns into the world and never got a rap for one of them."

The national health insurance scheme has at any rate checked the more unconscionable draughts which once used to be made upon the deep well of medical disinterestedness, but the profession still gives much for which it receives no direct return but gratitude and sometimes even that is left unspoken. That, however, is the penalty of altruism and an established reputation for kindness of heart and that is partly why the doctor holds his place in the public esteem, despite the satirists, the playwrights, and the novelists who still delight to poke their fun - on the whole not unfriendly - at his etiquette, his bedside manner, his scraps of weird Latinity, and the artifice with which the wild surmise of an impossible diagnosis may still be masked under the grave, slow smile of apparently assumed certainty.

THE REAL DOCTOR.

But if you want the portrait of the real doctor we go, not to books, but to life. We expect him, not in vain, to combine with knowledge the understanding that springs from intuition till it is most richly reinforced by experience to bear a tranquilizing influence, and to radiate confidence and hope. We expect him to exemplify, like the surgeon of whom Henley wrote:-

> Faultless patience and unyielding will,
> Beautiful gentleness and splendid skill."

caring always for life as a thing most precious, quick-and now happily well able - to spare the sufferer one unnecessary pang, the restorer of health a strong sure help in the more supreme moments:-

> "In many a house of care, when pain has forced a footing there,
> And there's a Darkness on the stair will not be turned away."

Such is the doctor, the family doctor, who is more to the public at large than the most learned and the most wise who dwell in those two long, unlovely, parallel streets of London, where the waters of healing are laid on at the main. He is still the same, even though he is called upon in these days to enter the service - the preventive service - of the Ministry of Health, disarming disease before it strikes, saving the firstborn, not by a smear of blood on the lintel, but by a dash of disinfectant in the drain, and sometimes purchasing the immunity of millions as cheaply as the restoration of a few convalescents to health. The doctor's professional qualifications may change as medical science advances; the qualifications he needs to win him the confidence of his fellows are unchangeable as human nature itself. That confidence it is the policy of this great Association and the desire of every one of its members always to deserve and for ever to retain.

From the "Trent and go wandering by" By R. G. Hogarth
The Thoroton Press

---

1 The Pay Bed Wing was opened in 1938 from a donation of £25,000 from John Player, plus £4,600 from the Nottingham Freemasons.
2 See Presidential Address
3 A book was produced for the occasion by J. Eric B. Snell, M.A., M.B., B.C, & N. P. R. Galloway, M.B., and was entitled "The Book of Nottingham 1926"
4 Memorial Nurses Home, opened in 1923 by the Prince of Wales, and provided 130 rooms. In 1927 a fifth storey was built adding another 40 rooms.
5 Walter Whitman, American poet, journalist and writer. Born 13 May, 1818, West Hills, Long Island, New York. Died 26 March, 1892, Camden, New Jersey.
6 The Ministry of Health was formed in 1919 from out of the Local Government Board, previously the poor Law Commissioners. 1919 also saw the formation of the General Nursing Council.
7 National Health Act was passed in 1911.

W.R. SMITH M.D. (London) F.R.C.S. (England)
President of the
Nottingham Medico-Chirurgical Society 1914-1919

William Robert Smith:- The Willows, Beeston, Nottingham. (Smith, Hannon & Cale). Doctor of Medicine, London, 1895; Bachelor of Medicine, 1892; Bachelor of Surgery (Honours) 1894; Fellow of the Royal College of Surgeons (England), 1896; Member of the Royal College of Surgeons & Licentiate of the Royal College of Physicians (London) 1892; Licentiate of the Society of Apothecaries, 1892 (Kings College); Honorary Medical Officer for the Beeston Orphans, and Medical Officer and Public Vaccination Officer for the Beeston and Wollaton District, Basford Poor Union. Surgeon for the Nottingham Hospital for Women and the National Shell Filling Factory, Chilwell, Nott's. Consultant Surgeon, Military Hospitals, Nottingham. Temporary Assistant Surgeon, Nottingham General Hospital. Chairman of the Nottingham Panel Committee; Certified Factory Surgeon; Surgeon to the Post Office. President of the Nottingham Medico-Chirurgical Society; Vice President of the Midland and West Countries Obstetric and Gynaecology Society. Fellow of the Royal Society of Medicine (Member of the Gynaecological Secretariat). Late:- Sambrooke Medical Registrar; House Surgeon and House Physician, Kings College Hospital. House Surgeon, St. Peter's Hospital;   Senior House Surgeon, Nottingham General Hospital.

Medical Directory 1919

Born at Honingham, Norfolk in 1869 William Smith was educated at Bracondale School, Norwich and King's College Hospital, which he entered with an exhibition. He won prizes and scholarships each year from 1887 to 1890. He qualified with the Conjoint Diploma and the London M.B. in 1892, took the B.S. in 1894, and gained the M.D. in 1895 and the Fellowship in 1896. After servicing as a house surgeon, house physician and medical registrar at King's he settled in Nottingham.

In 1896, while senior house surgeon at the Nottingham General Hospital, he installed the first X Ray apparatus, the year following Roentgen's discovery. It was installed in a disused bathroom at a cost of £100 paid for by Sir Charles Seely, the chairman of the hospital. Later Smith introduced electric heating in the Women's Hospital in place of the coal fires that were used in the wards and even in the operating theatre

Smith settled in Beeston, near Nottingham in 1898 and was in general practice there for fifty years. He also specialised in midwifery and from 1903 was for thirty years surgeon to the Castle Gate Women's Hospital, Nottingham. He was also surgeon to the Collins Maternity Hospital and consulting obstetrician to the Nottingham Corporation and the Nottinghamshire County Council

He was President of the Nottingham Medico-Chirurgical Society from 1914-1919, Vice President of the Section of Obstetrics and Gynaecology of the British Medical Association at its annual meeting in 1920, and Chairman of the Nottingham Division of the B. M. A., 1928-1929. He retired from hospital work in 1933 but continued his private practice till 1947. In the early days he made his rounds by a pony and trap, but bought a motorcar in 1906 which he drove for 100,000 miles before changing to a new one. He made his evening visits on a bicycle till 1947.

Smith was a handsome man with a bustling walk and smiling eyes and mouth which endeared him to all his patients. When he retired they gave him a handsome present which he spent on a tour of South Africa. He then settled in Sheringham, Norfolk living with a nephew and enjoying golf, bridge and gardening.

He was an active Mason and kept up life long friendships with his contemporaries from medical school, P. T. Beal F.R.C.S., whose father had been senior physician at King's and John Wood M.R.C.S., son of the senior surgeon. Smith died on 6th February 1966 aged 96 years.

Dr W.T. ROWE M.C., M.D. (London) M.R.C.P.
President of the
Nottingham Medico-Chirurgical Society 1919-1920

William Trethowan Rowe M.C. :- 36, Regent Street, Nottingham. Doctor of Medicine, London (Gold Medal), 1902; Bachelor of Surgery, 1901; Member of the Royal College of Physicians (London) 1910; Member of the Royal College of Surgeons and Licentiate of the Royal College of Physicians (London) 1897; (St. Barthlomews) Physician, Nottingham General Hospital; Physician, Ransom Sanatorium. Surgeon-Captain, South Nott's Hussars Yeomanry. Member of the British Medical Association. Ex- Vice President of the Abernethy Society. Formerly:- House Surgeon and External Midwifery Assistant, St. Bartholomews Hospital; Civil Surgeon attached to the R.A.M.C. and the National Field Force 1899-1900; House Surgeon, West London Hospital.

Medical Directory 1919

William Trethowan Rowe was born on 30th December 1874 at Constantine, Cornwall, and was educated at Chelmsford Grammar School and St. Bartholomew's Hospital, qualifying with the Conjoint Diploma in 1897. He graduated M.B., B.S. in 1901, and a year later proceeded M.D. and was awarded the gold medal. After two years resident appointments in his teaching hospital and at the West London Hospital, he volunteered for service in the Boer War and sailed for South Africa in 1899 as a civil surgeon to the Imperial Forces. He was present at the relief of Mafeking in 1900. He returned to England in 1902, having been awarded the Queen's Medal for South Africa with four clasps. He then set up in general practice in Nottingham. In 1906 he was elected to the honorary consulting staff of the Nottingham General Hospital, where he remained until his retirement as senior physician in 1946.

In 1905 he joined the South Nottinghamshire Hussars as a surgeon lieutenant. During the first world war he served with the rank of major, first at Gallipoli - where he was awarded the Military Cross and Bar - and afterwards in France. A member of the British Medical Association, he was a representative at the Annual Meeting in 1906, Chairman of the Nottingham Division in 1925-6, in which year he was also honorary secretary of the section of medicine at the Annual Meeting and, in 1927-8, president of the Midland Branch. During the second world war he was appointed group officer in charge of arrangements for the receipt of convoys in Nottingham.

In an obituary of Dr. Rowe by Patrick Henry O'Donovan it was said of him:- Dr. Rowe was a "character." He had a transparent honesty, and the gift of inspiring in his patients supreme confidence. The nursing staff were devoted to him and he was kindness itself to the hospital residents. He was probably the last of that type of practitioner who, although in general practice, also served on the staff of a large general hospital and had a big consulting practice. He had no false pride and was quick to call for a second opinion from a fellow and often younger, consultant.

He was a well known figure, being driven in a smart, always open, two-seater coupe, wearing a buttonhole supplied daily by a grateful patient. After retiring from the hospital staff he continued in practice in spite of increasing pain and disability from a severely arthritic hip. He was an active Mason, having been initiated in the Nottinghamshire Lodge in 1913. He was a keen golfer, and in 1934 was captain of the Nottinghamshire Golf Club.

The war service of Dr. W.T. Rowe M.D., M.R.C.P.

Gazetted Surgeon Lieutenant to the South Notts Hussars, 1905. Called up in August, 1914: went east in April, 1915 and to Gallipoli in August, 1915, as Medical Officer to the South Notts Hussars, the Sherwood Rangers, and the Derbyshire Yeomanry. Had a warm and very busy time at Suvla Bay, attending to wounded among burning scrub and under heavy fire, was mentioned in dispatches and awarded the Military Cross. Invalided in September, 1915, with paratyphoid. After that, home duties, then to a base hospital in France, and finally in February, 1917, officer in charge of a medical division. He was demobilized November, 1918, with the rank of

Lieutenant-Colonel.

> Extracts from the Historical Records of the South Notting-
> hamshire Hussars Yeomanry, 1794-1924, pp. 223, 228

Battle of Scimitar Hill. August 21st, 1915.

To make matter worse the scrub caught fire. The Medical Officer of the South Nott's Hussars, Captain Rowe, remained out in the open helping to rescue the wounded, under heavy shell fire. Captain Rowe's gallant conduct saved many lives.

October 2nd, 1915.

Captain Rowe, the regimental Medical Officer, was about this time sent to Hospital, much to everyone's regret, as his cheery words on sick parade did much to keep men going - even more so than his No. 9's.

Despite the devoted efforts of Captain Rowe, the regiment gradually decreased in number from disease and from casualties in the firing line. But the men of the South Nott's Hussars stuck it, one and all, and many remained on duty when they were almost too weak to walk, and only left for hospital under compulsion.

On November 3rd they were evacuated. The last march of this remnant of a Regiment, although it was but a two mile walk from the trenches to the beach, was a great effort to many, so weak was their condition, caused by dysentry and want of sleep.

J.F. BLURTON M.R.C.S. (England)
(1862 - 1949)
President of the
Nottingham Medico-Chirurgical Society 1920-1921

John Fredrick Blurton:- 11, Radcliffe Road, West Bridgford and Arkwright Street, Nottingham. M.B. Durham, 1887, M.R.C.S. (England), 1887 (Queen's College, Birmingham and University of Durham) J.P., Member of the British Medical Association. Late:- Resident Physician, Obstetrics and Oph-thalmology, House Surgeon, Queen's Hospital, Birmingham.

Medical Directory 1919

The information is from an obituary which appeared in the Nottinghamshire Guardian 6th May, 1949.

The death took place yesterday at 4, Valley Road, West Bridgford, of Dr. Frederick Blurton, for many years a well known medical practitioner and a Justice of the Peace for Nottingham since 1909.

Dr. Blurton, who was 87, was in practice over a long period at 11, Radcliffe Road and Arkwright Street, He was educated at Queen's College, Birmingham and Durham University, and took his Bachelor of Medicine degree at the latter in 1887, and also secured his membership of the Royal College of Surgeons in the same year. He was later ophthalmic house surgeon at Queen's Hospital, Birmingham.

During the period he has been associated with Nottingham he was a prominent member of the Southern Division Liberal Association and a member of the High Pavement Chapel Congregation.

He is an ex-president of the Nottingham Medico-Chirurgical Society and a member of the British Medical Association. His elder son died some years ago while experimenting with a new method of anaesthesia.

Local Studies Library,
Angel Row, Nottingham.

MISS SARAH GRAY (1921-1922)
President of the
Nottingham Medico-Chirurgical Society 1921-1922

Miss Sarah Gray, 21, Regent Street, Nottingham. F.R.C.S. "Ireland." 1900; L.R.C.P., L.R.C.S., "Edinburgh." Licentiate of the Royal Faculty of Physicians and Surgeons, "Glasgow," 1888. (London School of Medicine for Women). Honorary Surgeon to the Nottingham and Nott's Convalescent Homes; Medical Examiner to the Board of Education and Nottingham Education Committee. Member of the Federation Medical Women and the Nottingham Medico-Chirurgical Society. Late:- Resident Medical Officer East Hospital, Homerton; Assistant to Physicians in Outpatients, New Hospital for Women; Resident Medical Officer, Clapham Maternity Hospital. Author "Is Alcohol properly described as a Stimulant?" *Medical Magazine*, 1902; "Case of Osteomalacia," *Lancet, 1913.*

The Medical Directory 1941

1860 - 1941
F.R.C.S. Ireland, L.R C.P. Edinburgh.

Dr. Sarah Gray has an honourable place amongst pioneer medical women. Born in Tipperary she determined on a medical career at a time when such a course was still considered eccentric,for a woman if not improper. She studied in London. London granted no degrees to women, so in 1888 she took the Scottish conjoint qualification.

Three years later she settled down in Nottingham, the first woman to undertake general practice in that city. Opposition was bitter. Women doctors were not wanted, except perhaps by women; certainly not by the profession. The first years were bleak and discouraging. Nevertheless, in 1899 she was elected to her first public appointment. At the Women's Hospital, Nottingham, she became assistant surgeon in charge of outpatients and, as it was then called, chloroformist.

Her advent was viewed by most of her colleagues with distrust. For a whole year, one of them insisted on being present whenever she administered an anaesthetic, eager to discover and proclaim some negligence or inefficiency. She disappointed him. She applied for the post of consulting surgeon in charge of inpatients. Her suitability could not be questioned, yet some excuse had to be found for keeping her out. She was told that her qualifications, the highest open to women when she took them, were not high enough. Nothing daunted, at the age of forty, she took her F.R.C.S.I. The opposition was cowed and, in 1902, she became one of the two most highly qualified members of the staff. She became surgeon to the Nottingham and Notts Convalescent Home, medical examiner to the Board of Education and the Nottingham Education Committee. When her outstanding ability and her sense of duty failed to convince she carried the day by warm sympathy, her sense of humour, her volcanic energy, her Irish brogue, or her golden voice. She even mastered the early motorcar.

In the year 1921-22 she was elected the first, and up to that present time the only, woman president of the Nottingham Medico-Chirurgical Society. She could, and did, laugh at her difficulties. She had gained her rightful place. She had many interests in the city where she practised for 37 years. Temperance, foreign missions, rescue work, social reform in all aspects were sure of her sympathy and help. She was an eloquent speaker and contributed to articles to the medical press. Her life was rich and full and her loss will bring grief to many.

THOMPSON HENDERSON M.D. (Edinburgh)
(1879 - 1962)
President of the
Nottingham Medico-Chirurgical Society 1922-1923

Thompson Henderson:- 15, The Ropewalk, Nottingham. M.D., Edinburgh, M.B., Ch.B., 1900 (University of Edinburgh and Vienna). De Vincentiis Gold Medal, International Ophthalmic Congress, Naples, 1909. Surgeon, Nottingham and Midland Eye Infirmary; Ophthalmic Surgeon, Royal Midland Eye Institute for the Blind. Member of the Royal Medical Society, Edinburgh; Ophthalmic Society, British Medical Association. Late, House Surgeon, Ophthalmic Department, Royal Infirmary Edinburgh. Demonstrator in Anatomy, School of Medicine, Royal College of Surgeons, Edinburgh. House Surgeon, Eye Hospital, Bristol.

Medical Directory 1922

Dr. Thompson Henderson was born at Leghorn, Italy where his family had a business. From George Watson's College he went to study medicine at Edinburgh University where he graduated M.B., Ch.B., at the age of 21. For a time he was demonstrator of anatomy in the Royal College of Surgeons of Edinburgh and, after qualification, he worked as ophthalmic house surgeon in the Edinburgh Royal Infirmary. After further postgraduate study in Vienna and London he set up practice in Nottingham in 1904, marrying in the same year, and for nearly half a century he lived and practiced at the Ropewalk. In 1909 he was appointed honorary surgeon to the Nottingham and Midland Eye Infirmary. A year later he was awarded the gold medal offered by the 11th International Ophthalmological Congress in Naples for the best paper in connection with the treatment of hardening of the eye. In August, 1914 he volunteered for medical work in the Army and served throughout the first world war as a captain. In 1926 he gained the Doyne memorial medal at the Oxford Ophthalmic Congress and for several years his main research work was directed towards discovering the cause of glaucoma and its treatment. Even in his earlier years in Nottingham he undertook research work, installing his own laboratory at his surgery. In 1950 he published a book entitled *Principles of Ophthalmology*. He was also the author of several contributions on ophthalmological subjects. His discoveries brought him world-wide recognition and he was frequently in touch with leading ophthalmologists on the Continent and in America.

Dr. Henderson was president of the Nottingham Medico-Chirurgical Society in 1922/3 and president of the Midland Branch of the British Medical Association in 1935/6. Before this he had represented his Division at several Annual Meetings not long after he came to Nottingham. At the Annual Meeting of the B.M.A. in Nottingham in 1926 he was vice-president of the Section of Ophthalmology. As a relaxation he was fond of golf.

Adapted from an obituary notice.
B.M.J., June 25, 1960

DR E.H. HOUFTON M.D. (London)
(1872 - 1926)
President of the
Nottingham Medico-Chirurgical Society 1923-1924

Ernest Henry Houfton:- Bath House, Mansfield, Nott's. Doctor of Medicine, London, 1899: Bachelor of Medicine (Honours in Obstetrics) 1894; Member of the Royal College of Surgeons and Licentiate of the Royal College of Physicians (London) 1893; Leeds School of Medicine 1889. Medical Officer of Health, Mansfield Woodhouse Urban District Council; Honorary Surgeon, Mansfield Hospital. Formerly:- Resident Obstetrics Officer, General Infirmary Leeds.

Medical Directory 1919

Dr. Ernest Henry Houfton was educated at Leeds University where he gained the entrance medical scholarship in 1889, the junior silver medal in 1880-90 and the Thorpe prize for forensic medicine in 1892. In the following year he obtained the diplomas M.R.C.S., L.R.C.P., and in 1894 graduated M.B., B.S. (London) with honours in obstetrics; he proceeded M.D., in 1899. After holding the appointment of resident obstetric officer to the Leeds General Infirmary he commenced practice in Mansfield in 1903. He was honorary surgeon to the Mansfield Hospital and medical officer of health for the Mansfield Woodhouse Urban District Council. He took an active interest in the Nottingham Division of the British Medical Association; he was a representative in 1913-15 and a deputy representative in 1918-20 and 1925-26. He was vice chairman of the Division in 1920, and was a member for many years of the Contract Practice Sub-Committee of the Medico-Political Committee and the Midland Branch Council. He was a member of the Consultative Council on Medical and Allied Services and secretary of the Notts Panel Committee

In a tribute to Dr. Houfton two colleagues said:- Dr. Houfton was a busy and successful general practitioner and an accomplished surgeon. If he had devoted himself to surgery in his younger days he would have won eminence in that direction. In spite of the pressing demands of a large practice, he devoted much time to the service of his fellow practitioners. Twenty five years ago he was concerned in the formation of the Midland Medical Union, an association which ceased to function on the reconstitution of the British Medical Association. From that time Dr. Houfton was a thorough "B.M.A. man." He had been chairman of the Nottingham Division, and he served as representative during the stormy days preceding and following the passing of the 1911 National Health Insurance Act. He was also a member of the Nottingham Insurance Committee, and had served the Local Medical Panel Committee continuously as secretary, also the Contract Practice Subcommittee of the British Medical Association, and was afterwards appointed to the Consultative Council under the then Minister of Health. Much of his time in latter years was involved with the Mansfield Accident Hospital where, in addition to his active work as a surgeon, he was always ready to help the board of management with his advice.

The colliery surgeons of Nottinghamshire and Derbyshire will always remember Dr. Houfton with the deepest gratitude for his untiring efforts on their behalf in their many negotiations with the colliery clubs. Only those closely associated with him in this work can appreciate the devotion with which he laboured for the benefit of his fellow practitioners. He never spared himself in the service of his patients or of his professional brethren.

DR W STAFFORD M.R.C.S. (England)
President of the
Nottingham Medico-Chirurgical Society 1924-1925

William Stafford:- 110, Mansfield Road, Nottingham. Bachelor of Medicine, Glasgow, 1883; Member of the Royal College of Surgeons (England), 1883 (University of Glasgow). Medical Officer, Training College, University College, Nottingham; Medical Examination Board, Education. Formerly:- Lecturer of Physiology, University College, Nottingham; House Physician and House Surgeon, Western Infirmary, Glasgow; House Surgeon, Dispensary of Skin Diseases.

Medical Directory 1926

HERBERT BELL TAWES
(1878 - 1940)
President of the
Nottingham Medico-Chirurgical Society 1925-1926

Herbert Bell Tawse 16, Regent Street, Nottingham. M.R.C.S.. 8th December 1904; F.R.C.S. 8th December 1904; M.B., Ch.B. Aberdeen 1900. Senior Honorary Surgeon, Nottingham Children's Hospital; Honorary Surgeon Ear Nose and Throat Department, General Hospital, Nottingham; Aural Surgeon, Nottingham Education Committee. Member of the Committee in the Board of Education to enquire into the Prevention of Adenoids & Enlarged Tonsils; Fellow of the Royal Society of Medicine. (Member of the Laryngological Section). President of the Nottingham Medico-Chirurgical Society. Member of the British Medical Association. Late House Surgeon, Throat Hospital, Golden Square; Clinical Assistant, London Throat Hospital; Clinical Assistant, Aural & Throat department, London Hospital.

Medical Directory 1926

Mr. Tawse, was born in Aberdeen in 1878. He received his medical education at Aberdeen University. After a distinguished career as a student, he graduated with honours in 1900. Following subsequent study at King's College Hospital and the London Hospital he took the F.R.C.S. in 1904 and proceeded to devote himself to the study of laryngology, which was to be his life's work. After an appointment as house-surgeon to the Throat Hospital, Golden Square, he settled in Nottingham and, within a short time, was elected honorary assistant surgeon to the Children's Hospital and later, to the General Hospital, Nottingham. Later he was appointed honorary surgeon to the throat and nose department. He was also consulting laryngologist to the Ransom Sanatorium and the Nottingham and Nottinghamshire Education Committee.

In his earlier days Mr. Tawse was for a long time secretary of the Nottingham Medico-Chirurgical Society, one of the eldest medical societies in England, becoming its president in 1925. He did much to further its development and influence. He took a leading part in acquiring an old town house as its headquarters, which afforded not only an excellent lecture room and library, but also facilities for encouraging social life among the medical profession in Nottingham. Mr. Tawse was well known in laryngological circles throughout the country. When the British Medical Association met at Nottingham in 1926 he acted as vice-president of the Section of Laryngology and Otology. At the Aberdeen meeting of the Association in 1939 he was president of the Section of Oto-Rhino-Laryngology. He was a member of the British Medical Association for thirty years. He made many contributions to the literature on his speciality. He was a member of the committee appointed by the Board of Education to consider the causes and prevention of enlarged tonsils and adenoids.

Herbert Bell Tawse died on November 12th 1940. In a tribute a colleague wrote the following:-

By the death of Herbert Tawse the profession sustains a severe loss. He has been a notable and outstanding figure in the medical life of Nottingham for many years. Not only as an eminent exponent of his speciality but also as a man of affairs. I remember well a remark which was made by a senior member of the hospital staff soon after his arrival in Nottingham: "I am much impressed by such mature judgement in a young man." This quality, coupled with shrewd common-sense and a gift of expressing himself simply and directly, ensured that one could expect, and did in fact always receive, a helpful opinion, whether in consultation over a case or in committee in the matters relating to hospital management. His views were always regarded with respect. He was an intense worker and any project undertaken was pursued with unflagging resolution to its completion. With all this he had a keen and kindly sense of humour and was never at a loss in repartee. His interests apart from work were in a country life, especially with rod or gun. He delighted in extending hospitality to his many friends, whether at Wymeswold or in his Aberdeenshire house on the Don. They will long remember the thoughtfulness and kindness of a perfect host.

B.M.J., December 7, 1940.

J.C. BUCKLEY M.D.
(1868 - 1945)
President of the
Nottingham Medico-Chirurgical Society 1926-1927

James Charles Buckley:- 74, St. James Street, Nottingham and Southfield House, Bramcote, Nottinghamshire. M.D. Victoria, 1894, M.B., Ch.B. 1892; (Owen College). Consultant Physician, Venereal Diseases, Nottingham General Hospital. Medical Officer for Venereal Diseases, Nottinghamshire County Council Member of the Nottingham Medico-Chirurgical Society. Late:- Senior Assistant Honorary Physician and Senior Resident Medical Officer, General Hospital, Nottingham. House Physician, Hospital for Consumption, Brompton, London. and Manchester Royal Infirmary. Temporary Lt. R.A.M.C. Author:- "Laryngeal Tuberculosis." (Thesis).

Medical Directory 1926

James Charles Buckley, son of Joseph Mills Buckley, a Manchester Merchant Banker, was born in Manchester in 1868, and was educated at Leys School Cambridge, Owen's College and Manchester Royal Infirmary. After graduating at Manchester and holding various appointments Buckley engaged in General Practice in Nottingham. His interests were attracted to venereology and, by 1914, this speciality made up half his practice. When in the Royal Army Medical Corps his work was confined to venereology and in 1917 he was released for the purpose of starting the Nottingham Clinic. Under his direction the clinic was organized and expanded until it became one of the most important of provincial treatment centres. He was also in charge of clinics at Mansfield and for a time at Newark. He also carried on a large private practice. Although he retired from the Nottingham Clinic in 1938, his activities were not reduced, and he actually opened a centre at Worksop.

In an obituary to Dr. Buckley a colleague said:- Those who worked with Buckley remembered him for his great store of energy and excellent organizing abilities. Good tempered and kindly, he did not suffer fools gladly. This combination enabled him to run a large clinic with the minimum of friction. He played an important part in the growth of venereology as a speciality and, although he did not write many articles, his influence was felt in the committee room as a sound and practical planner who was really able to make things work. In his spare time Buckley bred racing pigeons and secured many successes, notably in long distance races from San Sebastian. During the year 1943/44 the pigeons he bred were used for military purposes.

Dr. Buckley died at his home address of Southfields, Bramcote on November 18th 1945.

B.M.J., December 22nd, 1945, page 905.

ALEXANDER ROBERT TWEEDIE
(1871 - 1936)
President of the
Nottingham Medico-Chirurgical Society 1928-1929

Alexander Robert Tweedie 14, Oxford Street, Nottingham. M.R.C.S. 8th November 1900; F.R.C.S. 12th December 1901; L.R.C.P. 1900. Junior Scholar, Anatomy & Biology, 1896. Honorary Surgeon, Ear Nose and Throat Department, Nottingham General Hospital; Honorary Laryngologist & Aural Surgeon, Royal Midland Institute for the Blind; Aural Specialist, Local Ministry of Pensions. Colonel Royal Army Medical Corps (Volunteers) (retired). Member of the Medical Committee, National Institute for the Deaf; Member of the Laryngological Section & Member of the Council, Otolaryngological Section of the Royal Society of Medicine; Member of the Nottingham Medico-Chirurgical Society. Late Junior Clinical Assistant, Hospital for the Diseases of the Throat, Golden Square; Casualty House Surgeon, Royal Free Hospital; Assistant Surgeon, Nottingham Children's Hospital; Civil Surgeon, South African Field Force. Member of the Collaborative Staff, Journal of Laryngology& Otology.

Medical Directory 1926

Alexander Robert Tweedie was born at Bickley, Kent, in 1871, the third son of Alexander Forbes Tweedie, J.P., of Rawlinson. After finishing his early education at Repton he proceeded to St. Bartholomew's Hospital, and in 1900 obtained the membership of the Royal College of Surgeons and Licentiate of the Royal College of Physicians diplomas. In 1901 he became a Fellow of the Royal College of Surgeons of England. After qualifying he held the appointments of casualty house-surgeon at the Royal Free Hospital and junior clinical assistant at the Hospital for Diseases of the Throat, Golden Square.

He had a remarkable military career. In 1893 he joined the New Zealand Mounted Rifles, and during the South African War he served as a civil surgeon. He then became surgeon lieutenant in the Kent Artillery (Volunteers) for four years and, on the establishment of the Territorial Army in 1908, he transferred to the Royal Army Medical Corps. He took an active part in raising the ambulance of the Notts and Derby Mounted Brigade. During the first world war Mr. Tweedie was present at the opening of the Gallipoli campaign and had command of a large medical organisation in Alexandria. He served all through the expedition to Tripoli against the Senussi. Later he administered a large medical district in Upper Egypt and commanded the Citadel Hospital in Cairo. He was senior medical officer of a division at the final assault on Gaza and in the pursuit of the Turks in the Jaffa-Jerusalem line and beyond. He was demobilised with the rank of lieutenant-colonel, was mentioned in dispatches, and received the Territorial decoration. He retired later from the Territorial Army with the rank of colonel.

In 1908 he was appointed honorary assistant surgeon to the Nottingham Children's Hospital, and in 1911 to the Nottingham General Hospital. In 1919 he became honorary surgeon to the Nottingham General Hospital, and in 1920 honorary surgeon to the newly created ear, nose and throat department. He was also elected to the Nottingham City Council and served on the Health, Asylum Visiting, and Mental Deficiency Committees.

In his professional life he was an outstanding personality. He was vice-president of the Section of Laryngology and Otology at the Annual Meeting of the British Medical Association held in Nottingham in 1926, President of the Nottingham Medico-Chirurgical Society in 1928. His other appointments included honorary laryngological and aural surgeon to the Royal Midland Institution for the Blind, local aural specialist to the Ministry of Pensions, and visiting aural laryngological surgeon to the City Mental Hospital (Mapperley Hospital). He was Fellow of the Royal Society of Medicine, and in 1931 was elected president of the Section of Otology, and at the time of his death was vice president of the Section of Laryngology. He had visited nearly every important aural clinic in Europe and had formed lasting friendships with the leading aural surgeons there. He was a corresponding member of the Austrian Otological Society and Laryngological Society of the Paris Hospitals and for may years was treasurer of the Collegium Oto-rhino-laryngologicum. Besides being a member of the collaborating staff of the *Journal of Laryngology and Otology,* nearly every issue of which contained some of his transactions, he was also a frequent contributor and his name was associated chiefly with his articles on labyrinthine nystagmus, vertigo, and the otolithic and neck reflexes.

For many years he was intimately connected with the Nottingham and Nott's Institute for the deaf and Dumb. It is largely due to his efforts that the institute was housed in an excellent building on Forest Road, Nottingham. He devoted every moment of his spare time to the welfare of the deaf and dumb. His wife was his constant and most able assistant. He was also an active member of the Medical Committee of the National Institute for the Deaf. He was a prominent Freemason, a past master of the Royal Sussex Lodge and had also held office in the Provincial Grand Lodge of Nottinghamshire.

Mr. Tweedie had a very special affection for his old medical school, Barts, and frequently revisited it. To his work he brought whole-hearted enthusiasm and any young men interested in aural surgery found in him a very real friend and helper. He was kindly and sympathetic by nature and full of genial humour. He was in much demand as an after dinner speaker and had great facility in the telling of amusing stories. His holidays were chiefly spent walking in Scotland. He had a great love of nature and a wide knowledge of all forms of bird life.

In a personal tribute to Mr. Tweedie by Mr. Herbert Bell Tawes, his successor, it was said:- Mr. Tweedie died in the midst of his medical friends and will long be remembered as a man who was devoted to his work, who lived for his colleagues, both at home and abroad.

B.M.J., April 4th, 1936, page 733

G.A. ROBINSON M.C., M.D., M.S., (LONDON)
President of the
Nottingham Medico-Chirurgical Society 1929-1930

George E.J. Antoine Robinson:- M.C.: 20 Park Row, Nottingham, M.S., London, 1927; M.D., 1901; M.B., B.S., 1900; F.R.C.S. Edinburgh, 1928; M.R.C.S., L.R.C.P., London, 1896. L.D.S.R.C.S. England, 1894 (Dublin University, King's College, London R.C.S. Ireland, Paris, Berne) Carmichael Medal in Surgery R.C.S. Ireland, Haughton Clinical Medal, Dublin University. Major, Royal Army Medical Corps, Territorial attached to the South Nott's Hussars R.H.A. T.A., Honorary Surgeon, Nottingham Hospital for Women. Member of the Nottingham Medico-Chirurgical Society. Late: Senior Honorary House Surgeon, Samaritan Hospital for Women, Nottingham; Honorary Surgeon Steevens' Hospital, Dublin; Resident Surgeon, Nottingham General Dispensary; Officer in Command of the Surgical Division of the 70th and 44th General Hospital's Author: 'Is Craniotomy Justified?'

Medical Directory 1929

J.W. SCOTT M.C., M.D. (Glasgow) M.R.C.P.
President of the Nottingham, Medico-Chirurgical Society 1930-1931

1st June, 1877 - 16th February, 1958.

Joseph Wilkie Scott M.C.- 40, The Ropewalk, Nottingham.
M.B. (1916) M.B., ChB. Glasgow (1898) M.D. Glasgow
(1902) M.R.C.P. (1919) F.R.C.P.(1933). Honorary Physician,
Children's Hospital, Nottingham & General Hospital, Nottingham. Captain, Royal Army Medical Corps (Volunteers)
7th Battalion, Sherwood Foresters; Member of the Nottingham Medico-Chirurgical Society. Late, Clinical Assistant,
Great Ormond Street Hospital for Children; House Physician
& Senior Resident Medical Officer, General Hospital, Nottingham; House Surgeon, Monkwearmouth Hospital.

Medical Directory 1934.

A native of Airdrie, Joseph Wilkie Scott was one of three sons of a school-
master, Alexander Scott and his wife Elizabeth. They all entered the medical
profession. He received his medical education at Glasgow University.
After holding house appointments at the Nottingham General Hospital, he
went into partnership in general practice in the city. This phase of his career was cut short by the First World War in which he became medical
officer to the 7th Battalion of the Sherwood Foresters (Robin Hood's).
While serving in France in 1916 he was awarded the Military Cross for
conspicuous gallantry in action. On his return to civilian life he quickly
achieved the Membership of the Royal College of Physicians of London
and was elected honorary assistant physician to Nottingham General Hospital and, later, honorary physician to both the General and Children's
Hospitals. Henceforth his work was chiefly in consulting medicine - general and paediatric. He acquired a well-deserved reputation for clinical
skill and soundness of judgement, not only in the city and county, but
more widely.

Dr. Joseph Wilkie Scott's association with Nottingham began in 1899 with his appointment as assistant house physician, and was uninterrupted until his retirement in 1946 from his consulting practice and from his unique position as honorary physician to the General and Children's Hospitals and visiting physician to the Nottingham City and Mental Hospitals.

He was an excellent teacher. His outpatient clinics and his ward-rounds on a Sunday morning at the General, and a Thursday Afternoon at the Children's, became tutorials. Practitioners owe much to his encouragement. Many could recall vividly cases demonstrated to them by Wilkie Scott. His enthusiasm in the quest of the right diagnosis and the means of achieving it, was best seen at open clinical meetings where he would marshal his facts and arguments with the skill of an advocate. He was a good committee man who would give his opinion firmly. Above all he was a loyal and kindly colleague with a saving sense of humour.

He lead an active life and won some much-prized honours. He was a staunch supporter of the Nottingham Medico-Chirurgical Society, a member of its council for two long spells, its honorary secretary and, in 1930, its president. His presidential addresses attracted a record attendance. Arrangements for a provincial meeting in Nottingham of the paediatric section of the Royal Society of Medicine in 1928 were almost entirely the work of Joseph Wilkie Scott. The meeting was adjudged something of a personal triumph. His eminence as a physician was acknowledged by his election to the College Fellowship, and as paediatrician by his holding the presidency of the British Paediatric Association in 1938. Though not greatly drawn to medical politics he held it to be his duty to take his share of the toil and sweat. He was chairman of the Nottingham Division of the British Medical Association in 1929-30 and president of the branch from 1938 to 1940. Earlier he served as a vice-president of the section of diseases of children when the Association held its annual meeting in Nottingham in 1926. His recreations were tennis, golf, and chess - particularly golf.

In 1926 he married Dr. Marjorie Godfrey, whom he first met as his house physician at the Nottingham Children's Hospital. She shared his life and his enthusiasms.

Joseph Wilkie Scott joined the Royal Army Medical Corps 1/7th Sherwood Foresters (Robin Hoods) in 1913. Mobilised August, 1914 and was in France for four and a half years, two years in the trenches. Finally he was in charge of the medical division of a base hospital.

In the History of the Robin Hoods, 1914-1918, two incidents are reported. One is of the disastrous attack on the Hohenzollern Redoubt in which both 1/7th and 1/8th Sherwood Foresters were engaged.

"The casualties very greatly exceeded the number anticipated and consequently Captain Scott was working at very high pressure, the Dressing Station being at all times under continuous shell fire. It would be impossible to speak too highly of the services rendered by him during the attack, and the wounded who were taken to the Dressing Station will always remember with gratitude the tender and expeditious manner in which they were treated before being sent to the rear."

The second occasion was the even more disastrous attack on Gommercourt. Here everything possible seems to have gone wrong. The mud in the trenches was so deep that supports and carriers were literally sinking fast and could not get up. The smoke screen failed and the attacking force, including Captain Scott, found themselves in the open before the German trenches without any protection.

"Of the 27 Officers and 600 men who went into action only 90 men came out. Of the 27 twelve were killed and 8 wounded. Captain Scott was among the lucky ones to be unwounded. Captain Scott managed to get back to the advanced British trench. Here he stayed all day, organising the defence of the trench, taking charge of the men as well as attending to the wounded.

The Brigadier-General recommended him very strongly for the D.S.O.. Later he was awarded the M.C. for most conspicuous bravery shown on this occasion and for the very excellent work he had done with the Battalion since their landing in France. Later Captain Scott was appointed in charge of a medical division in a base hospital with the rank of Major.

Dr. Scott was not a member of the Honorary Medical Staff at this time. He had been House Physician to the Hospital. He was elected Honorary Physician to the Children's Hospital and Honorary Physician to the General Hospital in 1919. Later he was elected President of the British Paediatric Association, 1938, as a tribute to his good work in that branch of the profession.

C.H. ALLEN O.B.E., F.R.C.S. (Edinburgh)
President of the
Nottingham Medico-Chirurgical Society 1931-1932

Charles Henry Allen O.B.E. :- 24, The Ropewalk, Nottingham. Fellow of the Royal College of Surgeons (Edinburgh), 1906; Bachelor of Medicine, Bachelor of Surgery (Edinburgh), 1900; (University of Edinburgh); Order of the Nile, 4th Class. Honorary Surgeon, Nottingham General Hospital; Consultant Surgeon, City Infirmary, Nottingham; Government Medical Reference, Working mans Compensation Act; Member and Ex-President of the Nottingham Medico-Chirurgical Society; Fellow of the Association of Surgeons, Great Britain. Formerly: Resident Medical Officer and Senior House Surgeon, Nottingham General Hospital.

A farmer's son from Mctheringham, Lincolnshire, Charles Henry Allen was a medical student at Edinburgh University, where he graduated M.B., Ch.B., in 1900. In the same year he joined the staff of the Nottingham General Hospital as assistant house surgeon and, having obtained the Fellowship of the Royal College of Surgeons of Edinburgh in 1906, was appointed to the honorary staff of the hospital in 1907. In his early days Mr. Allen was an active Territorial Army Officer, and at the outbreak of the first world war in 1914 was a captain in the 3rd North Midland Mounted Field Ambulance. He went to Egypt with the brigade in the spring of 1915 but later was detached from the field ambulance to command the Ras-el-Tin military hospital in Cyrenaica. He was three times mentioned in dispatches for his service in the field, twice by Lord Allenby, and was appointed O.B.E. and awarded the Order of the Nile (Fourth Class).

After the war he returned to his work at Nottingham as honorary surgeon at the General Hospital. Later he became senior surgeon and chairman of the medical committee of the hospital. He was for many years consultant surgeon to the Nottingham City Hospital. He was a Fellow of the Association of Surgeons of Great Britain and Ireland, and in 1931-2 President of the Nottingham Medico-Chirurgical Society. Because of the second world war and, at the request of the hospital board, he continued his work as a surgeon for four years past the retiring age and he eventually gave up active consultant work in 1946. A member of the British Medical Association for forty-two years, he served as a vice president of the section of Surgery when the Association held its Annual Meeting in 1926. He was also chairman of the Nottingham Division in 1927-8 and president of the Midland Branch in 1933-4.

A.C. REID M.D. (Aberdeen), D.C. (Oxford)
President of the
Nottingham Medico-Chirurgical Society 1932-1933

Alex Christie Reid:- 13, Wellington Circus, Nottingham.M.A., B.Sc Aberdeen 1897, M.B., Ch.B., (Honours) 1902, M.D. (Honours) 1905. (Aberdeen). Diploma of Opthalmics, Oxford, 1913. Opthalmic Surgeon, Mansfield and Worksop Hospital. Honorary Surgeon, Nottingham Eye Infirmary. Late:- House Surgeon, West Norfolk and Lynn Hospital. Temporary Captain, R.A.M.C. Author:- "Miners Nystagmus," Brain, 1906.

Medical Directory 1937

In an obituary to Dr. Reid by the Consultant Ophthalmologist, Dr. George Gordon-Napier he said:- Dr. Alexander Christie Reid was educated at Aberdeen University, taking the degrees of M.A. and B.Sc. before going on to do his medical studies. He graduated M.B. in 1902 and proceeded M.D. with honours in 1905. In 1913 he took the Oxford Diploma in Ophthalmology. For nearly 40 years he was honorary surgeon to the Nottingham and Midland Eye Infirmary, and for many years was consultant ophthalmic surgeon to the Kesteven County Council and the Mansfield and Worksop Hospitals. He retired from active consulting in 1946 and, for his distinguished service, was appointed consulting surgeon to the Nottingham and Midland Eye Infirmary. During the 1914-18 war he served as a captain in the Royal Army Medical Corps. Dr. Reid made a study of miners nystagmus and, to gain first-hand knowledge of working conditions went down the mine on many occasions. He always brought a clear analytical mind to bear on any difficult problem. Apart from his professional work his interests were wide and varied. Dr. Reid will be remembered with affection and admiration by all who knew him.

B.M.J. September 9th, 1950, page 632

G. OGG GAULD M.B., Ch.B. (Aberdeen)
President of the
Nottingham Medico-Chirurgical Society 1933-1934

George Ogg Gauld:- 16, The Ropewalk, Nottingham. M.B., Ch.B., Aberdeen, 1901.(Aberdeen, Dublin and London Hospitals) Fellow of the Royal Society of Medicine.

Medical Directory 1937

Born at 33, Hamilton Place, Aberdeen, on June 21st, 1873, G. O. Gauld was educated at Aberdeen Grammar School and Aberdeen University. He played cricket for Aberdeenshire in 1900, 1901 and 1902. His best performances with the ball, as a very fast right-arm bowler, were 7 for 9 v. Forfarshire and 5 for 6 v. Blairgowrie. He moved from Adberdeen to Elvington, Yorkshire, in 1902 and then to Nottingham in 1909. Whilst in Nottingham he became associated with Nottingham Amateurs C.C. and on June 12th, 1913, he scored 154 for that club v. Uppingham School. When A.O. Jones fell ill in 1913 Nottinghamshire was captained by G. T. Branston for two matches and then J. Iremonger. Dr. Gauld was invited to take over from Iremonger and made his first-class debut v. Kent at Trent Bridge on June 30th, July 1st and 2nd. He played in eight consecutive matches as captain until Jones had recovered sufficiently to return to the field. In 1914 Dr. Gauld again captained the side when Jones was forced to retire and v. Derbyshire at Trent Bridge he hit 90 in 65 minutes - his only notable score in first-class matches. His final first-class was v. A.I.F. at Trent Bridge on July 24th, 25th and 26th in 1919, when he came into the XI in place of Carr. His complete first-class record reads:

Batting	M.	Ins.	NO	Runs	HS	Aver.	100s	50s	0s	ct	st.
	14	19	—	350	90	18-42	——	1	1	7	—

Bowling	I.	Overs	Mdns.	Runs	Wkts.	Aver.	5i	10m	B/W
	11	70.1	13	250	5	50.00	__	____	84.

In 1920 he became a member of the Nottinghamshire C.C.C. Committee, finally retiring in 1947, and from 1922 to 1935 he was honorary secretary. in August 1934 Dr. Gauld was the medical practitioner involoved in the controversial withdrawal of Voce from the Nottinghamshire v. Australian match. Dr. Gauld resided at 16, The Ropewalk, and died at 7, Park Terrace, Nottingham, on June 16th, 1950.

Nottinghamshire Cricketers, 1821-1914

A.M. WEBBER M.S. (London) F.R.C.S. (England) (1879 - 1947)
President of the
Nottingham Medico-Chirurgical Society 1934-1935

Alexander Moxon Webber:- 2, The Ropewalk, Nottingham. M.R.C.S. 12th November 1903; F.R.C.S. 14th June 1906; M.B., B.S. London 1903; M.S. 1905; L.R.C.P. 1903; Honorary Surgeon, Nottingham General Hospital & Hospital for Women, Nottingham; Temporary Captain (Acting Major) Royal Army Medical Corps; Member (Ex-Honorary Secretary, Nottingham Division and general Secretary, 1926, Annual Meeting, Nottingham) British Medical Association; President of the Nottingham Medico-Chirurgical Society, 1934-1935. Late Obstetric Resident House Surgeon, Guy's Hospital; Clinical Assistant, Great Ormond Street Hospital for Children; Honorary Surgeon, Children's Hospital, Nottingham.

Medical Directory 1940

167

Born on the 4th August 1879 at Glen Lynden, Bedford, Cape Colony, South Africa, the seventh child and fourth son of Benjamin Webber, a landowner, and his wife Millicent Anne Nash. He was educated at St. Andrew's College, Grahamstown, and came home to take his medical training at Guy's Hospital where he served as house surgeon and obstretric registrar. He was also clinical assistant at the Great Ormond Street Hospital. After taking the Fellowship in 1906 he settled at Nottingham, in partnership with R. C. Chicken. In due course he became surgeon to the Children's Hospital and to the General Hospital, and consulting surgeon to the Hospital for Women. During the war of 1914-18 he served as surgeon specialist at the 27th General Hospital from early 1915 till December 1916, first at Mudros for the evacuation of the Dardanelles and later at Abbasiah, Cairo. From 1917 he was surgeon to the 52nd Lowland casualty clearing station, East Africa, with the rank of major, R.A.M.C. He was twice mentioned in despatches.

Webber was an active member of the British Medical Association. He was the representative of the Nottingham Division at the annual representative meeting for eleven consecutive years, 1919-30; in 1922-25 he was secretary of the division and its chairman in 1931-32. He also served on the B.M.A. Council, and was the general secretary when the Association met at Nottingham in 1926. He was president of the Nottingham Medico-Chirurgical Society 1934-35. He retired in December 1945 to Sandown, Isle of Wight, where he died on the 26th October 1947. He had married in 1909 Elizabeth Fullerton, who survived him with four daughters. For many years he suffered from Paget's disease of his leg. Webber was of great kindness and understanding and, though of retiring nature, was a born administrator.

B.R.B. TRUEMAN M.B., B.Ch. (Cambridge)
President of the
Nottingham Medico-Chirurgical Society 1935-1936

Bernard Renshaw Beckit Trueman:- 408, Mansfield Road, Nottingham. B.A.,Cambridge, 1897, M.B., B.Ch., 1900; M.R.C.S., L.R.C.P., London, 1900. (Cambridge and St. Bartholomew's Hospital).Medical Officer, Infant Welfare Clinics, Nottingham. Honorary Physician, Nottingham Children's Hospital.Late:- House Surgeon, Victoria Hospital, Folkestone; Assistant Medical Officer, Brook Hospital (M.A.B.). Flt. Lt., Royal Air Force Medical Service.

Medical Directory 1937

This information is from an obituary which appeared in the Nottinghamshire Guardian 27th October, 1947.

Dr. Bernard Renshaw Beckit Trueman died suddenly yesterday at his home, The Woodlands, Woodland Drive, Mapperley Park.

Dr. Trueman's father and grandfather were both doctors in the city and he himself practiced in Nottingham for over 40 years. He took an active interest in the Children's Hospital, and was associated with the city's infant welfare work. He was a former president of the Nottingham Medico-Chirurgical Society. On his retirement from private practice two years ago he was appointed honorary consultant physician to the Children's Hospital. He leaves a widow, one son Mr. J.R.B. Trueman, who is a solicitor in Kent, and a daughter Miss C.C.B. Trueman, who is a physiotherapist at the Nottingham General Hospital.

**Local Studies Library,
Angle Row, Nottingham.**

W BOOTHBY BLANDY, M.R.C.S., L.R.C.P.
President of the
Nottingham Medico-Chirurgical Society 1937-1938

Wilfrid Boothby Blandy:- "Hazelwood," Mount Hooton Road, Nottingham. M.R.C.S., L.R.C.P., London, 1902. L.D.S., R.C.S., England 1900, (Dent Hospital and Charing Cross Hospital). Entrance Scholar, Charing Cross Hospital. Huxley School, 1899. Honorary Consultant Surgeon, Nottingham General Dispensary. Late:- House Surgeon, Charing Cross Hospital.

Medical Directory 1937

Dr. Blandy took the L.D.S., R.C.S. in 1900 and the M.R.C.S., L.R.C.P. in 1902. He was a house surgeon at Charing Cross Hospital, where he received his medical training. For many years he practiced in Nottingham. He served in the Middle East with the Royal Army Medical Corps from 1917 to 1919. After returning to Nottingham, he was elected to the local council as a member of the Meadows Ward. He was president of the Nottingham Medico-Chirurgical Society in 1937 to 1938 and he had a great deal to do with the Ransom Sanatorium at Newstead. One of his principle interests was work in connection with the Nottingham Branch of the Red Cross Society of which he became county director. He was also a member of the University College Council in Nottingham and a past chairman of the Board of Governors of the Nottingham High School.

Dr. W. B. Blandy's died on 1st April, 1947. He was survived not only by his widow but also two sons, one of whom was Dr. [1] Anthony Charles Blandy. who became a consultant paediatrician at the Nottingham Children's Hospital, the Mansfield General Hospital and the Newark Hospital as well. He too was a member of the Nottingham Medico-Chirurgical Society and served on its council from 1960 to 1965.

The President's Badge of Office, which is worn by the president at all meetings of the society, was presented to the society as a gift from Dr. W. B. Blandy during his term as president. He personally invested his successor, Dr. H. Smith Wallace with it at the inaugural meeting of the society on the 5th October, 1938.

The name Blandy is still to this day kept alive at Kingsmill Hospital, Sutton-in-Ashfield, Nottinghamshire, by a ward which bears the name.

B.M.J., May 3rd, 1947, page 619.

[1] See Appendices

H SMITH WALLACE M.B., Ch.B. (Edinburgh)
(Born: Feb 2nd 1886 - Died: Aug 25th 1961)
President of the
Nottingham Medico-Chirurgical Society 1938-1939

Herbert Wallace Smith:- 23, Regent Street, Nottingham. M.B., Ch.B., Edinburgh, 1908 (University of Edinburgh), Assistant Honorary Physician and Honorary Dermatologist, General Hospital, Nottingham; Assistant Honorary Physician, Children's Hospital, Nottingham. Late:- House Surgeon, North Riding Infirmary, Middlesborough; House Physician, General Hospital Nottingham.

Medical Directory 1937

William Trethowan Rowe wrote: Herbert Smith Wallace was born at Prestonpans on February 2, 1886, the seventh of ten brothers. Graduating M.B., Ch.B. at the University of Edinburgh in 1908, he became house surgeon to the North Riding Infirmary, Middlesborough and, in 1910, house physician at the Nottingham General Hospital. Four years later he was appointed honorary assistant physician to the hospital. Soon after his appointment to the honorary staff, Dr. Wallace, an enthusiastic Territorial Officer, was mobilized with the Notts and Derby Mounted Brigade Field Ambulance and went east with them in 1915. He was soon posted as officer-in-charge of the medical division of No. 88 General Hospital, where he served until demobilization in 1919.

Returning to Nottingham after the war, he decided to specialize in dermatology and was appointed honorary dermatologist in 1920, an appointment he held until 1948 when he became consultant dermatologist until his retirement in 1951. He also held honorary appointments in the Children's Hospital, Nottingham and in Newark General Hospital but his main duties were with the General Hospital in Nottingham.

He was an active supporter of the British Medical Association and of the Nottingham Medico-Chirurgical Society. From 1924 to 1928 he was joint secretary and treasurer of the Nottinghamshire Division and, at the British Medical Association Meeting in Nottingham in 1926, he was honorary secretary of the Section of Dermatology. His early work as secretary was recognized by his becoming chairman of the Nottingham Division in 1935-6. Later he became president of the Nottingham Medico-Chirurgical Society in 1938-9.

His interests were not entirely in the field of medicine. As a young man he was an enthusiastic footballer and played both Association and Rugby football in the same season. Later golf became his hobby and his weekly relaxation was a four ball match at Hollinwell. Even in retirement he maintained his interest in sport and took up archery with his customary enthusiasm. An ardent Freemason, he became not only Master of his Lodge but was promoted to Provincial Grand Lodge honours.

Dr. Wallace was a popular member of the hospital staff and took a great personal interest in his younger colleagues. His brisk walk, his incisive speech, his puckish grin, and his fund of common sense were long remembered with gratitude by those who had the pleasure of being his colleagues.

British Medical Journal, September 30, 1961. Page 902.

FREDERICK CROOKS
(1887 - 1950)
President of the
Nottingham Medico-Chirurgical Society 1940-1946

Frederick Crooks:- 6, The Ropewalk, Nottingham. M.B., B.Ch., B.O.A., Belfast, 1911., M.Ch., 1914, F.R.C.S., Edinburgh, 1919. (Belfast). Honorary Assistant Surgeon with charge of Physiotherapy & Orthopaedics Department, General Hospital, Nottingham. Visiting Orthopaedic Surgeon, City Hospital, Nottingham; Orthopaedic Surgeon & Director of the Fracture Clinic, Royal Hospital, Chesterfield; member of the Orthopaedic Section of the Royal Society of Medicine; Member of the British Orthopaedic Association. Late Senior House Surgeon, General Hospital, Nottingham

Medical Directory 1940

Frederick Crooks was an Ulsterman who came to Nottingham as a House Surgeon immediately after qualifying at Belfast in 1911. He was born in 1887 at Maghera County Derry. The son of the late William John Crooks he was educated at Cookstown Academy and Queen's University Belfast where he qualified as a House Surgeon after gaining his Bachelor of Medicine, Bachelor of Surgery and Bachelor of Obstetrics. In 1914 he became a Master of Orthopaedic Surgery. For the first two years of the 1st World War he served as a senior house surgeon and then later joined the Royal Army Medical Corps as a Captain. He was to see service in India as a surgical specialist and was later put in charge of a surgical unit in a military hospital. After he was demobilised he took his Edinburgh Fellowship and was appointed as Honorary Assistant Surgeon to the Nottingham Children's Hospital in 1920. He became an Assistant Surgeon to the General Hospital in 1939. He was also an Honorary Consulting Surgeon to the Nottingham Cripples' Guild from 1923 onwards. He was recognised in the local press as an "orthopaedic surgeon" in 1932, but there was no such appointment at the General Hospital until Noel Birkett was appointed in 1947. Frederick Crooks continued practising general surgery as well as orthopaedics until he died in 1950.

178

Of his experiences in the two world wars, Dr. Jacobs, a colleague, author of "An History of the General Hospital, Nottingham," asked Frederick Crooks for his impressions:-

"In the first war", he said, "the struggle against suppurative and anaerobic infection at times appeared almost hopeless. The amount of disability from compound fractures was almost appalling. In the second war the whole picture was changed, particularly in the last two years by the regular use of Sulphonamides and Penicillin. We used to receive casualties from Italy in 8 or 10 days after injury. They had received Sulphonamides at regular intervals, and arrived looking fit and well. I was able to do primary sutures and plastic operations almost immediately after their arrival. One was also able to close up many compound fractures and treat them as simple fractures. I can only think of one patient who suffered from severe toxaemia, and one who developed gas gangrene."

Frederick Crooks was to die of brucellosis in 1950 at the age of 63 years. Although he had been ill for several years he continued working until a few hours before his death. In an obituary to Mr. Crooks written by Mr. A. Sheenan it was said of him:-

"He was a brilliant surgeon who combined speed and dexterity greatly to the benefit of his patients. The excellence of the present orthopaedic and accident department of the Nottingham General Hospital is a tribute to his organising ability and hard work and the department will be a lasting memorial to him. The naming of the operating theatre at the Nottingham Children's Hospital - "The Frederick Crooks Operating Theatre" - gave him great happiness. He was able to imbue his colleagues with his own enthusiasm. No house surgeon ever asked for help without receiving it in the kindest way."

Mr. Alan Bell Tawes who knew Frederick Crooks for many years wrote: "My impression is that he was the perfect example of the true general surgeon who was as at home in the abdomen as he was pinning a fracture of the neck of the femur - both of which he did superbly well."

A physiotherapist who worked with Frederick Crooks said of him. "He spoke with a strong Irish accent and it was difficult to make out what he said, particularly as he always had a cigarette dangling from the corner of his mouth. Although he was a shy man, he had no hesitation in speaking his mind, especially when treatment was not going according to plan. He was nonetheless appreciative of good work." When that same physiotherapist was leaving to get married he said of her, "although her post would be filled, she herself would never be replaced".

From the "Development of Orthopaedics in Nottingham Area"
by William Waugh.
Pages, 145, 146, 148 & 149.

Dr A.E. NEWTH M.B., B.S. (London) D.P.H.
(1887 - 1958)
President of the
Nottingham Medico-Chirurgical Society 1946-1947

Alfred Arthur Edmund Newth:- 28, Chaucer Street, Nottingham. Bachelor of Medicine, Bachelor of Surgery (London), 1912; Licentiate in Medicine and Surgery, Society of Apothecaries, London, 1911; Diploma in Public Health, Oxford, 1923 (Westminster Hospital); Senior School's Medical Officer, Nottingham; Honorary Captain (Late R.A.M.C.); Fellow of the Society of Medical Officers of Health, and President (1946-47) of the Nottingham Medico-Chirurgical Society; Member of the British Psychological Society. Formerly:- House Surgeon, Derbyshire Royal Infirmary and Wolverhampton General Hospital; House Physician, Westminster Hospital.

Medical Directory 1947.

Alfred Arthur Edmund Newth was born in Sussex on September 17th, 1887, his father being a general practitioner at Haywards Heath. Educated at Epsom College and the Westminster Hospital, he qualified L.M.S.S.A. in 1911 and graduated M.B., B.S., in the following year. After holding house appointments at the Westminster Hospital, the Wolverhampton General Hospital and the Derbyshire Royal Infirmary, he was appointed assistant school medical officer in Nottingham in 1914 and continued in the service until his retirement in 1954.

During the first world war he served in the Royal Army Medical Corps. In 1923 he took the D.P.H. of Oxford University and, shortly afterwards, he was appointed senior school medical officer in Nottingham. An honorary fellow of the Society of Medical Officers of Health, he was a president of the Nottingham Medico-Chirurgical Society and, at the annual meeting of the British Medical Association in Harrogate in 1949, he was vice-president of the Section on Child Health. After retiring from the school health service he accepted an invitation to become a medical officer at Mapperley Hospital in Nottingham.

In an obituary a colleague wrote of Dr. Newth saying:- Dr. Newth was one of those with a naturally and persistently inquiring mind. If he felt that something needed investigating he would go to no end of trouble to complete the inquiries. His personal typist would often find herself involved in a questionary which had to go to many authorities or to experts on the subject. I well remember the interest he took in the question of physical examination prior to schoolboy boxing contests. He felt this was a waste of time or, if it was not, then all youngsters prior to many activity involving hard physical work should have a physical checkup, so where would it all end? In 1943 he revived the School Health Service Group of the Society of Medical Officers of Health, a group which was then almost non-existent. He become secretary, a post he retained until 1957. His special interest was in "handicapped pupils," In 1945 he was appointed by the Minister of Education to serve on the Advisory Committee on Handicapped Pupils. He realized that maladjustment was something which could be present in a child and this encouraged him in 1937 to visit and inquire into the work of child guidance clinics. He finally persuaded his authority in 1938 that one was necessary in Nottingham. In 1952 he was awarded the O.B.E., an honour he well deserved, for he had made himself one of the experts in the work of the school health service.

In 1949, faced with the choice of operation or deep x-ray therapy (Radiotherapy) for an illness, he chose the latter, facing the issue with that patient fortitude that was part of his nature. On recovery he came back to his office and that was the end of it so far as he was concerned. When he retired in 1954 he went as a senior hospital medical officer to the local mental hospital, where he felt he could give something to the patients there. They quickly came to know him and to look to him for that cheerful encouragement which is so essential in that type of work.

The death of Dr. Newth occurred on 30th July, 1958; he was aged 70. It was said in his obituary: "The funeral service was held at St. Jude's Church, Mapperley, Nottingham, when very many friends, including a group of nurses from Mapperley Hospital attended. They came to show their affection and for the high regard in which he was held."

BMJ., August 16th, 1958. Pages 452, 453.

**DR J BATTERSBY M.B., Ch.B. (Victoria) L.D.S.
(England) President of the
Nottingham Medico-Chirurgical Society 1947-1948**

John Battersby:- 17, Regent Street, Nottingham. (Battersby & Glaister). Bachelor of Medicine, Bachelor of Surgery Victoria 1904; Licentiate in Dental Surgery, Royal College of Surgeons (England) 1908; (Victoria University, Manchester). Honorary Dental Surgeon, Nottingham General Hospital; Fellow of the Royal Society of Medicine; Member of the Nottingham Medico-Chirurgical Society and the British Medical Association. Formerly:- Senior House Surgeon, Bury Infirmary. Honorary Dental Surgeon, Hyson Green, Nottingham Dispensary.

Medical Directory 1947

JOHN LLEWELLYN DAVIS
(1889 - 1963)
President of the
Nottingham Medico-Chirurgical Society 1948-1949

John Llewwllyn Davies:- Castle Bank, 5, Lenton Road, The Park, Nottingham. B.A., Cambridge (National Science Tripos), 1912, M.B., B.Ch., 1919 F.R.C.S. England, 1922, M. 1914; L.R.C.P. London, 1914 *(St Bartholomew's);* Sizar & Scholar, Emmanuel College, Cambridge. Honorary Consultant Urological Surgeon, Nottingham Women's Hospital; Consultant Urological Surgeon, Nottingham City Hospital; Consultant Surgeon, Harlow Wood Hospital; Honorary Surgeon, Nottingham General & Children's Hospitals. Fellow of the Royal Society of Medicine; Association of Surgeons of Great Britian & British Association of Urological Surgeons. Member of the Society International d'Urological: Late Temporary Captain, Royal Army Medical Corps; House Surgeon & Resident Surgical Officer St. Peters Hospital for Stone.

Medical Directory 1949

Born in Nottingham, where his father was a general practitioner who died young, leaving a widow with three small children, a son and two daughters. His early life was spent on his uncle's farm in Oxfordshire where he acquired his lifelong interest in wild life and in fishing and shooting. He was educated at Nottingham High School, Emmanual College, Cambridge and St. Bartholomew's Hospital where he qualified in 1914.

He then entered the Royal Army Medical Corps and served throughout the war, returning to St. Bartholomew's in 1919. He was house surgeon, at St. George's and at St. Peter's Hospital where he became resident surgeon to C.H. Allen and, in 1931, was appointed assistant surgeon to the Nottingham General Hospital. He had to wait until 1946 to become full surgeon as all staff appointments were frozen during the war of 1939-45. He retired from the active staff in 1955 but remained a member of the committee of management of which he was vice-chairman and was also chairman of the general purposes committee.

He was a city councillor and in 1957-58 an alderman, becoming Lord Mayor of Nottingham in 1961-62. In 1962 he was appointed a Deputy Lieutenant of the County of Nottingham. He was a deeply religious man, widely admired and respected. He died on 27th September 1963 survived by his wife, son and daughter.

**From the
Lives of the Fellows of the Royal College of Surgeons of England
1952-1964.
R.H.O.B. ROBINSON, M.A., F.R.C.S. And W.R. Le FANU, M.A.,
F.S.A.**

I.R. SPARK M.B., Ch.B. (Aberdeen)
(1897 - 1974)
President of the
Nottingham Medico-Chirurgical Society 1949-1950

Ian Robert Spark: 9a, The Ropewalk, Nottingham. M.B., Ch. B. Aberdeen, 1921. Honorary Anaesthetist, Nottingham General Hospital.

Medical Directory 1949

Medical Directory 1949.

Ian Robert Spark, a son of the manse, was born in Kincardineshire on 6th March, 1897. During the first world war his medical studies at Aberdeen University were interrupted while he served for two years as a surgeon probationer in the Royal Navy. He then returned to the university, graduated in 1921, and went to Nottingham as an assistant. Later he set up in general practice on his own. He developed a great interest in anaesthetics and eventually was appointed to the City Hospital as a consultant anaethetist. Other appointments to the General Hospital, Women's Hospital, and Children's Hospital soon followed. After the inception of the National Health Service he took his full share of committee work to help to formulate the new concept in the Nottingham area and served as chairman of the medical committees at the City and General Hospitals. A past president of the Nottingham Medico Chirurgical Society, he was one of its most ardent supporters. He was also a founder member and first president of the Nottingham and East Midlands Aberdeen Graduates Association.

Ian Spark worked at all the Nottingham hospitals during the period from the days of chloroform and ether to well into the era of modern anaesthesia. From the early thirties he was an exponent of spinal and epidural anaesthesia and, until he retired, he kept abreast of modern developments. He enjoyed working with children with whom he achieved an immediate rapport aided by a chiming watch hidden in his clothing or the bed. A great sportsman, he had been in his youth a robust rugby forward, playing in five Scottish trials and, after settling at Nottingham, he played for some years for Nott's Rugby Club. He was an excellent shot but most enjoyed salmon fishing at which he was successful and accomplished. At Nottingham he made an immense number of friends of all ages and they, with the many patients who have cause to be grateful for his skill and care, mourned his passing. His first wife, whom he married in 1924, died eight years before him. His son and daughter both qualified in medicine at Aberdeen University. Shortly before he died he married Miss Jane Holloway, who had been his nurse, companion and housekeeper for several years.

B.M.J., 30th November, 1974.

**N.P.R. GALLOWAY M.B., Ch.B. (Edinburgh), D.O.
(Oxford) President of the
Nottingham Medico-Chirurgical Society 1950-1951**

Norman Patrick Galloway: 16, Upper College Street, Nottingham. M.B., Ch.B, Edinburgh 1917. Diploma in Ophthalmology 1923 (University of Edinburgh). Honorary Surgeon, Nottingham and Midland Eye Infirmary. Member of the Oxford Ophthalmic Congregation, Ophthalmic Society, U.K. The Midland Ophthalmic Society, and the Nottingham Medico-Chirurgical Society. Late, Honorary Physician, Royal Infirmary, Edinburgh.

Medical Directory 1949.

Information from two reports in the Nottingham Guardian, dated, 20th February, 1959 and 29th April, 1960

Norman Patrick Galloway was a graduate of the University of Edinburgh. Before coming to Nottingham he was appointed honorary house physician at the Edinburgh Royal Infirmary. In 1922 he was appointed clinical assistant and anaesthetist to the Nottingham and Midland Eye Infirmary. Five years later, in 1927, he was to be elected to the position of honorary surgeon. He held this appointment until the inception of the National Health Service in July 1948 when he became consultant ophthalmologist.

Mr. Galloway was a member of the British Medical Association and was also a member of the Regional Hospital Consultants and Specialists Association. He also held the presidency of the Midland Ophthalmological Society from 1951 to 1953 and from 1950 to 1951 was the president of the Nottingham Medico-Chirurgical Society. He was also a member of the Ophthalmological Society of the United Kingdom, the British Orthoptic Society, the ophthalmological section of the Royal Society of Medicine and the Ophthalmological Congress.

After his retirement in March 1959, the Hospital Board of the Nottingham General Hospital decided in April 1960 to award Norman Patrick Galloway the title of Surgeon Emeritus to the Nottingham Eye Hospital in recognition of 34 years service to the Hospital.

Local Studies Library, Angel Row, Nottingham.

192

J.T. KNOX M.B., B.Ch., B.A.O.
(1901 - 1965)
President of the
Nottingham Medico-Chirurgical Society 1951-1952

John Leslie Templeton Knox: 27, Victoria Embankment, Nottingham. B.A., B.Ch., B.A.O., Belfast, 1924. Member of the British Medical Association and the Nottingham Medico-Chirurgical Society.

Medical Directory 1953.

John Leslie Templeton Knox was born in Belfast in 1899. He studied medicine at Queen's University and graduated M.B., B.Ch., B.O.A. in 1924. During his student days he was a keen athlete and played rugby and waterpolo for the university. After graduation he proceeded to postgraduate study in London and then joined Dr. J. H. Thompson of the Embankment, Nottingham, whom he later succeeded. He remained in this practice until he retired from the Health Service in September 1963.

For two years until the time of his death on the 28th September, 1965 he was fully occupied with regional medical boards and various other appointments. During his life in medical practice he was outstanding as member, chairman, and representative of such bodies as the Nottingham Insurance Committee, the Nottingham County and City Local Medical Committee, and the Local Executive Council. He found time to give unstinting service for many years. For this he was awarded the O.B.E. in 1963. His fellow general practitioners considered it a well merited honour. He was at one time president of the Nottingham Branch of the British Medical Association and in 1951 to 1952 president of the Nottingham Medico-Chirurgical Society. In addition to this he did valuable work for the British Red Cross Society over many years. He was appointed president of the City Division in 1948 and assistant branch director of the Nottinghamshire Branch in 1953, when he was made a life member.

F.C. HUNT F.R.C.S., F.R.C.S. (England)
President of the
Nottingham Medico-Chirurgical Society 1952-1953

Frederick Cecil Hunt:- 40, The Ropewalk, Nottingham. Member of the Royal College of Surgeons (England), Licentiate of the Royal College of Physicians (London) 1922; Bachelor of Medicine Bachelor of Surgery (London) 1922; Fellow of the Royal College of Surgeons (Edinburgh) 1928 (London Hospital). Honorary Surgeon, Nottingham General Hospital, Honorary Consultant Surgeon, Ilkeston General Hospital and Heanor Hospital; Visiting Surgeon, Nottingham City Hospital; Consultant, Nott's County Council in General Surgery and for Treatment of Malign Diseases by Radium and Radiological Methods; Fellow of the Association of Surgery, Great Britain and Ireland; Associate Member of the Society of Thoracic Surgeons, Great Britain and Ireland; Member of the British Medical Association. Formerly:- Clinical Assistant Medical Out-Patients, Emergency Officer; House Surgeon and Receiving Room Officer, London Hospital; Casualty Officer, House Surgeon and Senior Resident Medical Officer, Nottingham General Hospital.

Medical Directory 1949

Frederick Hunt served the General Hospital, Nottingham, for 40 years as casualty and house officer, surgical assistant and honorary surgeon. For many years he was an active member of the nurses' committee and lecturer to nurses. As registrar in charge of radium he was largely responsible for the formation of the radiotherapy department. He was a meticulous general surgeon and was unsparing in his advice and help when asked.

On retirement in 1964 he went to live in Thorpe, Derbyshire. He was a voracious reader. His great delight was gardening and walking over the local hills. He became a lay preacher, churchwarden, and a member of the diocesan synod. His wife, died a few years after his retirement; he was survived by his three daughters and grandchildren.

B.M.J., 3rd April, 1993.

196

H.A. SUMMERS M.B., Ch.B. (Glasgow)
President of the
Nottingham Medico-Chirurgical Society 1953-1954

Herbert Arnold Summers: Oak Hill, East Leake, Nr. Loughborough, Leicestershire. M.B., Ch.B., Glasgow 1929, (University of Glasgow). Medical Officer to the Ministry of Supply, Ministry of Labour and Ministry of Pensions. Author: "Aids to First Aid."

Medical Directory 1953.

SYDNEY ALAN STORMER MALKIN (1892-1964)
President of the
Nottingham Medico-Chirurgical Society 1954-1955

Sydney Alan Stormer Malkin:- 54, The Ropewalk, Nottingham: C.B.E. 1952; M.R.C.S. 1915; F.R.C.S. England ad eundem 1948; L.R.C.P. London, 1915 *(University College Hospital);* F.R.C.S.Edinburgh. 1922; M.B., B.S. London 1922; Senior Surgeon & Surgeon Superintendent, Harlow Wood Orthopaedic Hospital, Associated Out Patients Clinics & Children's Hospital, Grindley; Orthopaedic Surgeon, Mansfield & District General Hospital, Retford Hospital& Newark & Grantham General Hospitals. Member of the Standing Advisory Committee on Limb Fitting, Ministry of Health. Fellow & Ex-President of the British Orthpaedic Association; Fellow of the Association of Surgeons of Great Britain. Late Resident Surgical Officer, Military Hospital & Woodlands Orthopaedic Hospital, Birmingham; Senior House Surgeon, Royal National Orthopaedic Hospital

Medical Directory 1956

Born on the 13th August 1892 Sydney Malkin was educated at Epworth College, Rhyl, and University College Hospital, London. He qualified M.R.C.S., L.R.C.P. in 1915 then went on active service in France as a regimental medical officer. After the war he returned to his studies, graduating M.B., B.S. in 1922 and obtaining the fellowship of the Royal College of Surgeons of Edinburgh. Later he went on to hold resident posts in London at the Royal National Orthopaedic Hospital, St. Bartholomew's and the Hospital for Sick Children and in 1923 became resident surgical officer at what is now the Royal Orthopaedic Hospital, Birmingham.

Orthopaedics was a young speciality at that time and Sydney Malkin was inspired by the work of Sir Robert Jones, who developed the treatment and rehabilitation of the war wounded on a national scale. Centres for rehabilitation, like ones developed at Shepherd's Bush, London, and others of a similar scale, pioneered the way to the training and rehabilitation of the physically handicapped.

Some years earlier Sir Robert Jones and Gathorne Robert Girdlestone had put forward a National Scheme for the Care of Crippled Children. Under the presidency of Winifred, Duchess of Portland, citizens of Nottingham formed a Cripples Guild and in 1923 Sydney Malkin was appointed their first orthopaedic surgeon. Plans were made to build an orthopaedic hospital and a site near Mansfield was given by the Duke of Portland. Jesse Boot, Lord Trent, chairman of Boots, offered the services of his company to build the hospital without profit. This culminated in 1929 when Harlow Wood Orthopaedic Hospital was opened by the Duke and Duchess of York (King George VI and Queen Elizabeth). Sydney Malkin was appointed surgeon-in-charge and under his supervision the hospital expanded and became well known throughout the orthopaedic world.

After the second world war he planned the Portland Training College, which eventually opened in 1950 with, again, local generous support. He was next involved with Nottinghamshire Education Committee's project for a school for handicapped children, which was completed in 1957 at Thieves Wood near the hospital and training college.

Sydney Malkin held appointments at Newark, Grantham, Loughborough, Mansfield and Retford hospitals, and was President of the Nottingham Medico-Chirurgical Society. He was President of the Nottingham branch and chairman of the Orthopaedic group of the British Medical Association and was elected an Honorary Fellow of the Association in 1961. He was President of the section of orthopaedics in the Royal Society of Medicine in 1936 and of the British Orthopaedic Association in 1948-49. He presided at the joint meeting of the British and Canadian Orthopaedic Associations at Quebec in 1948, and initiated with R. I. Harris of Toronto a scheme for interchange of visits among young American, British and Canadian orthopaedic surgeons. In the same year he was elected to the fellowship of the Royal College of Surgeons of England. He was also a fellow of the Societe Internationale de Chiurgie Orthopedique et de Traumatologie. His work was further recognized by his being appointed C.B.E. in 1958.

During the 1920s he introduced the operation of trochanteric osteotomy for osteo-arthritis of the hip joint. He wrote both on surgical technique and on training of the disabled. The training and welfare of orthopaedic surgeons and orthopaedic nurses was ever on Malkin's mind. Shortly before he died the new nurses' building at Harlow Wood Hospital was named the Alan Malkin House.

His writings were varied, ranging from scientific papers on techniques which he had found useful in the operating theatre, to advances in rehabilitation and the training of the disabled. His presidential address delivered before the British Orthopaedic Association was "The Scientific Approach to Orthopaedic Surgery," a subject in which he had a life long interest. After his retirement in 1958 he was appointed surgeon emeritus at Harlow Wood, but he continued to take an active part in the resettlement of the disabled.

In an obituary William Waugh related on the retirement of Sidney Malkin:-

"It was natural that he should continue to take a great interest in everything that went on at Harlow Wood. He was a member of the management committee and his knowledge of organisation and administration was always available to members of the staff. His advice was frequently asked - no problem was too small or too large to be carefully discussed. His aims and objects were clear: the first thing to be considered was what was best for the patient. His simple criterion led to straightforward solutions of many complicated problems. He was also particularly concerned about the training of orthopaedic nurses and gave much time and thought to improving their conditions of service. His interest in rehabilitation of the disabled never ceased; at the invitation of the Sheffield Regional Hospital Board he began resettlement clinics in Nottingham, Chesterfield, and Mansfield in 1961. Although he had created a comprehensive service based on Harlow Wood he continued to look to the future and up till the time of his death he was making plans for improvements."

Sir Herbert John Seddon (President of the British Orthopaedic Association, 1960-61) writes of Malkin as a surgeon and as a friend:-

"Robert Jones's ability to pick winners was never more evident than the choice of Malkin. Harlow Wood and the Portland Training College were all Malkin's doing and there was hardly a national body or committee concerned with the welfare of the disabled that he did not influence. It might be thought from this that he had little time for the practice of surgery. But he was an able and soundly conservative clinician; independently of McMurray, he devised the best operation we know for osteo-arthritis of the hip and if he had not been so modest it would possibly have borne his name."

"Malkin was not so clever as some of his contemporaries, but he rose above them because of his superb character. Here was a man devoid of personal ambition, caring for nothing except the great cause he espoused. His tenacity was increased by opposition or indifference; he was like a bulldog, he never let go; he could move in only one direction, forward. We have lost not only a dear friend but one whose example rebuked self-seeking, timidity, and ennui."

Norman Capener (President of the British Orthopaedic Association, 1958-59) describes what he did for his specialty beyond the Midlands:-

"He did original work himself: one of the most notable being his early recognition in the 1920s of the curative effects of trochanteric osteotomy for osteo-arthritis of the hip-joint. In his earlier life he had been influenced particularly by Naughton Dunn in Birmingham and by Reginald Cheyne Elmslie in London. He had a great capacity for organisation; and he took infinite trouble to watch the affairs of the disabled nationally through the Central Council of the Care of Cripples, of which he was a member for many years. In public affairs he gave of his best. In private, he had a quiet personal charm which was altogether delightful. He was temperate in all things. His modest exterior sometimes led people to impose upon him, but he had an extraordinary intuition and he read character to many a person's discomfiture."

"Orthopaedics in Great Britain has, like other branches of medicine, developed as an art and a science but, more than most, also as a social service. In all three Malkin made his mark. Not only did he develop a hospital for the routine treatment of cripples from the industrial areas around, but he also built up a place of orthopaedic learning and teaching, which I know he had hoped would form the basis of a great new medical teaching centre in the midlands.

R. G. Pulvertaft Orthopaedic Surgeon, Harlow Wood Hospital, sent the following personal appreciation:-

"Alan Malkin will be remembered for his grace and quiet confidence and for his single-minded devotion to the care of the disabled. For him responsibility did not end until all had been done to restore ɛ patient to the art of living. To him, people mattered and it was natural for him to go beyond the line of duty to help them. This was particularly noticeable in his relations with the young men who came to Harlow Wood for training. He was constantly thinking of their future and many owe their position today to his guidance. Alan Malkin sought little for himself except to be given the means to advance the work he had at heart. His humanity and integrity were outstanding and never in the twenty-five years of our friendship did I hear him say a word of unkind or unjust criticism of others."

R. S. C. returned to his work as a teacher:-

"Alan Malkin was a good friend to many people but perhaps especially to the young men of orthopaedics. At Harlow Wood Orthopaedic Hospital the annual course, which is so successful, has always started with a small speech of welcome by this tall kindly man who took an interest in the problems and ideas of all the students. Since his official retirement his thoughts were constantly on how to improve the facilities for training and research in the Nottingham area, even when pruning his many apple trees or riding the lanes around his home. A generous man of high ideals, he was consumed by an inner fire and he dedicated his life to orthopaedics. How many of us will be able to leave such a tribute to our work as the unique orthopaedic trio of Harlow Wood Orthopaedic Hospital, the Portland Training College for the disabled, and the Thieves Wood School for Handicapped Children, within arrow shot of each other in Sherwood Forest.

After his death on the 22nd February, 1964, his family formed a trust with a gift from his estate as he had wished. This made it possible to establish a scholarship to sponsor travel by young surgeons and non-medical staff who were based at Harlow Wood Hospital. His contribution to the hospital is also commemorated by the annual 'Alan Malkin Memorial Lecture.'

Dr A GORDON M.R.C.S., L.R.C.P.
President of the
Nottingham Medico-Chirurgical Society 1955-1956

Arthur Gordon:- 113, Melton Road, West Bridgford, Nottingham. (Gordon & Maclean). M.R.C.S., (England) L.R.C.P., (London), 1923 (Cape and Guy's Hospital). Anaesthetist, Nottingham General Hospital. Anaesthetist, Women's Hospital, Nottingham. Education Committee and Royal Midland Eye Infirmary. President of the Arthur Gordon:- 113, Melton Road, West Bridgford, Nottingham. (Gordon & Nottingham Medico-Chirurgical Society.

Medical Directory 1956

P.H. O'DONOVAN M.D. (London) F.R.C.P. (London)
President of the
Nottingham Medico-Chirurgical Society 1956-1957

PATRICK HENRY O'DONOVAN
1900 - 1977.
Honorary Librarian of the Nottingham Medico-Chirurgical Society 1934 to 1937.

Patrick Henry O'Donovan:- 16, The Ropewalk, Nottingham. M.R.C.S., L.R.C.P. 1923, M.B., B.S., London 1924; M.D. 1928; M.R.C.P. 1928; F.R.C.P. 1944; Honorary Physician, General Hospital, Nottingham; Visiting Physician, City Hospital, Nottingham; Consultant Physician, Ilkeston Hospital, Stamford Infirmary & Skegness Hospital. Member of the Nottingham Medico-Chirurgical Society & Derby Medical Society. Late Resident Medical Officer, National heart Hospital, London; House Physician, General Hospital, Nottingham; Clinical Assistant Surgeon, Out Patients, London Hospital

Medical Directory 1961

Patrick O'Donovan was proud to have been born in London within the sound of Bow Bells. He was the son of Patrick O'Donovan, civil servant, and his wife, Beatrice Gibson, daughter of an iron foundry owner. He attended Cooper's School and the London Hospital Medical College. He came to Nottingham General Hospital as house physician in 1925. In 1928 he was given leave of absence to study for MD and MRCP. He served as RMO in the National Heart Hospital during this time and was successful in both examinations. He was appointed honorary assistant physician to the Nottingham General Hospital in 1930, honorary physician in 1937 and when the Health Service started in 1948, consultant physician. He was honorary librarian of the Nottingham Medico-Chirurgical Society from 1934 to 1937, and in 1956 the Society (composed of members from all medical disciplines in the area) conferred upon him its highest honour by electing him president for the year. He was a member of the British Heart Society for many years.

He was appointed honorary assistant physician at a time when there were very few trained specialists available outside teaching centres. The Nottingham Medical School was not to be established for another thirty years. He quickly showed his specialist interest and skill in cardiology and it was not long before he was widely recognised as giving an outstanding opinion in the Midlands. His private practice therefore made increasing demands upon his time. He never neglected his hospital patients and for many years did a regular ward round on Sunday mornings.

In 1932 he married Mary Dobson and they had two sons. He continued to live in Nottingham after his retirement.

Patrick O'Donovan was not an easy man to get to know. He had few close medical friends. All his colleagues had the highest regard for his professional skill and personal integrity. He was a shy man, quiet but firm. If he was convinced that a cause deserved his support, it was given with vigour and determination. On the other hand, if he felt something was wrong he had no hesitation in opposing it, even though this could be unpopular.

In his earlier days he enjoyed a little golf and an occasional day's shooting but work claimed a great deal of his time. He enjoyed reading and, in his later years, took up bowls. One of his unique experiences was to receive a blank cheque from John Dane Player of the wealthy tobacco family. He did not complete it but had it framed and showed it to his visitors who thus gained an interesting insight into his character.

Throughout his life he was a committed Roman Catholic. One of his great joys was the Papal Honour, *Bene Merenti*, bestowed on him a year before he died.

W.S. WHIMSTER M.D. (London) F.R.C.P.
President of the
Nottingham Medico-Chirurgical Society 1958-1959

William Swanson Whimster: "Parkdale," Pevril Drive, The Park, Nottingham. M.D., London 1928, M.B., B.S., 1926; M.R.C.P., London 1929; M.R.C.S. England; L.R.C.P. London, 1925 (Guys): Physician General, Highbury and City Hospitals, Nottingham. Fellow of the Royal Society of Medicine; Member of the Nottingham Medico-Chirurgical Society. Late, Resident Medical Officer Ancoats Hospital, Manchester; House Physician Warneford Hospital, Leamington Spa; Senior House Surgeon, Royal United Hospital, Bath.

Medical Directory 1959.

William Swanson Whimster, Born 12th May, 1902, Died 30th May, 1969. M.R.C.S., L.R.C.P. (1925) M.B., B.S. London (1926) M.D. (1928) M.R.C.P. (1929), F.R.C.P. (1960)

William Swanson Whimster was born at Wood Green in Middlesex, the elder son of William Swanson Whimster, an emigre Scot and hardware merchant and Catherine Whimster (nee Cameron).

He became clinical assistant to Sir (then Dr.) Charles Symonds at the National Hospitals for Nervous Diseases, Queen Square, London, where he attended weekly until the outbreak of war.

He was medically unfit for military service and so continued his practice with the help of assistants. He was educated at the City of London School and entered Guy's Hospital in October 1919, qualifying M.R.C.S., L.R.C.P. in 1925 and M.B., B.S. in 1926. He enjoyed his time at Guy's, taking part in the athletics and rugby, and often recalled the teaching of Sir Arthur Hurst and John Ryle. After resident appointments at the Warneford Hospital, Leamington Spa, and the United Hospitals in Bath, he took the post of medical officer on the cargo ship TSS Cachas of the Blue Funnel Line and sailed from Liverpool in August 1927 to China and Japan. In the Indian Ocean he experienced his first attack of atrial fibrillation which lasted for four days and troubled him intermittently until 1955 when it became continuous.

In February 1928 he was appointed resident medical officer at Ancoats Hospital, Manchester. During this appointment he proceeded M.D., took the M.R.C.P. and met his wife.

In May 1930 he took over a single-handed general practice in Nottingham. He was attracted to this because it was a university town and offered opportunities for what he called a 'centre of town physician and honorary hospital appointments. By 1931 he was clinical assistant at the Nottingham General Hospital and medical officer to the University College and to Raleigh Industries. He became medical officer to No.1 Ordnance Field Park, Royal Canadian Ordnance Corps, which was stationed in Nottingham. In 1941 he was appointed honorary physician to Mansfield General Hospital and became senior physician and chairman of the Medical Committee there. In 1944 he was made assistant physician to the Nottingham General Hospital and physician in 1946. From the inception of the National Health Service he held appointments as consultant to the General, City, Highbury, and Mapperley Hospitals in Nottingham, and to Saxondale Hospital, Radcliffe-on-Trent. He continued general medical practice with neurology of which he remained the only local practitioner up to his retirement.

He was a founder member of, honorary treasurer and finally president of the East Midlands Society of Physicians. He served on the Council and, in 1958-59 was president of the Nottingham Medico-Chirurgical Society. He was member of the Nottingham No.4 Hospital Management Committee chairman of the Highbury Hospital Medical Committee, and honorary secretary of the General Hospital Management Committee. From 1961 to 1966 he was a member of the Sheffield Regional Board. For the last 15 months before his retirement he was senior physician at the Nottingham General Hospital and the last physician to have come to hospital consultantship through general practice.

William Whimster was a thoughtful, energetic man whose sympathetic and encouraging manner was well suited to the long-term problems of neurological patients. He developed a most satisfactory relationship with the psychiatrists (he was consultant to the local mental hospitals) and with neurosurgeons in Derby. He did not often publish but was sought after as a speaker and committee man with a strong sense of public duty. He was particularly aware of the need for hospital administration to be tempered by medical humanity
.

In 1930 he married Madge Elizabeth Edwards, M.B. Ch.B. (Manchester) youngest child of Frederick Fountain Edwards of Manchester. He was fortunate to live to see his three sons married and qualified as a pathologist, a veterinary surgeon, and a consulting engineer.

He had a deep knowledge and love of the English countryside and its history. In later years he travelled abroad to visit his doctor son in Fiji and Jamaica. He also visited the continent and Egypt. He was an enthusiastic photographer whose colour slides enhanced his travel talks which were in demand after his retirement. His accomplished public speaking and many tit bits of information came from his wide reading and long membership of the Rotary Club and the local Magdala Debating Society. His junior staff and his sons greatly appreciated the byways of learning, both medical and lay, into which he led them.

From the Lives of Fellows of the Royal College of Physicians.

Munks Roll, pages 456 and 457.

HAROLD JORDAN MALKIN
(1898 - 1978)
President of the
Nottingham Medico-Chirurgical Society 1959-1960

Harold Jordan Malkin   26, The Ropewalk, Nottingham. C.B.E., F.R.C.S. (Edinburgh) 1925, M.R.C.S. (England) L.R.C.P. (London) 1923. M.D. London, 1926; M.B., B.S., 1924. F.R.C.O.G., 1938 (University College Hospital, London) Surgeon, Nottingham Womens Hospital Gynaecology and Obstetric Surgeon, City Hospital and Firs Maternity Hospital, Nottingham. Gynaecology Surgeon, Newark Hospital; Consultant Obstetrician Surgeon, Victoria Hospital, Mansfield, Notts. Obstetric Specialist, Nottinghamshire County Council. Exam Centre, Midwifery Board. Association Exam London, M.B., B.S. Member of the Council of the Royal College of Obstetrics and Gynaecologists. Fellow of the Royal Society of Medicine and Nursing of England Obstetric Society. Late:- House Surgeon and House Physician, Royal North Hospital. House Surgeon, Obstetric House Surgeon, Obstetric Registrar and Associated to Obstetric Unit, University College Hospital, London.

Medical Directory 1948.

Harold Jordan Malkin came to Nottingham in 1928. He was connected with the Old Samaritans' Hospital before it changed to the Nottingham Women's Hospital. From 1937 he was on the staff of the Nottingham City Hospital and before that, the Newark Hospital. He was attached to Mansfield General Hospital from 1932 to 1945.

In 1956, Mr. Malkin was chosen to be a member of the Government committee set up to enquire into the country's maternity services, a committee that was led by Lord Cranbrook. During his long career with hospitals he was able to introduce many changes and advances in after-care.

Among his many duties Mr. Malkin held the position of president in the North of England Obstetric Society and the obstetric section of the Royal Society of Medicine.

He was elected President of the Nottingham Medico-Chirurgical Society from from 1959 - 1960. At that time he was vice-president of the Council of the Royal College of Obstetrics and Gynaecologists.

He retired from the National Health Service in 1963 but retained his position as chairman of the Obstetric Committee of the Nottingham City and County Health Executive until his retirement in 1969.

Harold Jordan Malkin died in December 1978 aged 80. In a memorial service held in January 1979 a tribute was paid to him. It said; "Selfless dedication of his outstanding gifts in teaching and administration. Younger people, had been ready to respond to the inspiration of his example and the encouragement of his counsel."

Nottingham Local History Library

"Obituary"

British Medical Journal, 6th January, 1979.

Mr. Harold Jordan Malkin, formerly consultant obstetrician and gynaecologist at Nottingham died on the 13th December, 1978 he was aged 80. He was survived by his wife Joyce and two daughters.

Harold Jordan Malkin was born on 27th April 1898 and educated at Epworth College and at University College and Hospital. During the first world war his studies were interrupted by service in the Royal Field Artillery. After qualifying in 1923 he held house appointments at University College Hospital and at the Royal Northern Hospital. He took the Fellowship of the Royal College of Surgeons, Edinburgh in 1925 and proceeded MD in 1926. Two years later he became consultant obstetrician and gynaecologist at Nottingham and held the appointment until 1967. From then until 1975 he was director of postgraduate studies at the Royal College of Obstetricians and Gynaecologists of which he had been a fellow since 1938.

Harold Malkin will be remembered in many places as the kindest and most considerate of friends, as a great obstetrician, a leader in the councils of his specialty, and a broadminded and tolerant seeker after the best outcome for us all and not merely for his own profession. He, and Miss Glen Bott established his specialty in Nottingham at a time when it seemed firmly under the dominance of the surgeons yet contrived to avoid the strife that so often attended such a development. He built up a centre that could compare with any, despite the limitations of hospital resources. He will be remembered for that achievement in the city to which he gave a life's work, far into the future. He taught many who were to look back on their time with him with gratitude and affection for the one who led by unmatched example. He was to play a large part in the establishment of the new medical school, even though he had ceased by then to be an active teacher. His devotion to Nottingham did not prevent him from playing a major part in the college of which he was to be vice-president, and in which he was to hold many offices. His last long service to the college as director of postgraduate education came at a time when that side of medical education most needed his talents of persuasion and patience. Harold was an original member of the Joint Consultants Committee at a time when that body played a crucial part in the inception of the National Health Service, a part too seldom recognised at the present time. His role in the N.H.S. was always constructive and fair and locally of the greatest importance. He was not merely active at the national level, but visited Africa, the Middle East, and the Far East on behalf of his college. He was one of the original group of regional assessors who made the confidential investigation into maternal deaths the outstanding success it became, and he served in that capacity for 20 years. This was a life of service to medicine at every level seldom equalled and never surpassed; but Harold's memory will be cherished by all who had the privilege of his friendship or of his professional help being the man he was, even more than the great doctor he also was.

JOHN D PROCTOR
(1902 - 1966)
President of the
Nottingham Medico-Chirurgical Society 1961-1962

John Douglas Proctor:- 16, Park Terrace, The Park, Nottingham; B.A. Cambridge, 1923 M.R.C.S., L.R.C.P., 1925 *(Cambridge & University College)*; M.R.C.P. 1928; M.A., M.B. BChir, 1929 M.D. 1937; F.R.C.P. 1962; Physician, Nottingham General Hospital & Nottingham Children's Hospital; Member of the British Medical Association (President of the Nottingham Division); Fellow of the Royal Society of Medicine; Late Honorary House Physician, Mansfield General Hospital; Assistant to the Medical Unit & House Physician, University College Hospital.

Medical Directory 1963

John Douglas Proctor was born at Longton, Stoke on Trent, where his father, Percy John Proctor, was a china and earthenware factor. His mother, Isabella Hodgkinson was the daughter of a draper. John Proctor was educated at Epworth College, Rhyl, in North Wales and later at Gonville and Caius College, Cambridge. Here he obtained a BA degree in the Natural Science Tripos in 1923 and then went up to University College Hospital in London, where he qualified with the Conjoint diploma in 1925. He served this hospital as house physician, house surgeon and obstetric house surgeon between 1925 and 1927, when he spent a further four years as an assistant to the Medical Unit under T. R. Elliott. He obtained the Cambridge MD in 1937 with a thesis on 'Factors influencing gastric acidity'.

In 1931 he was appointed clinical assistant at the Nottingham General Hospital, a post which he held until 1937, when he obtained a post on the staff of the Mansfield General Hospital. In 1946 was appointed physician to the Nottingham General Hospital and the Nottingham Children's Hospital, both of which posts he held till his death. He was elected an FRCP in 1962, and was always interested in the work of the BMA, of which he was elected a Fellow in 1966. He was Chairman of the Sheffield Regional Consultants and Specialists Committee and was a member of the Central Consultants and Specialists Committee from 1955 till 1958.

John Proctor was a good, careful, conscientious and popular doctor whose opinion and advice was often sought and always willingly given. He was particularly interested in patients with diabetes. He was devoted to music and was a competent performer on both the piano and the violin. Among his greatest pleasures were the meetings of the Nottingham Music Club of which he was an active member.

His wife, Ellen Elizabeth Sargent, the daughter of a rubber and metal merchant, whom he married in 1929, was a keen musician herself, as were his son and two daughters.

In 1962 John Proctor suffered a coronary thrombosis which reduced his activities. He seemed to have made a good recovery and was resuming much of his normal life when he suffered a second and fatal coronary thrombosis on the golf course.

E.J. GILROY GLASS T.D., F.R.C.S. (Edinburgh) D.L.O.
(1901 - 1980)
President of the
Nottingham Medico-Chirurgical Society 1962-1963

Edward James Gilroy Glass:- 32a, The Ropewalk, Nottingham; M.B., Ch.B., Edinburgh, 1924; F.R.C.S. Edinburgh. D.L.O. England 1930; *(University of Edinburgh & Paris)* E.N.T. Surgeon, Nottingham Group of Hospitals; Fellow of the Royal Society of Medicine (President of the Section of Laryngology); Member (Vice President) Midland Institute for Laryngology; Late Colonel Royal Army Medical Corps; Assistant E.N.T. Department, Royal Infirmary, Edinburgh; House Surgeon, General Hospital, Nottingham

Medical Directory 1963

Edward James Gilroy Glass was born at North Berwick, Scotland, on 5th April 1901 and graduated in medicine from Edinburgh University in 1924. He was appointed house surgeon to the Ear Nose and Throat Department at the Nottingham General Hospital in 1926. Two years later he took the Fellowship of the Royal College of Surgeons (Edinburgh). The next year he was appointed honorary assistant Ear Nose and Throat surgeon to Mansfield and Nottingham City Hospitals and continued his work at the general Hospital, becoming honorary assistant surgeon in 1935. During the 1930s Roy Glass studied at Philadelphia and visited clinics in Paris Vienna, and Holland. His career was interrupted by the war. Since 1927 he had been medical officer in the Territorial Army. In 1938 he was promoted to major and posted as ENT surgeon to No. 16 General Hospital serving in France, retreating and subsequently evacuating that country. In 1941 he was appointed to raise and command No. 80 British General Hospital for service in India, later commanding No. 57 India General Hospital. He finished his war service as assistant director of medical services Central Command India.

When Roy Glass returned to civilian life he was appointed senior ENT surgeon to the Nottingham General Hospital, where he was able to use his flair for administration in getting the department through the early years of the Health Service. He was instrumental in setting up combined clinics in conjunction with the school health service. Later he served for three years as chairman of the group medical committee and as a member of the management committee. In 1962 he was elected president of the section of laryngology of the Royal Society of Medicine. At the same time he was president of the Nottingham Medico-Chirurgical Society. Roy retired in 1966 and moved to Guernsey where he was able to pursue his two lifelong interests, fishing and gardening.

Dr. W. K. S. Moore wrote:- Roy Glass was a man of parts. Some saw the distinguished surgeon, some knew the senior RAMC officer, but beyond these aspects of his life was a keen fisherman, a knowledgeable gardener, a skilful embroiderer, a yachtsman and, above all, a warm-hearted and steadfast friend. Roy was a man of his word, never undertaking anything he could not fulfil. Without being gregarious, he enjoyed the company of friends both young and old with whom he delighted in exploring Guernsey and talking over affairs old and new. He retained his soldierly bearing and neatness all his life and never lost the slightly formal good manners of his Scottish upbringing.

British Medical Journal, 22nd March, 1980. Page 873.

JOHN BARR COCHRANE M.B., CH.B., F.R.G.O.G
(1912 - 1986)
President of the
Nottingham Medico-Chirurgical Society 1963-1964

Mr. John Barr Cochrane:- M.B., Ch.B., Edinburgh, 1963; M.R.C.O.G., 1947 (University of Edinburgh) F.R.C.O.G. 1959; Address, 41, Burlington Road, Sherwood & 36, The Ropewalk, Nottingham; Consultant Obstetrician and Gynaecology, City Hospital and Firs Maternity Hospital, Nottingham; Member of the Nottingham Medico-Chirurgical Society; Fellow of the North of England Obstetric and Gynaecology Society; Late:- House Surgeon, Royal Infirmary, Bolton. Medical Officer, Municipal General Hospital, Burnley.

Medical Directory 1963

Mr. John Barr Cochrane was born in Elgin and educated at the academy there, where he was captain of the school. He graduated in medicine from Edinburgh University in 1936 and moved to Nottingham the following year. He was appointed house surgeon at the City Hospital in 1937 and spent the rest of his professional life there, being made consultant at the inception of the National Health Service.

Mr. Cochrane was a man of immense energy with a prodigious workload who set high standards in the personal care of his patients and the administration of his department. He had a great interest in the City Hospital and did much to develop it from a local authority hospital with a house staff of six to a modern teaching hospital with a medical staff of over 100. He was proud of the Nottingham Medico-Chirurgical Society of which he was a trustee and former president. For many years he collected on behalf of the Royal Medical Benevolent Fund and was also active on behalf of Cancer Research and the nearby Convent Hospital.

Outside medicine he was in his younger days a very competent jazz drummer and a keen cricketer, leading the City Hospital's team for many years. Before his death in November 1985 he became president of the Nottinghamshire County Cricket Club and Nottinghamshire Cricket Association.

British Medical Journal. Volume 292, 15th February, 1986.
Page 493.

A.C. GLADSTONE M.B., B.S., M.R.C.S., L.R.C.P.
President of the
Nottingham Medico-Chirurgical Society 1964-1965

Albert Clemenston Gladstone:- The Croft, 8, Church Street, Eastwood, Nottinghamshire. M.B., B.S., London 1932, M.R.C.S., England. L.R.C.P., London, 1932 (St. Thomas's). Late:- Senior Obstetric House Physician, St. Thomas's Hospital, House Surgeon, Royal North Hospital; Orthopaedic House Surgeon, Derbyshire Royal Infirmary.

Medical Directory 1964

J.P. CAMPBELL M.B., Ch.B. (St.A.),
(1907 - 1976)
F.R.C.S. (Edinburgh) President of the
Nottingham Medico-Chirurgical Society 1965-1966

James Pollock Campbell:- 3, Albemarle Road, Woodthorpe, Nottingham. Consulting Rooms, 1, Park Terrace, The Ropewalk, Nottingham. M.B., Ch.B., St. Andrews 1930, F.R.C.S., Edinburgh 1936 (Dundee). Surgeon Superintendent, Harlow Wood Orthopaedic Hospital, Mansfield. Orhopaedic Surgeon, Nottingham General Hospital, Nottingham Children's Hospital and Ilkeston Hospital. Fellow of the British Orthopaedic Association. Member of the British Medical Association and former President of the Nottingham Branch. Member of the International de Chir Orthopaedic et de Traumatol. Late:- Senior Orthopaedic Surgeon, City Hospital, Nottingham.Orthopaedic Surgeon, Newark Hospital Lecturer:- Regional Avatomy, University College Dundee (St. Andrews University).

Medical Directory 1964

James Pollock Campbell graduated at the University College of Dundee in 1930 and became a lecturer in anatomy before beginning his surgical career. He took the Fellowship of the Royal College of Surgeons (Edinburgh) in 1936. His early orthopaedic training was at Manchester with Sir Harry Platt and at the Robert Jones and Agnes Hunt Orthopaedic Hospital at Oswestry. This experience formed the basis on which he was to develop a lifetime's devotion to the practice of orthopaedic surgery. He came to Nottingham in 1938 and joined Alan Malkin at Harlow Wood Orthopaedic Hospital. He was on the staff of the Nottingham City Hospital for a number of years and also at Nottingham General and Nottingham Children's Hospital. When Alan Malkin retired in 1957 James Campbell succeeded him as surgeon superintendent at Harlow Wood and dedicated himself to improving the hospital in every way. He believed firmly that orthopaedic surgery was best practised in a special hospital which was designed for that purpose and he was determined to preserve the integrity of the unit with which he was so closely associated. At the same time he played an active part in the busy accident service at the Nottingham General Hospital.

James Campbell was a kind and generous man. He was a strong supporter of the long established Nottingham Cripples Guild and president of the Nottingham Sports Club for the Disabled. Many patients in Nottingham have reason to be grateful for his sound judgment and surgical skill. He was particularly interested in the use of femerol osteotomy for osteoarthritis and other conditions of the hip and published an important paper on this with one of his colleagues. He was a fellow of the British Orthopaedic Association and a member of the Societe Internationale de Chirurgie Orthopedique. He was elected president of the Nottingham Medico-Chirurgical Society in 1965 to 1966, and was also president of the Nottinghamshire Branch of the British Medical Association. James had many friends outside his work and was a popular figure at the Notts Golf Club where he played with notable skill. He was also a past president of the Nottinghamshire and District Scottish Golfing Society.

BMJ, 28th August 1976. Page 535.

PHILIP RONALD KIRTLEY BRADBURY
President of the
Nottingham Medico-Chirurgical Society 1966-1967

Philip Ronald Kirtley Bradbury:- Crich House, Villiers Road, Woodthorpe, Nottingham. M.B., Ch.B., Edinburgh; 1934. Member of the Nottingham and Nottinghamshire Local Medical Committee. Member of the British Medical Association. President of the Nottingham Medico-Chirurgical Society.

Medical Directory 1968

PAUL COWELL BARKLA V.R.D., F.R.C.S.
(1911 - 1986)
(Edinburgh), F.R.C.O.G President of the
Nottingham Medico-Chirurgical Society 1967-1968

Paul Cowell Barkla, V.R.D.:- 37, Private Road, Sherwood Nottingham. (Consulting Rooms) 9, Regent Street, Nottingham. M.B., Ch.B., Edinburgh, 1933; F.R.C.S., Edinburgh, 1937; F.R.C.O.G., 1957; M. 1939; (Edinburgh) J.P.. Obstetric and Gynaecologist, Women's Hospital, Nottingham and City Hospital, Nottingham. Gynaecologist, Newark Hospital and Ilkeston General Hospital. Member of the North of England Obstetric and Gynaecologist Society and the Birmingham and Midland Obstetric and Gynaecologist Society. Late:- Surgeon , Lt Commander, R.N.V.R. (Retired). External Examiner Obstetric and Gynaecologist, University's of Manchester Sheffield. House Surgeon, Royal Maternity Hospital, Edinburgh.

Medical Directory 1968

Paul Cowell Barkla came from a distinguished family: his father was professor of physics at Edinburgh University and won the Nobel prize. Paul had a spectacular athletics record as a student and took part in the University Olympics in Darmstart. He graduated M.D., Ch.B., at Edinburgh in 1933 and moved in 1939 to Nottingham, where he was to spend the rest of his professional life, apart from six years during the war when he served with the Royal Naval Volunteer Reserve. He was appointed consultant at the City and Women's Hospitals in 1948 and retired in 1975. He took a full part in the life of both hospitals and was chairman of the group medical executive committee. He was also President of the Nottingham Medico-Chirurgical Society between 1967/68. Outside medicine he retained an interest in matters naval, supporting the local sea cadets and the Royal National Lifeboat Institution, of which he was the local president. He became a magistrate in 1963.

Paul Cowell Barkla was considered a very kind and compassionate man who loved other peoples company and was thoughtful and generous in his invitation to others; he received excellent support from his wife Eleanor. He was considerate to his patients and junior medical staff and his concern for others was expressed in his "Save the Children" movement. He had a great sense of humour and a remarkable ability to coin an amusing phrase or recount a stimulating anecdote. Everyone was relaxed and at ease in his company and ward rounds were enlivening. He had a remarkable ability to interpret other people's reactions in the best possible light. This, together with his attractive personality and technical competence, made him a very capable chairman of committees. Among a gathering of colleagues he was always a uniter and a peacemaker.

B.M.J., Volume 292. 12th April, 1986. Page 1022, 1023.
See Appendices

ERNEST LUCAS LOEWENTHAL
President of the
Nottingham Medico-Chirurgical Society 1968-1969

Ernest Lucas Loewenthal:- 292, Derby Road, Nottingham. (Loewenthal, Fisher, Giedrys and Sprackling). M.B., B.S., London, 1938. District Obstetrician, Royal College of Gynaecologists, 1946 (University College Hospital). Member of the Nottingham Medico-Chirurgical Society. Late:- Anaesthetist, Nottingham Women's Hospital, Casualty Officer, Queen Mary's Hospital, Stratford; Obstetric House Surgeon, City Hospital.

Medical Directory 1969

J.C. BUCKLEY T.D., B.A., M.B., B.Chir., F.F.A.
President of the
Nottingham Medico-Chirurgical Society 1969-1970

John Charles Buckley: Southfield House, Bramcote, Nottingham. B.A., Canterbury, 1929; M.B., B.Chir, 1934: M.R.C.S., England; L.R.C.P., London, 1934. F.F.A. R.C.S., England, 1953. D.A. England, 1937 (Cambridge and St Thomas'); Consultant Anaesthetist, General Hospital, City Hospital, Women's Hospital and Thoracic Surgical Unit, Nottingham. Member of the Association of Anaesthetists, Great Britain. Fellow of the Royal Society of Medicine. Late: Anaesthetist, Westminster Hospital; Honorary Anaesthetist, Memorial Hospital Woolwich and Princess Beatrice Hospital.

Medical Directory 1969

REGINALD JOSEPH TWORT M.A., M.D., F.R.C.P.
President of the
Nottingham Medico-Chirurgical Society 1970-1971

Born: 21st March, 1911. Died: 16th June, 1971.

Reginald Joseph Twort:- 6, The Ropewalk, Nottingham. M.A., Cambridge, 1938, B.A., (1st Class, National Science Trope Part 1) Cambridge, 1932. M.D. (Commended, Aberdeen, 1944, M.B., Ch.B. Distinction) 1936; F.R.C.P., London, 1963; M., 1940; F.R.C.P. Edinburgh, 1957. M. 1940; (Cambridge and Aberdeen). Gold Medal in Pathological Maternity Medicine and Clinical Medicine. Smith Prize for Disabled Children and Alex Anderson Travelling School of Medicine, University of Aberdeen. Medical Physics Department, Nottingham General and City Hospitals. Examiner to the General Nursing Council. Member of the Thoracic Society, Member of the British Cardiac Society. Late:- Medical Registrar, Royal Infirmary, Aberdeen; Resident Medical Officer, West End Hospital for Nervous Diseases. Wing Commander, O.C., Medical Division, R.A.F.V.R.

Medical Directory 1970

Reginald Joseph Twort: B.A. Canterbury (1932), M.B., Ch.B., Aberdeen (1936) M.A., Canterbury (1938) M.R.C.P. (1940) M.R.C.P. (Edinburgh), (1940) M.D., Aberdeen (1944) F.R.C.P. (Edinburgh) (1957) F.R.C.P. (1963).

"Reggie" Twort was born at Bagshot in Surrey, the son and grandson of general practitioners. He was educated at Fettes College and Peterhouse, Cambridge. Then he went to Aberdeen where he graduated in medicine with distinction in 1936. His intellectual quality had previously shown itself when he was at Cambridge, for he achieved a First in the Natural

Sciences Tripos and was elected a life scholar at Peterhouse.

After house officer appointments at the Royal Infirmary at Aberdeen, Addenbrookes and the Brompton, he served as a resident medical officer at the West End Hospital for Nervous Diseases and as medical registrar at the Royal Infirmary at Aberdeen. By this time the 1939-45 war had erupted and he served as a medical specialist in the Royal Air Force for five years, achieving the rank of Wing-Commander and Officer in Charge of a Medical Division. On demobilisation he was appointed physician to the Nottingham City and General Hospitals and also to Mansfield General Hospital.

Dr. Twort developed a special interest in cardiology. He was an excellent general physician and had great energy, administrative ability, wit and charm. He had a very large consulting practice and all who knew him had great respect and affection for him. When Nottingham was chosen for a new medical school he took a prominent part in the planning of the hospital aspect and served on the Council of the University. He died at his home in the Ropewalk at Nottingham when he was 60. He had married Francis Alice Smith, the daughter of Henry Smith. There were two sons of the marriage, one of whom continued the family tradition of medicine.

MUNKS ROLL
Page 441.

Dr. P. J. Toghill wrote:- "Reggie Twort was a fine physician, with enormous energy which he applied not only to his clinical work, but to many other aspects of his very full life. He was particularly interested in cardiac and thoracic disease and was in charge of the Cardiac Clinic at the General Hospital, Nottingham. His professional ability and integrity were widely recognised by his colleagues, and at the time of his death, he had just completed his term as president of the Nottingham Medico-Chirurgical Society, an honour of which he was justifiably proud. Throughout his career he maintained a particular affection for his old medical school and became president of the Aberdeen Graduates Society. With the formation of the Nottingham Medical School he was called upon to utilise his considerable administrative experience and skill as chairman of the Medical Advisory Committee when the new academic units were being integrated into the service departments of the Nottingham hospitals and the new University Hospital Management Committee was being established.

"His untimely death, after a short illness, coming at the height of his career, came as a shock to his many friends and colleagues. He had a particularly keen understanding with his junior hospital staff, who served him with great loyalty. He followed their subsequent careers with interest and encouragement. In his busy life he found time to travel far and wide in search of salmon and trout and he also greatly enjoyed his shooting. His large circle of friends will remember with affection the delightful evenings of entertainment at his home where so many were made welcome."

The Lancet, July 17th, 1971.
Page 171, 172.

IAN ALISTAIR MURDIE MACLEOD
T.D., M.B., Ch.B., F.R.C.S.(Edinburgh)

Born: 4th October, 1913. Died: 27th September, 1980.

**President of the Nottingham Medico-Chirurgical Society
1971 - 1972.**

Ian Alister Murdie Macleod T.D. :- 28, The Ropewalk, Nottingham. M.B., Ch.B., Edinburgh, 1937; F.R.C.S. Edinburgh, 1940 (University of Edinburgh). Consultant Ear Nose and Throat Surgeon, General Hospital, City Hospital and Children's Hospital, Nottingham. Major, R.A.M.C. (T.A.) Fellow of the Royal Society of Medicine. Member of the Otolaryngology Society; Late:- Clinical Tutor, Royal Infirmary, Edinburgh.

Medical Directory 1972

Mr. John Barr Cochrane wrote:- Ian Alistair Murdie Macleod was born in Edinburgh on 4th October, 1913 and educated at Edinburgh Institution and Edinburgh University, graduating in medicine in 1937. After house appointments in Edinburgh he became a clinical tutor in the ENT department of the Royal Infirmary. He joined the R.A.M.C. in 1941 as a surgical specialist, serving in Nigeria, India, and the Far East, until he was demobilised at the end of the war with the rank of lieutenant-colonel. In 1947 Ian Macleod was appointed assistant surgeon to the Ear Nose and Throat department of the General Hospital, Nottingham, attaining full surgeon status a year later when he obtained similar appointments at the Childrens and City Hospitals. His special interests were the treatment of Meniere's disease and the fenestration operation for otosclerosis. To gain further experience of this operation he was granted leave of absence for six months in 1949 to work in the New York clinic of the late Jules Lempert.

An active Fellow of the Royal Society of Medicine and member of the Scottish Otolaryngological Society, Macleod maintained his Army interests by acting as medical officer to the Territorial Battalion of the South Notts Hussars from 1947 to 1962, for which he received the Territorial Decoration. A lifelong member of the B.M.A., he was also a past president of the Nottingham Medico-Chirurgical Society and of the East Midlands Edinburgh University Medical Graduates Club.

A charismatic Scotsman, wholly dedicated to the hospitals to which he devoted so much of his life, Ian Macleod, by his quiet and methodical approach to the care of his patients, imbued them with complete confidence. He was painstaking to a degree, whether in his clinical practice or in giving his considered opinion in committee. Ian brought a wealth of experience to bear on his judgements which were always treated with respect by his colleagues. His friendship was acquired in the same gradual manner but, once established, it was generous and abiding. From his parents - both natives of Sutherland - he acquired a great love for the remote Western Scottish Highlands and eagerly awaited his annual visits to Inchnadamph to relax and fish the local waters for trout and salmon. Macleod was an enthusiastic and excellent shot. For many years he convened the 'doctors shoot' in North Nottinghamshire where he not only enjoyed himself to the full but also provided pleasure for many of his colleagues.

Mr. Macleod died soon after he retired. He was survived by his wife Mary whom he married in 1950 and his daughter, Margaret, who is a senior member of the nursing profession in a London teaching hospital.

Obituary
British Medical Journal, Volume 281, 8th November, 1980.
Pages 1293/1294.

KENNETH SOMERLED MACDONALD-SMITH
M.B., F.R.C.S. (Edinburgh) President of the
Nottingham Medico-Chirurgical Society 1972-1973

Kenneth Somerled Macdonald-Smith:- (Resident) Craigmore, 388, Westdale Lane, Mapperley, Nottingham. (Surgery) 1, Beck Street, Parliament Street, Nottingham. M.B., Ch.B., Edinburgh 1927; F.R.C.S., Edinburgh, 1933; (University of Edinburgh); Royal Victoria Hospital for Tuberculosis. Trust Gold Medal, 1927. Member of the Nottingham Medico-Chirurgical Society.

Medical Directory 1972

**E.B.Z. MASTERMAN M.A., M.D., F.R.C.S.
(England) President of the
Nottingham Medico-Chirurgical Society 1973-1974**

President of the Nottingham Medico-Chirurgical Society
1973 - 1974

Ernest Bertram Zellar Masterman:- 17, Magdala Road, Mapperley Park, Nottingham, and 36, The Ropewalk, Nottingham. B.A. (National Science Tripos) Cambridge, 1931, M.D., 1939, M.A., B.Ch., 1936; F.R.C.S., Edinburgh, 1947. M.R.C.S., England; L.R.C.P. London, 1934 (Cambridge and St. Bartholomew's). Surgeon, City Hospital Nottingham and Highbury Hospital, Bulwell. Fellow of the Royal Society of Medicine; Fellow of the Association of the Surgeons of Great Britain. late:- Major, R.A.M.C., Surgeon Specialist; Resident Surgical Officer, City Hospital, Nottingham; House Surgeon, St. Bartholomew's Hospital.

Medical Directory 1973

JAMES MACMASTER MACFIE T.D., F.R.C.S.
(1914 - 1998)
(Edinburgh) President of the
Nottingham Medico-Chirurgical Society 1974-1975

1914 - 1998

James MacMaster Macfie TD:- (Consulting Rooms) 32, The Ropewalk, Nottingham, and 5, Lucknow Avenue, Nottingham. M.B., Ch.B., Edinburgh, 1936. F.R.C.P. Edinburgh, 1947; M. 1939; (Edinburgh). Physician, Nottingham City Hospital. Clinical Teacher in Medicine, Nottingham University. Area Director of Postgraduate Medical Studies, Nottingham. Fellow of the Royal Society of Medicine, Edinburgh. Late:- Major R.A.M.C. (T.A.); Medical Registrar, Professorial Unit, Queen Elizabeth Hospital, Birmingham. Kirk Duncanson Medical Research Fellow, Royal College Physicians, Edinburgh. Author:- "Vasodilator Fibres in the Ulnar Nerve.

Medical Directory 1974

James MacMaster Macfie was a keen member of the Royal Medical Society, serving as president in 1936. He was called up in the Terrtorial Army in 1939 and served in the Royal Army Medical Corps, largely in India and Paiforce. His interest in post graduate education kindled in Bagdad in 1943 when he ran a refresher course for Polish prisoners of war who had been released by the Russians. He was closely involved in the metamorphosis of an adequate municipal hospital into one of high repute closely linked to the new medical school and in the development of postgraduate training. He was area director of postgraduate education and initiated one of the first general practice vocational training schemes long before they became mandatory. He developed a first class library and also introduced a new blood clinic and diabetic clinic. The award of an honorary Doctor of Medicine by Nottingham pleased him particularly because the other holder of the degree at that time was his old mentor, Sir Derrick Dunlop. He served on many committees and, after retirement, continued to serve on medical appeals tribunals. His main interests outside medicine were golf and gardening.

BMJ, Volume 316, 7th March, 1998. Page 782.

WILLIAM KEITH STEVENSON MOORE M.A.,
M.B., B.Ch. President of the
Nottingham Medico-Chirurgical Society 1975-1976

William Keith Stevenson Moore:- Pendennis, 47, Mapperley Hall Drive, Mapperley Park, Nottingham. M.A., M.B., B.Chir., Cambridge, 1942; (Cambridge and Manchester). Chief Medical Officer, The Boots Company Ltd., Member of the British Medical Association and the Nottingham medico-Chirurgical Society. Late:- Registrar, the Department of Haematology and House Physician, Manchester Royal Infirmary. Major R.A.M.C., A.E.R.. Author:- "Occupational dermatitis caused by Ethylene Oxide." British Journal of Industrial Medicine, 1955.

Medical Directory 1975

**Dr Alan Murphy MBE, MB ChB (Manch) FRCGP
President of the Nottingham Medico-Chirurgical
Society 1976 - 1977**

Alan Murphy, who was President of the Society for the 1976/77 session combined his work in a busy practice in Long Eaton, Nottinghamshire with that as a Reader at Attenborough Church and Military Service in the Army Emergency Reserve.

Alan Murphy was born in North Manchester and educated at the North Manchester Grammar School. He was awarded a Manchester City medical scholarship in 1942 to enter Manchester University from where he qualified MB ChB in 1947. His Pre-registration Posts were as House Physician and House Surgeon at the Manchester Royal Infirmary from where he went as Senior House Officer to the Thoracic Unit at the Frenchay Hospital, Bristol. After National Service in the Royal Army Medical Corps as Medical Officer to the 1st Battalion Royal Warwickshire Regiment he was for a period Surgical Registrar at the Radcliffe Infirmary, Oxford.

He entered general practice at Long Eaton in 1952, retiring as senior partner in 1992. During this time he delivered 2000 babies, 1500 at home and the last 500 in hospital when beds became available to G.Ps at the Queen's Medical Centre and at the City Hospital Nottingham. He was an advisor in obstetrics for the Medical Defence Union and an Assessor in Obstetric Units for the Royal College of Obstetrics and Gynaecology.

After National Service, Alan Murphy joined the Army Emergency Reserve as Medical Officer to 81st Port Regiment, Royal Engineers. Later that year he transferred as Major to the 10th Field Ambulance RAMC. In 1958 at the age of 33 he was promoted to Lt-Col commanding the 10th Field Ambulance.

With the development of the new Nottingham Medical School in the early 1970s Alan was quickly identified as an ideal doctor to forge links between the Medical School, the Hospital and satellite general practices which also involved him working to build the Post Graduate Education Centre at the Queen's Medical Centre. Accordingly he was appointed a part-time lecturer in General Practice to the University of Nottingham and a Clinical Assistant to Professor J R A Mitchell, the Foundation Professor of Medicine. Both of these jobs were combined with his full-time general practice work and continued until 1991.

For his services to General Practice and to Medical Education he was awarded the MBE in 1988.

A churchman all his life, Alan made a profound contribution to his local Church in Attenborough and was a Reader there for 43 years.

**WILLIAM MATTHEW GRAY M.B., CH.B.,
F.R.C.S. (Edinburgh) President of the
Nottingham Medico-Chirurgical Society 1977-1978**

William Matthew Gray:- Woodside, Vicarage Lane, Farnsfield, Newark. F.R.C.S. (Edinburgh) M.R.C.S. (England); L.R.C.P. London 1937 (Kings College Hospital). Surgeon, General Hospital and Nottingham City Hospital. Member of the Nottingham Medico-Chirurgical Society. Fellow of the Royal Society of Medicine. Late:- Resident Surgical Officer, Royal Infirmary, Huddersfield: House Surgeon, Prince of Wales Hospital, Tottenham. Major R.A.M.C. T.A.

Medical Directory, 1977.

Mr. William Matthew Gray, F.R.C.S. (Edinburgh) was a consultant surgeon in Nottingham from 1947 to 1979. He was born in Oxford in 1914, and was educated at Oxford High School and later Kings College Hospital, London, qualifying as a Member of the Royal College of Surgeons and Licentiate of the Royal College of Physicians in 1937. During the war he served in the Grenadier Guards as a medical officer and later as a surgical specialist seeing service in the Middle East, Yugoslavia, and Italy.

During the time of his service in Nottingham Mr. Gray had a reputation as a fine general surgeon. However, he was to gradually become more and more interested in genitourinary work and when the renal dialysis unit was set up at the Nottingham City Hospital this enabled him to form the genitourinary unit, which later became a teaching unit as part of the Nottingham University's Faculty of Medicine.

Mr. Gray's retirement was plagued by constant ill health which finally ended his life on 11 June 1990. His memory is still cherished by the members of the Nottingham Medico-Chirurgical Society who knew him.

BMJ Volume 301 12-25 August, 1990. Page 384.

Atholl H. MacLaren
MBE MB ChB FRCGP
President of the Nottingham Medico-Chirurgical
Society 1978-1979

The Society was extremely fortunate to be able to call upon one of its most distinguished members, Atholl MacLaren, to become President during 1978/9 when it celebrated its 150th anniversary.

Atholl MacLaren was born in Renfrewshire, Scotland and educated at Elgin Academy and Aberdeen University where he qualified MB ChB in 1942. After service in the Royal Air Force he moved to Ruddington, a village just outside Nottingham where he was to remain in general practice for the next 41 years. In addition to his clinical work he shouldered a heavy burden of administrative responsibilities. These included being a member of the BMA Local Medical Committee from 1970 - 90 (Chairman 1978-88), a member of the Nottinghamshire Family Practitioners' Committee (Chairman 1978 -88) and member of the Society of FPCs of England and Wales (President 1984/5). He was also a much respected member of the Nottingham Health Authority

As he did not have enough to do during this period (!) he served as a member for Basford Rural District Council from 1952 - 65 and Medical Officer to Nottingham Forest FC from 1960 - 72.

Atholl MacLaren joined the Medico-Chirurgical Society shortly after arriving in Ruddington, became President in 1978/9, a life member in 1985 and later a trustee. During his memorable year of Presidency, during the 150th celebrations he supervised a splendid Anniversary Dinner at County Hall attended by local dignitaries and luminaries. It is sufficient to say that his speech was the best of the evening! The Presidential year was, of course, dominated by the celebrations and his own Presidential Address dealt amusingly with many of the characters that had contributed to the medical scene over the years. In conjunction with Mr. J B Cochrane, Dr. Sandy Saunders and Dr. James McFie he wrote a Commemorative Anniversary Book for the Society.

He was appointed MBE in 1974.

Mr James Fulton Neil MA, MB BChir (Cantab), FRCS (Edin) DLO
(1979 - 1980)

James Fulton Neil, an otological surgeon at the General Hospital and later the Queen's Medical Centre, emulated his father Mr W F Neil, who had been a surgeon at the General Hospital Nottingham, by becoming President of the Nottingham Medico-Chirurgical Society.

James Neil, always known to his friends as Jimmy, was educated at Uppingham School, Rutland from where he went up to Queens College Cambridge just before World War II. He completed his clinical studies at the Middlesex Hospital graduating MB BChir in 1943, having qualified as Member of the Royal College of Surgeons (England) and Licentiate of the Royal College of Physicians (London) in 1942.

He saw service as a Captain in the Royal Army Medical Corps from 1943 to 1946 and on return from the Army began training as an Ear Nose and Throat (ENT) surgeon at the Institute of Laryngology and Otology Hospital in London and later as an ENT registrar at the General Hospital Nottingham. During this period he was elected to the Fellowship of the Royal College of Surgeons of Edinburgh in 1947 and gained the Diploma in Laryngology and Otology (DLO) in 1951.

Appointed consultant initially to the General Hospital Nottingham and Kings Mill Hospital Mansfield he moved to the Queen's Medical Centre, Nottingham when it became the first new medical school in the UK since the opening of the Welsh School of Medicine at the turn of the 19th century. As a senior surgeon in Nottingham he undertook a heavy administrative load both in the NHS and with the expanding new medical school. As a clinical teacher he was responsible for introducing otolaryngology into the curriculum and proved a popular teacher with undergraduates and postgraduates.

At a national level Jimmy Neil's distinction in the speciality was recognised by his Presidency of the Section of Laryngology of the Royal Society of Medicine in 1978/9 and by Presidency of the Midland Institute of Otology from 1981 to 1984.

He was very much a natural choice for the Presidency of the Medico-Chirurgical Society having been an active supporter over the years. Many will remember his outstanding Presidential Address, wonderfully supported by audio-visual effects including an example of Cleo Lane's phenomenal vocal range! In his retirement he was able to enjoy making his own music, as an accomplished cellist, in a local orchestra.

Dr Stanley James Harris
MB BS (Lond) MRCS (Eng) LRCP (Lond)
President of the Nottingham Medico-
Chirurgical Society (1980 - 1981)

Stanley Harris. President of the Society in 1980/81, was for 42 years a single handed General Practitioner in the NHS and still continues to practise as enthusiastically as ever. And, what is more, he continues to enjoy it!

Stanley Harris was born in London and educated at St Clement Dane's School. He entered Guy's Hospital Medical School at the age of 16 and qualified MB BS in 1947. After completing his pre-registration jobs he joined the RAF for his National Service where he served mainly on an operational flying station, but also looked after a small service hospital, an occupational works area, and families of Service Personnel. This experience was to serve him well in his subsequent career in General Practice.

He married Joan in 1948, and left the RAF in 1950, during the harsh austerity years of post-war Britain, and became a Trainee Assistant in Stratford-on-Avon. His principal there, Dr Archibald McWhinney was an excellent Doctor and teacher, and this appointment was, in essence, the forerunner of modern vocational training. (Incidentally, Archibald McWhinney's brother Robert, was a well known medical practitioner in Wollaton.) Whilst there Stanley Harris was involved in the care of patients in an epidemic of infective hepatitis (Hepatitis A); despite taking the usually recommended precautions, he caught the disease himself! He also looked after the actors at the Shakespeare Memorial Theatre, and, with his friend the local Vet, officially attended horse racing meetings, where the horses seemed to be much more important (valuable) than the local celebrities and punt ers. In the 1950s opportunities for newpractices were few and far between, but after a second assistant in Accrington, he applied for, and was successful in being appointed to a single-handed practice vacancy in Nottingham. This was to be his mode of practice for the rest of his professional life.

An enthusiasm and interest in industrial medicine led to Stanley Harris being appointed Factory Doctor in Nottingham and Medical Advisor to Raleigh Industries, to Birds Food products and to various other manufacturing companies. He also became Medical Officer to the Nottingham General Dispensary in Broad Street, from 1954, dealing with rheumatology and physiotherapy. When that institution closed in the 1990s he continued as Trustee to the Charity. Interestingly, in its early days, the Nottingham Medico-Chirurgical Society used to meet at these premesis at Broad Street before moving to 64 St James' Street.

With his two children becoming keen swimmers, he took a technical interest in Sports Medicine, being Medical Officer to the Nottinghamshire Amateur Swimming Association, and the Midland ASA. He also dealt with the British team when it trained at Loughborough.

The 70s, 80s and 90s were to prove times of medico-political reorganisation and evolution, during which time Stanley Harris undertook an increasing burden of administrative duties. He was elected to the BMA Local Medical Committee in the 70s, became a member of the Nottinghamshire Family Practitioners Committee (renamed the FHSA) and was a member of the Practices Vacancy Committee and other associated committees, serving his colleagues, until he retired. He was Chairman of the Professional Advisory Committee, which directed and monitored the activities of the Deputising Services in the City and County, and which set out the framework and principles for the current out of hours work, although he rarely used the service himself. On retirement from the NHS he was appointed to the Appeals Authority of the Dept of Health.

A member of the BMA since qualifying, Stanley Harris became Chairman of the Nottingham Division in 1981 and again in 1998. During his first Chairmanship he attended the BMA Meeting in San Diego, where he addressed the students of the University of Los Angeles on the subject of General Practice in the UK. He is a member of the BMA Supporters scheme.

He became a member of the Medico-Chirurgical Society shortly after arriving in Nottingham, and served the Society loyally for many years. He was Librarian for 4 years, and Secretary for 4 years, being involved then in the negotiations for the move of the Society from St James' Street to the Postgraduate Centre at the City Hospital in 1972. He was elected a life member of the society in 1993.

His daughter, Elizabeth teaches in London, and his son, Simon, is a GP in Hove. A senior, well known and respected figure in the local medical establishment, Stanley Harris enjoys in his spare time, photography, jazz, gardening, the internet and reading (until 2am)!

Mr R T Sears
MA MB BChir FRCS FRCOG President of
the Nottingham Medico-Chirurgical Society
1981 - 1982

Mr Richard (Dick) Tankard Sears was a popular choice for President for the 1981/2 session. Being appointed consultant he was already well known in the City having worked in Nottingham earlier as a Registrar. Before the expansion of medical services associated with the new Medical School in the early 70s, he, with his colleagues, had shouldered an enormous burden of clinical work with limited resources and junior staff. It is a measure of the man that even with improved staffing and facilities he continued throughout his professional lifetime to continue with this heavy workload being well known to give a personal service to all his patients.

Dick Sears was born in Chesterfield, Derbyshire and was educated at Chesterfield Grammar School and Epsom College, the latter school being famous for nurturing future doctors. From there he went up to Emmanuel College Cambridge and completed his medical studies at the Middlesex Hospital London, qualifying MB BCh (Cantab) in 1948.

Having decided to become an obstetrician and gynaecologist he passed the Membership to the Royal College of Obstetrics and Gynaecologists examination in 1964 and the Fellowship to the Royal College of Surgeons examinations the following year. He came to Nottingham firstly as a registrar at the City Hospital and moved to a senior registrarship at the Jessop Hospital, before returning to Nottingham as a consultant.

In his presidential year Dick Sears recruited local doctors to describe their hobbies outside medicine. Many will remember with pleasure the erudite and entertaining lecture on local archaeology given by Dr Salisbury about his studies of the Trent.

Dr Brendan Jacobs
MA MRCS (Eng) LRCP (Lond) 1944 FRCGP
President of the
Nottingham Medico-Chirurgical Society 1983 - 1983

Those meeting Brendan Jacobs for the first time might be forgiven for imagining him to be a Cambridge don. The enigmatic smile of welcome, the cultured words of greeting, the flowing white hair, coloured shirt and sports coat all seemed to fit the bill! The first impression would of course be incorrect for Brendan was a respected partner in a busy practice in Arnold, a bustling working class suburb of Nottingham. He became President of the Nottingham Medico-Chirurgical Society in 1982/3 and still claims to looks back in some awe and amazement at being invited to take up the office.

Brendan Jacobs was born in Dublin and educated at Oundle and Cambridge. He completed his clinical studies at the Westminster Hospital qualifying Member of the Royal College of Surgeons and Licentiate of the Royal College of Physicians in 1944.

From 1944 to 1951 he undertook posts at the Westminster Hospital, Kent and Canterbury Hospital, and the Westminster Children's Hospital and a 6-month course in Obstetrics at the Rotunda Hospital, Dublin. A period of National Service intervened from 1945 - 47.

In 1953 Brendan and his wife decided that General Practice was to be their future and Brendan was lucky enough to be accepted by a practice in Nottingham. One of the partners was Dr, Jon Graham, with whom Brendan immediately established rapport. Their subsequent friendship resulted in what they claimed was the basis for a respected Practice. The practice had a long history of single-handed doctors working from and living in the same house - Arnold House on Church Street. The practice moved to the Health Centre on High Street and, by the time Brendan retired, the Practice had grown to a seven partner teaching practice.

For Brendan, who had had 15 years as a Nottingham GP, the coming of the new Medical School with associated departments and staff provided a fresh stimulus. The Nottingham Vocational Training Scheme (VTS) developed from the early 70s and, on his own admission, with some trepidation Brendan Jacobs became one of the early trainers. This was the embryonic germ of the University Department of General Practice which was to grow from strength to strength over the next three decades. The attachment of students and postgraduates was, in Brendan's view, one of the best preventatives of partners becoming stale.

In the late 1950s and early 1960s the psychoanalyst, Dr Michael Balint of the Tavistock Clinic, became well known for his interest in what the GP can do for the wide variety of neuroses and the high prevalence of hidden emotional disorders. Having read his seminal work- The Doctor, His Patient and The Illness - Brendan was hooked. After rigorous inquiry about reasons for wanting to join his seminar group at the time Brendon went to weekly sessions for a year. It helped him to practise a part of General Practice that he had never learned in Medical School.

Brendan Jacobs became a member of the Nottingham Medico-Chirurgical Society, then based at 64 St James St, Nottingham in 1954. He remembered well the lanternslides, the tangle of wires to trip over, the uncomfortable chairs - but a most attractive Georgian House. Before the coming of the Medical School the Nottingham Medico-Chirurgical Society was almost the only facility for postgraduate study for GPs. It was, and still is, a good place for doctors of all disciplines to meet each other and benefit from a "getting to know each other" kind of way. As Honorary Secretary in the 1970s he found the job of (amongst others) summarising the wisdom of the visiting lecturers words for the Minute Book a challenge and good for the "listening ear".

This latter topic he took for the subject of his Inaugural Address to the Society entitled "Visual Language" which was very well received, as was the remainder of his programme. Many will recollect with delight the talk given by his old friend P D James (later Baroness James), the detective storywriter. It was possibly one of the shortest given to the Society - but undoubtedly one of the best!

A cultured man of wide interests, Brendan Jacobs personified general practice at its very best. In his retirement he continues to contribute wise thoughts to the journals and can be found swimming every morning in the local pool.

266

Lives of the Presidents J B Bittiner
Dr John Bruce Bittiner, TD, MB ChB
(Born 1920 - died 1998)
President of the Nottingham Medico-Chirurgical
Society 1983 - 1984

Dr John Bittiner, was consultant venereologist at Nottingham General Hospital from 1962 until his retirement in 1986.

He was educated at Aberdeen University, qualifying MB ChB in 1943. He served with the Royal Army Medical Corps in India when newly qualified and, at the end of the War, returned to England to complete his postgraduate training at Leeds General Infirmary where he was Casualty Officer and Senior Registrar. He published the first described cases of asymptomatic carriage of gonorrhoea in men in 1955.

He was appointed consultant in Nottingham in 1962 and quickly established a first-rate department at the General Hospital. He delighted in teaching medical students, nurses, midwives and doctors. This skill was aided by a rapport with young people and an impish sense of humour.

In the early 1960s he predicted the changes caused by the sexual revolution and by the contraceptive pill, which were to alter the demography of the clinics from domination by men to virtual parity with women. At the same time effective antibiotics and contact tracing put the traditional sexually transmitted diseases, gonorrhoea and syphilis, into decline.

John Bittiner took great pride in his department, his staff and the hospital and in 1990 published "Nottingham General Hospital - Personal Reflections". He was an excellent administrator and his wise judgement, experience and diplomacy led to his being much in demand as a committee member and chairman. Amongst other appointments he was Chairman of the Nottingham Stroke Appeal which culminated in the establishment of a chair in stroke medicine and an associated research department.

As an enthusiastic Territorial Army Officer he travelled widely and gave valuable advice to the Forces in relation to his speciality. He was awarded the Territorial Army decoration.

As President of the Medico-Chirurgical Society he recruited a wide range of speakers and was greatly supported by his delightful wife Pauline, who was later elected a life member of the Society.

In his all too short retirement he enjoyed driving his Porsche and cultivated his many interests including horticulture, motor caravanning and art classes.

Dr James Spiers Nelson

MB BCh BAO (Belfast) DMJ (Clin)
President of the Nottingham
Medico-Chirurgical Society (1984 - 1985)

James Nelson a well-known and respected Nottingham doctor was President of the Society for the 1984-1985 session.

He was born in Rathfriland, Co. Down, and educated at the Public Elementary School there, moving on to the Friends' School Lisburn later. He entered Queen's University, Belfast from which he qualified MB BCh BAO in 1949, gaining the diplomas LRCP LRCS Ed, LRFPS (Glas) in the same year. He settled in Nottingham at an early stage in his career and was appointed to the City Hospital and to the Children's Hospital where he gained an excellent grounding in paediatrics. This was to serve him well in his subsequent career.

He became a general practitioner in Sneinton, Nottingham, the birthplace of General Booth of Salvation Army fame. This was a busy inner city practice, based in later years at the Sneinton Health Centre, which was fortunate in having a doctor with Dr Nelson's expertise, able to deal with human life in all its aspects. He became involved in the psychiatric services of the City working as a clinical assistant at St Francis Hospital. With Dr Maurice Everton he was one of the first GPs in the area to have this close liaison with the psychiatric hospitals and the psycho-geriatric population.

An interest in medico-legal matters led Jimmy Nelson into police work and from 1954 to 1988, where he became Senior Police Surgeon to the Nottinghamshire Constabulary, it was once said that one of his favourite occupations was "arguing with lawyers." He obtained the Diploma in Medical Jurisprudence of the Society of Apothecaries of London in 1971.

From 1980 to 1992 he was physician in charge of the Nottingham BUPA Clinic.

Throughout his career James Nelson was held in high esteem by his patients and colleagues. He was always easily approachable and ready to help colleagues. His successful Presidency of the Society was characterised by excellent speakers, including the formidable Professor Sheila Sherlock, one of the few leaders of the profession to address the Society on more than one occasion. Those who were fortunate enough to enjoy the pre-lecture dinners will remember with pleasure Christine's hospitality and her cordon bleu cooking. Both are keen golfers - Christine pursuing her game with consummate skill and James with enthusiasm! Finally, James was well known for his prowess as a hockey referee within the East Midlands.

Margaret Sprackling MB BS (Lond), MRCS (Lond), LRCP (Lond), F.R.C.P. (Lond)
President of the Nottingham Medico-Chirurgical Society (1985 - 1986)

Margaret Ellen Sprackling (nee Hughes), Consultant Physician in the Department of Health Care of the Elderly, became the second woman President of the Society after Miss Sarah Gray (1921-1922)

She was born in London and educated at Romford County High School for Girls (Essex) and Beckenham County Grammar School for Girls (Kent). To both schools she gratefully acknowledged the debt for opening up the world of learning. She trained at the Middlesex Hospital Medical School from 1953-1958, qualifying MB BS with Distinction in Medicine at the University of London in 1958.

She arrived in Nottingham newly qualified and registered. Her early career was spent as a clinical assistant and doing GP locums as she juggled career, domestic and maternal commitments. She worked in the newly created Department of Geriatric Medicine, as it then was. Passing the Membership of the Royal College of

Physicians (London) examination enabled her to apply for Senior Registrar and later a Consultant Physician post at the City Hospital, Nottingham. She well remembered her first visit to the City Hospital which reassuringly not only resembled the Central Middlesex Hospital of her student days, but also had the same long corridors! Sherwood Hospital also had its full complement of eight redbrick ward blocks, each housing sixty patients.

The advent of the new Medical School brought many changes, and her Department became the Department for Health Care of the Elderly. She enjoyed the added stimulus of teaching medical students, contributing to preclinical teaching (third year), and to clinical teaching on the wards (fifth year).

On arrival in Nottingham in 1960, Margaret joined the Nottingham Medico-Chirurgical Society which then met in its beautiful Georgian period house at 64, St. James' Street, Nottingham. She was an active member over the years, serving as Treasurer and Trustee, and was elected Honorary Life Member. Believing that each President had a personal and unique contribution to make to the Society, she arranged to have the Society's collection of painting restored and re-hung in the Society's newly decorated Council Room. She presented a specially made bookcase for the safe keeping of the Society's historic Minute Books dating back many years.

A prominent member of the Medical Women's Federation, she served locally (East Midlands Association) as Council representative, Careers Advisor for Nottingham and President, and nationally as Federation representative on the European Communities (EC) Committee of the British Medical Association (BMA). This proved to be a fascinating task, as the BMA Committee, as well as meeting quarterly in London, also travelled to attend the Standing Committee of Doctors of the EC at its annual Plenary Assembly to discuss matters of mutual interest with other EC doctors. She became Federation President 1988-1989.

Her commitment to community work in Nottingham and Nottinghamshire Victim Support where she chaired the Serious Crime Committee for its nine years, and Soroptimist International, where she was Club and Region President, again taking a special interest in the international aspects.

A quiet, cultured and knowledgeable person, Margaret was keenly interested in the arts throughout her life, especially painting, sculpture and textiles; she also enjoyed music, particularly opera. These interests, along with ancient history and architecture formed the basis of some fascinating holidays. However, in retirement her greatest pleasure was spending time with children, grandchildren and friends.

Maurice John Everton MB ChB (B'ham)
President of the Nottingham Medico-Chirurgical Society
(1986 - 1987)

During the 1980s the role of the Medico-Chirurgical Society evolved from a Society primarily concerned with postgraduate educational to a professional forum for medical life within the City. Coming to the Presidency of the Society after many years as a general practitioner in the City, Maurice Everton was well placed to cement bonds between the established family doctors. This he did with considerable aplomb, introducing speakers and activities of interest to all branches of the profession and fostering good will amongst the members.

Maurice Everton, a midlander by birth and education, went to Kings Norton Grammar School, Birmingham and then moved on to Birmingham University where he qualified M.B Ch B in 1950. After working as a pre-registration House Officer at Walsall Manor Hospital, he was conscripted into the Royal Army Medical Corps (R.A.M.C.) for his National Service, working as an Embarkation Medical Officer in Southampton dealing with all aspects of medicine with regard to troopships.

His wife, Jean, had worked as a physiotherapist at the General Hospital and she persuaded him to move to Nottingham where he entered practice on the Woodborough Road. His routine work expanded to take in sessions as a clinical assistant at Mapperley Psychiatric Hospital where, with Dr J Nelson, another President of the Society they became two of the earliest GPs to contribute to the work of a Psychiatric Hospital in Nottingham.

The respect with which his colleagues held Maurice Everton led to his being Chairman of the Nottinghamshire Local Medical Committee, a position he held for five years.

He became a member of the Nottingham Medico-Chirurgical Society shortly after arriving in Nottingham and before long was inveigled into becoming Social Secretary by the irascible, charismatic but persuasive gynaecologist J.B. Cochrane who was then President. A request from 'J B' could not be refused! After 5 years as Social Secretary he moved on to the Society's Council at a time of important change when the Society was selling the previous home in St James Street to the Postgraduate Centre at the Nottingham City Hospital. He was elected President of the Society in 1987.

An affable and popular man Maurice Everton enjoyed a full and active social life within the City being at times President of Nottingham Round Table, President of the Nottingham "41" club and President of Queen Anne's Bowling Green.

Dr Peter J Toghill
MD FRCP (Lond), FRCP (Edin)
President of the Nottingham Medico-Chirurgical Society
(1987 - 1988)

Peter Toghill had first worked at the General Hospital as House Physician and Senior House Officer at which time he came under the influence of Dr J D Proctor an earlier President of the Nottingham Medico-Chirurgical Society, whom he regarded as the best physician he had ever met.

He was educated at Watford Boys' Grammar School, University College, London (as an Exhibitioner) and University College Hospital Medical School graduating MB. BS. in 1955.

After National Service as a Captain in the Royal Army Medical Corps, and various postgraduate appointments in Nottingham and Sheffield, he returned to University College Hospital, London, as Medical Registrar and British Empire Research Fellow with Professor (later Lord Rosenheim) and Professor Tom Prankerd. His research work there with Tom Prankerd on "Red Cell Pooling in the Spleen" led to the award of a Doctorate in Medicine in the University of London. He became Senior Registrar to the Liver Unit at Kings College Hospital before moving back to Nottingham when he was appointed as Consultant Physician to the General Hospital, Nottingham in 1968, moving to the Queens Medical Centre when it opened ten years later.

Peter Toghill had been attracted by the prospect of the new Medical School in Nottingham. During the period 1968 to 1970, shortly after he arrived, there was an enormous expansion of medical staff and facilities. The Queen's Medical Centre had already been planned. Amongst others coming to Nottingham during those halcyon days were Tony Mitchell, Michael Langman, John Hampton, David Hull, Jack Hardcastle and Malcolm Symonds with David Greenfield as a charming and unifying Dean.

Peter Toghill's clinical interests were in gastroenterology and haematology and initially he continued his research on splenic function in disease. He had a wide interest in general medicine and was regarded by the local medical community as the "physician's physician." With the arrival of students at the new Medical School his interest began to turn to medical education and he became, in turn, medical tutor, clinical sub-dean and later Director of Education at the Royal College of Physicians of London. He wrote extensively and one of his books, "Examining Patients," became a standard textbook for new medical students on the wards.

He joined the Nottingham Medico-Chirurgical Society shortly after arriving in Nottingham and was Hon. Secretary in the 1970s. In 1978 he was awarded the Society's travelling Fellowship to review the medical arrangements and to give medical advice to the Falkland Islands. A grateful momento of this visit, in the form of a painting by a local artist from Port Stanley, hangs in the Society's Council Room at the City Hospital. His Presidential Address to the Society was entitled "Medical Apprentices" and dealt with the development of the Nottingham Medical School.

In later years he was much involved with the activities of the Royal College of Physicians of London being an examiner for the Membership exams, Councillor, Censor and Foundation Director of Education. In this last post he was responsible for introducing the concept of formal continuing medical education to consultant physicians.

In his earlier days he was an enthusiastic and competent cricketer, captaining his medical school and playing for United Hospitals. With his playing days were over he became an active member of Nottinghamshire County Cricket Club and wrote a series of articles for the journals on old cricketers, notably, Dr W G Grace and C B Fry.

Dr Bernard Gwilym Spilsbury
MB ChB (B'ham)
President of the Nottingham
Medico-Chirurgical Society (1988 - 1989)

Bernard Spilsbury was brought up in rural Worcestershire and educated at the King Charles 1st School in Kidderminster. From there he went on to Birmingham University to graduate MB. ChB in 1951. He was a pre-registration house physician and surgeon in Birmingham at the West Hallam Hospital, West Bromwich before entering the Medical Branch of the Royal Air Force.

The RAF station at Newton provided Bernard Spilsbury with his first introduction to Nottingham, where he was to spend most of his medical career. After various locum posts, he became a general practitioner in the Meadows, part of the inner city Nottingham, in 1957 and worked there until his retirement in 1992. Whilst this area may have been 'meadows' in the distant past, they were certainly not the idyllic pastures that the initial image might conjure up! It was a rough and tough area for a single-handed doctor to handle.

In 1966 he became Chairman of the Nottingham Division of the British Medical Association and was responsible for negotiating major changes and improvements for general practitioners. This was a time of much discontent within all branches of the profession and Bernard well remembers the verbal fisticuffs, which enlivened many of the meetings - at times the verbal fisticuffs verged on the physical! Nevertheless one of the important changes resulting from the negotiations at that time was open to access to the hospitals for G.P.s for X-Rays and laboratory tests.

In the late 1960s both Nottingham General Hospital and the Nottingham City Hospital were overstretched and overcrowded and the news that a new Medical School was to be built in Nottingham was received enthusiastically. The building of a large new hospital and teaching hospital complex (the Queen's Medical Complex) together with the injection of new academic staff for teaching clinical services was exciting news. As a respected and experienced local general practitioner Bernard Spilsbury was appointed to Nottingham No1 Hospital Management Committee to help co-ordinate many of these changes based at the General Hospital. He was one of an influential group of doctors who were able to forge a link between 'Town and Gown'.

With an enviable knowledge of Nottingham and its history, it was natural for Bernard to talk about the city in his Presidential Address to the Society. During the 1988/89 Session he saw the expansion of the charitable function of the Society, particularly for scholarships and help with student electives. Bernard Spilsbury continues to serve the society as Senior Trustee where his wide experience is utilised to the full.

Having retired to the country Bernard still retains the affections of his many friends and colleagues. Brought up in a farming community he now enjoys village life to the full - departing to the mountains each winter for his skiing holiday.

PROFESSOR TONY MITCHELL
**President of the Nottingham
Medico-Chirurgical Society (1989 - 1990)**

Tony Mitchell was a Lancashire man and it is not surprising that he became a medical student at Manchester. There his progress was no less than triumphant. Effortlessly he won every prize open to him and topped the examination lists time after time. It was in Manchester, as a student, that he consolidated his natural gifts of clear thinking, plain speaking and cool clear logic. These were to serve him well in the years to come.

After qualification he became resident house physician to Robert Platt where he learned that talking to patients was more important than talking about them, that he needed to be involved yet emotionally detached, and that at all times he was required to be in command of his professional skills. He established for himself some basic ground rules: offer facts first and opinions later, challenge established ideals, and ignore cant and rhetoric.

After a spell of national Service in the Royal Army Medical Corps, Tony Mitchell was appointed Registrar to Sir George Pickering, Regius Professor of Medicine at Oxford. He had in fact been appointed to a registrarship at the Hammersmith Hospital, London the day before his Oxford interview but he kept the Postgraduate Medical School waiting until he obtained the post he really wanted. This showed, as a young man, his cheerful antipathy to authority and to the establishment which he kept for the rest of his life. At Oxford he developed his personal philosophy of academic medicine from which he never deviated and which sometimes led him into conflicts with other academics whose feet were not so well grounded with the mud of the real world. But he was a true academic in the sense that he asked questions and required answers based on facts rather than opinions and Oxford convinced him of the intrinsic role of the academic physician. He was to apply these academic standards to clinical medicine when he moved to Nottingham.

His basic laboratory research contributions on thrombosis and platelets were made during those eleven years at Oxford. His chiefs were Professor Gwyn Mcfarlane and Sir George Pickering though it was Pickering who was really his mentor. Michael Oliver, a colleague at the time, recalls that Pickering instructed Tony to team up with Colin Schwarts, a young Australian pathologist who, at the time, was working with Robb Smith. Armed with a bacon slicer, countless hearts and post-mortem angiograms they became a series of innovative studies on the role of thombosis in the genesis of myocardial infarction (heart attack). This work gained Tony a D.Phil and was summarised in his book 'Arterial Disease' which he wrote in collaboration with Schwarts.

The turning point in Tony's career came in 1968. In July 1964 Mr. Anthony Barber, who was then Minister of Health, had announced that the new medical school that had been promised to the country was to be established in Nottingham. Many wondered why Nottingham had been chosen as the site of the new medical school, the first in the UK since the Welsh National School of Medicine was created in 1938. There were two reasons – one good and one bad. The good reason was that Nottingham had already the site of a thriving University with facilities as old as theology and as new as social sciences. The bad reason, necessitating the creation of a new medical school in the East Midlands, was for many years this part of the UK had been a medically deprived region. It was short of hospitals, short of doctors and short of money.

By a happy chance, Sir George Pickering, a reforming medical educationalist, was selected to chair the Medical School Advisory Committee which published its report in 1965 recommending a Teaching Hospital and Medical School   complex adjacent to the University campus. It came as no surprise that Tony Mitchell was appointed to the Foundation Chair of Medicine.

At this time, when the motorway had scarcely reached Nottingham, the new Medical School was housed in dreary, flat buildings on the University site, affectionately known as the cowsheds (later gentrified to Cherry Tree Buildings). The two old, but much respected Victorian hospitals in the city were renovated and expanded to cope with the influx of new medical students and work was started on what was to be the Queen's Medical Centre. At this time Tony was joined by Michael Langman as Senior Lecturer he was later to become Professor of Therapeutics in Nottingham and Professor of Medicine in Birmingham. In the ensuing years Tony Mitchell never missed an opportunity of making something from almost nothing. He channelled his abundant vigour into administration, research, teaching and patient care to convert the deprived Nottingham hospitals into centres of excellence. Provided there was space in his diary he never turned down a request for help; determined and careful planning were of critical importance. With John Hampton, later Professor of Cardiology, Stan Heptenstall, Keith Morris and Bob Wilcox, he welded together a formidable team which showed the world how to conduct trials of therapy in cardiovascular disease. With the opening of the Queen's Medical Centre in the early 1970s, activities prospered and the flow of publications to prestigious journals was but a trivial marker of the calibre of his team's work. Though he was much in demand as a speaker – and indeed if Oscars were given for lectures he would have won many – he was never away long from his department.

When Tony arrived in Nottingham as Professor of Medicine, he also came as a much needed additional consultant physician at both the Nottingham City and the General Hospitals, where not only facilities but staff were at dangerously low levels. Perhaps not surprisingly many local people expected the new professor to take over the care of those patients with rare and exotic diseases which had been perplexing his local consultants for years. Characteristically Tony had different ideas! He chose to look after patients with common but neglected diseases. His particular contribution was the care of patients who had had a stroke and he encouraged and supervised the development of the Nottingham Stroke Unit. He had the happy knack of being able to talk to patients in their own language and wasn't afraid to call a spade a spade or whatever he wanted to call it! His own notes, written in that neat hand, rarely corrected, were for the benefit of others only. He never needed to refer to them again. His prodigious memory allowed him to remember every detail years later.

On the wards he was never an internationally famous professor trailing a retinue of assistants and visitors. His were working rounds where he knew every patient, every nurse and every ward assistant. For one so tough and incisive in the committee room or lecture hall he could talk with gentleness and humility to those frightened little old ladies who were his patients.

Tony held strong views about many topics in contemporary life. For him private practice had no place in the NHS and his own special patients were largely ordinary folk with ordinary diseases; though it must be said that he collected more than a few bizarre problems! He couldn't stand the do-gooder health educationalists, a breed he regarded with particular distrust and suspicion. He abhorred clap-trap and pomposity and could indulge in a remarkably effective character assassination when he really put his mind to it.

As is often the case with busy people, this talented man had a full and productive life away from his professional work. He was blessed with a happy marriage to Muriel, whom he met at school and whose quiet support brought stability and continuity into his eventful life. His interests were numerous and to all of them he brought great enthusiasm, energy, efficiency, common sense and a rich store of knowledge generated by his splendid memory. He was into boats from his early days, out with the trawlers in Morecambe Bay. In later years he confessed surprisingly, of his own nervousness in high seas. When he became land-locked in Nottingham he took to the canals, those rivers which run uphill, which never failed to fascinate him. Whilst in Oxford he took to gliding and at coffee times there were tales of downdrift, cumulus clouds and wind gradients. But perhaps his greatest love was music and it was in Nottingham that he achieved one of his major ambitions – to join an orchestra! There he discovered that his own medical students played better than he did, but of course he was able to compensate by providing erudite and witty programme notes.

He took much pride in his adopted city and within a year or so of arrival he knew more of the geography and history of Nottingham than many of those born and bred there. He accepted the Vice-Chairmanship of the Nottingham Civic Society with some reluctance, preferring to be a rank and file member, happily trudging through the backstreets, captivating his companions with snippets and titbits from the past. In the year of his retirement, to the great delight of his colleagues, he honoured the Nottingham Medico-Chirurgical Society by becoming its president.

Sadly he died, suddenly and unexpectedly, in 1991, having enjoyed no more than a few months of pleasurable retirement. His bust, sculpted by a colleague, Kelvin Thomas, FRCS, which stands in the entrance hall of the Nottingham Medical School, bears this inscription:-

Professor J R A Mitchell, BSc, MD (Manchester), MA,
DPhil (Oxford), FRCP
Foundation Professor of Medicine, 1968-90
Si monumentum requiris, circumspice
If you seek his monument look around you

Dr Arthur Courtenay Saunders
MB ChB (L'pool)
President of the Nottingham
Medico-Chirurgical Society (1990 - 1991)

Arthur Courtenay Saunders never used his second Christian name. To everyone he was Sandy. This was a pity, because in an earlier age Courtenay would have fitted perfectly with his adventurous vacation life style, which complemented his busy career as a general practitioner in Nottingham. Away from his practice he was, at various times, ocean yachtsman, skier, golfer, walker and hilltrekker.

Sandy Saunders saw war service from 1943 - 46 with the Royal Electrical and Mechanical Engineers as a Radar Officer and in the Glider Pilot Regiment, as part of the Army Air Corps. He suffered terrible 40% burns, being one of the early patients at Birmingham and later at the Queen Victoria Hospital, East Grinstead becoming one of Sir Archibald MacIndoe's 'Guinea Pigs.'

He entered Liverpool University and qualified MB ChB in 1952. After various house appointments at Liverpool Stanley Hospital he became a general practitioner in Nottingham where he was to spend the rest of his professional career. He developed special interests in psychiatry and obstetrics. In the second half of his career he undertook training in hypnosis and gained the Diploma in Hypnosis at the University of Sheffield, becoming a Member of the British and the International Societies of Hypnosis.

Always a good "committee man" Sandy was for many years a member of the Family Practitioner Committee, Nottinghamshire District Health Authority and the Nottingham Local Medical Committee. From 1976 until 1992 he was Medical Secretary of the LMC with a Medical Service Committee advisory role.

Shortly after arriving in Nottingham he became a member of the Nottingham Medico-Chirurgical Society which he served loyally over many years being, in turn, Librarian (1960-62), Secretary (1970-74), President (1990-91) and Life Member in 1994. Given his background and interests it came as no surprise to the Members of the Society that, in his Presidential Address, they were transported to the Himalayas for a trekking Expedition.

Though having a successful Presidency, Sandy will be well remembered by the Society, for his time as Secretary, by elevating the reading of the minutes to an art form. At the beginning of each meeting, the Society had an amusing and perceptive summary of the previous meeting, not infrequently spiced with Latin and Greek! Never before in the history of the Society has each reading of the minutes been greeted with prolonged applause!

In retirement Sandy was trek doctor on the Khumbu trek in 1990, the Annapurna Sanctuary trek in 1998 and the Langtang trek in 2000. He was a crewmember in the Atlantic Rally for Cruisers Las Palmas to St Lucia in 2002.

Jean Lesley Baker
MB ChB (Sheff) FRCOG

President of the Nottingham
Medico-Chirurgical Society (1991 - 1992)

Leslie Baker (President 1991- 2), who was born in Winterton, North Lincolnshire, came from a family with a strong medical background. Her grandfather, great aunt and both parents were doctors and her brother also became a general practitioner.

Brought up during WW2, she went to boarding school, firstly at Ackworth, a Quaker School, and then, for 9 years, to Penrhose College for girls, a Methodist School in Colwyn Bay and Chatsworth. Following her parents' example she entered Sheffield University to study medicine, qualifying MB ChB in 1954.

Her pre-registration posts were at the Sheffield Royal Infirmary where she worked for those stalwarts of the Sheffield medical scene in the 1950s and 60s - Dr Skipper, Mr Clifford Jones and Mr Derek Randall. At this stage in her career she had virtually decided on a career in general practice and with this aim in view, took up an obstetric post in Leamington Spa before returning to Sheffield to work at the Children's Royal Hospital with Professor Illingworth. After a period of doing locums in North Lincolnshire she decided that further education in Obstetrics and Gynaecology would be useful in general practice in rural England, particularly as family doctors were still performing many domiciliary deliveries.

This proved to be the turning point in Miss Baker's career and after a year as senior house officer with the formidable Gladys Dodds at the Mile End Hospital, London, she became a registrar at the Norfolk and Norwich Hospital. With Obstetrics and Gynaecology now well and truly in her sights she returned to the Jessop Hospital for Women in Sheffield for further training, including a spell in Gynaecological Pathology. Having obtained Membership of the Royal College of Obstetrics and Gynaecology in 1962 she joined the University Department of Obstetrics under Professor Scott Russell and Sir Jack Dewhurst as a lecturer.

In 1965 Lesley Baker was appointed as Consultant Obstetrician for Nottingham City Hospital, the Firs Maternity Home and Grantham Kesteven Hospital. She remained at the City Hospital for the next 30 years, but, after local staff appointments, she left Grantham in 1973. During the 1960s and early 1970s, all active Obstetrics and Gynaecology was carried out by the consultants at the City Hospital - Mr Cochrane, Mr Barkla and Miss Baker, together with the consultants at Peel Street -Mr Maxwell, Mrs Marrow, Mr Sears and Mr Barkla. The various consultants at the City Hospital and Peel Street covered outlying hospitals at Newark, Mansfield, Heanor and Ilkeston and the Firs and Highbury. The General Practitioners and midwives did a considerable amount of domiciliary work and there was still a 40% home delivery rate; there was an active GP Obstetric group.

The arrival of the new medical school in the early 1970s changed the scene in Nottingham considerably. A new University Department of Obstetrics and Gynaecology headed by Professor Malcolm Symonds was initially established at the City Hospital and a new Obstetric Unit was opened on the campus in 1972. A further new unit was opened a few years later at the Queen's Medical Centre to which Professor Symonds moved. Following these developments hospital confinement rose in the area to 99% and gradually the peripheral units closed as active obstetric units. From the 1970s onwards the consultant staff in the Nottingham area expanded enormously. However General Practitioners retained access to Obstetric beds at the City Hospital for many more years. The flying squads, which had been functioning until the mid 1970s, were gradually dismantled with their place being taken by Paramedical Emergency Ambulance Teams.

Throughout her consultant career Miss Baker continued to practice general obstetrics and gynaecology with oncology and fertility work. She was very highly respected, not only as a skilled gynaecologist, but also as a caring doctor who always put the needs of her patients first. She would appear in the wards at any time, day or night, without warning. If she had a fault it was that her punctuality was not always perfect!

Deprived of work after her retirement from the NHS in September 1995, she went out a month later, to work as a voluntary Locum Consultant in Obstetrics and Gynaecology at a small Roman Catholic mission hospital called Kitovu in Uganda. Over the next 6 years she worked out there for 6 to 8 weeks at a time doing very active Obstetrics and Gynaecology with such problems as malaria, HIV, and obstructed labour being everyday events. In 1997 she became involved further with the obstetrical and surgical skills courses in Dilla, run by Abergavenny Hospital. She was an active member of the Jima group from the City Hospital which supported the medical school in Ethiopia and she visited several times to teach and to operate. These visits were much appreciated by those involved.

In the time that was left over in her professional career Miss Baker enjoyed sailing, wild flowers, cooking, gardening and entertaining - and very positively keeping in contact with her family and the younger generations. Sadly medicine now is training few surgeons with the commitment, virtuosity and stamina shown by Lesley Baker.

Dr. Edmund Clarke
MB ChB DIH, FFOM RCP (Lond)
**President of the Nottingham Medico-Chirurgical Society
(1992 - 1993)**

Edmund (Eddie) Clarke, who was President in 1992/3, served the Nottingham Medico-Chirurgical Society with particular distinction over a period of many years. He was one of the select band of occupational physicians who were to hold the Presidency during the long history of the Society.

A Yorkshireman, born in 1927, and educated at Ecclesfield Grammar School in the West Ridding, qualifying MB., ChB. at the University of Sheffield in 1951. After House Officer posts at the Royal Hospital, Sheffield, and Rotherham Hospital, he served in the Royal Air Force as a Flight Lieutenant from 1952 to 1954. On leaving the RAF, he entered an industrial general practice where he remained for four years before moving into full-time Occupation Health, which was destined to be his life's work over the next 40 years. He was awarded the Diploma in Industrial Health of the Society of Apothecaries in 1961 and was elected Fellow of the Faculty of Occupational Health of the Royal College of Physicians, London in 1993.

His first appointment was in London as the Medical Officer to the Morgan Crucible Company, Battersea, following which he became M.O. at the Ministry of Defence, Landsdown House, Berkeley Square, London and Woolwich Arsenal. In 1965, he was posted to Nottingham as Medical Officer to the Royal Ordnance Factory, on Kings Meadow Road, Central Ordnance Depot, Chilwell, and TSD Old Dalby, Melton Mowbray, Leicestershire. In 1976 he was appointed Senior Medical Officer to the Imperial Tobacco Company where he remained for ten years. After 1986 he held sessional appointments in Occupational Health at the Queen's Medical Centre, Nottingham, BUPA, Northern Foods and Hepworth Industries.

President of the Nottingham Society of Occupational Health 1969, Eddie Clark was Honorary Secretary of the Nottingham Medico-Chirurgical Society from 1989 to 1990 and was elected its President for the session 1992-93. He was keenly interested in the Society's extensive archives and produced a series of fascinating historical exhibits for the Society's display cabinet in the lounge of the Post Graduate Education Centre, Nottingham City Hospital. His interest in the role of the Doctor in the Crimean War resulted in him becoming a member of the Crimean War Research Society. In retirement, he continues to research the role of the Doctor in the Crimean War with particular reference to Dr. E. M. Wrench, whose letters he discovered whilst researching the Society's ancient books at the Hallward Library, Nottingham University.

Although retired and recovering from a stroke, he remains keenly interested in all aspects of medicine and continuing progress of the Society and he hopes, with the aid of further research, to publish the letters of Dr. Wrench, in book form.

Mr Nicholas R Galloway BA (Cantab), MB ChB (Edin), MD (Edin), FRCS (Edin)
President of the Nottingham
Medico-Chirurgical Society (1993 - 1994)

Nicholas (Nick) Galloway, an ophthalmic surgeon, was President of the Nottingham Medico-Chirurgical Society during the 1993/4 session. His father Mr N.P.R. Galloway, also an ophthalmic surgeon, had been President in 1950/51,.

Nick Galloway was educated at Shrewsbury and at the Universities of Cambridge (BA, 1956) and Edinburgh, qualifying in medicine MB., ChB. from Edinburgh in 1959. He was house surgeon at the Western General Hospital, Edinburgh from 1959 to 1960 and was senior registrar at Moorfields Eye Hospital from 1963 to 1965.He gained the Diploma of Ophthalmology (Eng) in 1963 and was elected a Fellow of the Royal College of Surgeons of England in 1966.

He returned to his home City as a consultant surgeon at the Nottingham Eye Hospital in 1967 and later, with the development of the new Medical School in Nottingham, to University Hospital at the Queen's Medical Centre. It is of interest that in those early days the secretary of the Nottingham Eye Hospital was the same Mr Wilson who supervised the affairs of the Nottingham Medico-Chirurgical Society and, with his wife, lived in the flat above the Headquarters of the Society at St James Street.

Throughout his clinical career Nick Galloway was always very much the "physicianly" surgeon and was much in demand for his opinion about complex cases. Always a prolific writer, he contributed widely to the literature and published several books including Ophthalmic Electrodiagnosis (1981), Common Eye Diseases and their Management (1985) and Ophthalmology (1988). In 1988/90 his burgeoning reputation in the speciality was recognised by his Mastership of the Oxford Ophthalmological Congress. Though national and international reputations often take their owners away from their clinical base this was certainly not the case with Nick Galloway. Throughout his career he gave sterling service to his hospital and was always available to help his fellow consultants and local general practitioners.

In his busy life he had served as Treasurer of the Nottingham Medico-Chirurgical Society before later becoming President. He recalls that he was more fortunate than his father in that all his speakers arrived on time for the meetings. In earlier days during his father's Presidency in 1950/51 one of the speakers, a Dutch Professor had to be collected from Sheffield. In those days "pea soup" fogs were commonplace in the winters in the north and the speaker of the evening had to walk in front of Mr Galloway Snr's car burning sheets of evening newspapers to show the way. President and speaker eventually made it!

Dr. P. C. Lawson
JP BSc MB ChB MRCGP FSOM
President of the Nottingham
Medico-Chirurgical Society (1994 - 1995)

Peter Charles Lawson, who was President for the 1994/95 Session had the unusual distinction of serving the Nottingham Medico-Chirurgical Society continuously, in one office or other, for a total of 28 years.

He was born in Egypt, in Alexandra, on the 1st April 1931 (under an eclipse of the moon!). His father had worked there for many years with the Navy, Army and Air Force Institutes. The family returned to England for a while when Peter was a small child, but in 1936 his father was sent with the military to Libya and then on to Palestine where the family soon joined him. There were many local troubles at that time and the family had to leave following threats from the Arabs. Peter's father's chauffer was subsequently murdered for working for him.

From there it was back to Cairo where Peter Lawson when to a small Private School and then on to Victoria College in Alexandra. After a brief spell in England the family returned to Cairo just before the outbreak of the war where Peter continued his education at Victoria College which had by then moved to Cairo. In 1940 his father was sent to Greece but was taken prisoner of war. With the German invasion of Egypt the family were sent to South Africa where Peter continued his education at De La Salle as a day boy and St. Aiden's as a boarder. With the repatriation of his father in 1943, Peter returned to England in 1944 by ship, being made a Boy Scout in Mid-Atlantic! After further wartime moves Peter was able to stay at Wallasey Grammar School for five years where he rowed for the 1st Crew for three years.

On leaving school Peter Lawson went to Liverpool University where he qualified MB., BCh. in 1956, being awarded the Clinical Exhibition prize and, having taken an intercalated Honours BSc in Anatomy. With general practice already in his sights he did pre-registration posts in Clatterbridge Hospital and a pre-registration appointment in Surgery, Orthopaedics, Ear Nose and Throat at Victoria Central Hospital. After registration he took a three year Short Term Commission in the Royal Air Force and was posted to RAF Newton, Nottinghamshire where he served for the full three years.

On leaving the RAF, he joined the redoubtable Dr. Ian Loch in General Practice and was happily in partnership with him for 25 years in Mansfield Road and Woodborough Road, Nottingham, until Ian Loch retired in 1985. Having examined Airline Pilots for the then Department of Aviation when on Royal Air Force service Peter Lawson became one of the first few civilians to be appointed to examine for the Ministry of Aviation later CAA, in 1960, and for the FAA in 1966 and for the Australian CAA. During the 1980s he spent a number of holidays acting as Ship's Doctor and cruised both in the Mediterranean and in the Caribbean and South America.

In 1972, with Dr. Brendon Jacobs, be became one of the first General Practice Trainers in Nottingham and acted as a trainer until his retirement.

In 1984 Peter was made a Fellow of the Society of Orthopaedic Medicine and lectured on a number of courses both in the UK and in Canada and the USA.

He was appointed a Justice of the Peace in 1972 and served 19 years on the Bench.

Joining the Nottingham Medico-Chirurgical Society after coming to Nottingham he was soon heavily involved with the Social Committee where he was eventually appointed as the Social Secretary, organising the Medical Ball for 20 years. The Society was delighted to ask him to become President for the 1994/95 session and made him Honorary Life Member in 1998.

Mr A N Fawcett MA, MB, MChir, FRCS

Nigel Fawcett came from a family with strong medical links. His father Alan Wordsworth Fawcett F.R.C.S. was a Consultant Surgeon at Sheffield Royal Infirmary, his mother Janet, an Anaesthetist and his grandfather, Professor Edward Fawcett FRS was Professor of Anatomy at Bristol University.

From 1948 - 54 he was educated at Clifton College, Bristol, captaining the Rugby Fives team, being Head of House and Deputy Head Boy. Entering Trinity Hall, Cambridge as an Open Scholar he read for the Natural Science Tripos in the first two years and Part 2 of the Law Tripos in his third year. Moving on to St Bartholomew's Hospital for his clinical training in 1958, he qualified MB. BChir. in 1961.As a medical student he captained London University at Rugby Fives and was awarded a Full Purple.

Having decided at an early stage to embark on a surgical career, he became house surgeon firstly to Mr. I. P. Todd (later Sir Ian Todd, President of the Royal College of Surgeons) and then secondly to Mr A W Badenoch at St. Bartholomew's Hospital, London. After further posts in Pathology at St. Bartholomew's and Casualty and Surgery at Bristol Royal Infirmary, Nigel Fawcett became a Surgical Registrar at Sheffield Royal Infirmary and passed the Final Fellowship of the Royal College of Surgeon's (Eng) exam in 1966.

A period in research in pancreatic secretion in the University Department of Surgery led to an M.Chir. thesis from Cambridge. In 1969 he was appointed to the Sheffield Senior Registar Rotation spending two years with Mr. D. H. Randall at Sheffield and 18 months with Mr. K. F. Wood at Leicester.

In January 1973 Nigel Fawcett was appointed Consultant General Surgeon to Nottingham General Hospital (later moving to the Queen's Medical Centre Nottingham), Ilkeston General Hospital and Heanor Memorial Hospital. Throughout his career he maintained a wide interest in General Surgery. Initially he specialised in the surgical management of duodenal ulcers but, with the advent of effective drug treatment for that condition, the need for surgery passed. Later in his career the advent of increasing specialisation threatened to limit his lines of treatment but never quite did! The advent of laparoscopic surgery provided new challenges and he was the first person to perform a laparoscopic cholecystectomy in an NHS Hospital in Nottingham. Late in his surgical career he fell from a tree when pruning, and broke both wrists but was back operating with his usual flair in a short time.

From childhood onwards Nigel Fawcett had a passion for aeroplanes and had always wanted to become a pilot. This ambition was fulfilled when he joined the Cambridge University Air Squadron in 1956. There he learned to fly in Chipmunks and passed the RAF Instrument Rating at that time. Reverting to flying when he became a Senior Registrar in Leicester, he gained his Pilot's Licence and Night Rating and flew Aerobatic Cessnas. On being appointed to Nottingham, he joined Sherwood Flying Club and over the years flew a variety of aerobatic and non-aerobatic aircraft; in 1974 he won the club aerobatic competition.

The sea and sailing ships also held attractions. Starting as a Sea Scout he progressed to sailing trips across the Channel in the 70s and flotilla sailing in the Aegean, yachting round Turkey and in the Mediterranean. More recently his sailing has been confined to windsurfing.

Having played golf intermittently for most of his life, Nigel Fawcell really started to play in earnest in1980. He joined Notts Golf Club at Hollinwell and subsequently Beeston Fields Club. On a steep learning curve he rapidly became a single figure handicap golfer, won numerous competitions and represented his club at local and national levels. He is said to have indulged two of his passions by flying low over the fairway at Hollinwell, much to the consternation of his fellow members!

An enthusiast for all types of physical activities Nigel Fawcett started snow skiing in 1960 in many resorts in Europe and the USA and took up water skiing in 1973. An intrepid traveller he has visited, with his wife, all the continents, except Antarctica, including touring Tibet and going round the world twice.

Surgeons are often"larger than life" characters. This one certainly is!

Dr Thomas Leopold Venables MA(Cantab), MB BChir (Cantab)FRCP FRCGP
President of the Nottingham Medico-Chirurgical Society
(1996 - 1997)

Dr Thomas Leopold (Tom) Venables, a distinguished local general practitioner, broadcaster and medical teacher was President of the Nottingham Medico-Chirurgical Society for the 1996/7 session.

He was educated at William Hulme's Grammar School, Manchester. On leaving school he entered the Royal Air Force for National Service from 1956 to 1958 being commissioned as a Pilot Officer (Fighter Controller). After serving in the RAF, he entered Downing College, Cambridge (BA 1961, MA 1964), completing his clinical studies at the Westminster Hospital, London and graduating MB. BChir. (Cantab) in 1964.

After qualification Tom was appointed to pre registration posts at his own teaching hospital. He then re-entered the RAF in its Medical Branch serving as a Flight Lieutenant from 1965 to 1970 as Senior Medical Officer, RAF

Henlow and later as a Medical Specialist at the RAF Hospital, Ely. He became a Member of the Royal College of Physicians in 1970.

Tom Venables joined the Calverton practice in 1970 and remained there throughout his professional life becoming Senior Partner in 1997. He was a clinical assistant in cardiology at the City Hospital from 1970, an organiser of Postgraduate Education for General Practitioners in Nottingham from 1974 to 1978 and a Lecturer in General Practice at the University of Nottingham from 1972 till 1997. He has published many articles on therapeutics and on the economics of drug prescribing.

After becoming a Member of the Royal College of General Practitioners in 1972 he served the College in various capacities over many years. He was heavily involved with the Membership of the Royal College of General Practitioners examination being an examiner, member of the Examination Executive and a member of the Board of Censors. He was elected Fellow of the Royal College of General Practitioners in 1980 and his services to general practice and medical education were recognised by his election to the Fellowship of the Royal College of Physicians - an unusual and well-deserved honour.

Tom's voice became familiar to local and national listeners in the 1980s and 90s when he was "radio doctor" and a member of the BBC Radio Nottingham Team. His broadcasting led to several awards including the Smith Kline Gold Award for Medical Journalism, a Sony Award (Bronze) for Radio and the British Association of Insurers Silver Medal for Services to the Community. He received the Society's President's Prize in 1993

Like many Presidents, Tom Venables had, in earlier years been Secretary to the Nottingham Medico-Chirurgical Society. As a Member of the Society he had been awarded a Travelling Fellowship by the Society to go to China to study medicine and the art of acupuncture. This led to an unusual distinction in 1986 - the Diploma in Acupuncture of Shanghai College of Traditional Chinese Medicine.

Tom Venables has been and remains one of the more familiar figures on the Nottingham medical scene. An academic interest in the history of medicine led him into several societies including the Wellcome Trust, the John Snow Society and the Osler Club. Osler was in fact the subject for his memorable and carefully researched Presidential Lecture.

John Edwin Forde Bruce MRCS Eng LRCP Lond, MB BS (Lond), FRCS (Eng),FRCOG

President of the Nottingham Medico-Chirurgical Society
(1997 - 1998)

Educationally the late 90s were years in which the Colleges were introducing formal continuing education and many pessimists within the profession saw no future for the long established local Medical Societies. How wrong they were! John Bruce, a popular and enthusiastic President, set his seal on the Society by introducing, during his year of office, a programme of speakers of the highest quality who were able to both educate and entertain. The Nottingham Medico-Chirurgical Society showed itself again to be a unique forum where hospital consultants, family doctors and academics could meet to enjoy good fellowship and continuing medical education for their mutual benefit.

John Bruce was born in Doncaster, and educated at Rossall School, Fleetwood and St Mary's Hospital Medical School, London from which he qualified as Member of the Royal College of Surgeons and Licentiate of the Royal College of Physicians and MB. BS. in 1962. During his student days he was a formidable rugby footballer, representing St Mary's when it was a top class club within the UK.

After various house appointments at Harold Wood Hospital, Essex and St Mary's he embarked on training in Obstetrics and Gynaecology in an enviable series of posts that including appointment as Senior House Officer at the Hammersmith Hospital, Registered Medical Officer at the Samaritan Hospital for Women and Queen Charlotte's Maternity Hospital, Registrar at St Mary's and Senior Registrar at King's College Hospital London. Along the way he became Fellow of the Royal College of Surgeons (Eng) in 1967 and a Member of the Royal College of Obstetrics and Gynaecology in 1970.

With such a pedigree it came as no surprise when he was appointed Consultant Obstetrician and Gynaecologist together with clinical teaching at the Nottingham City Hospital in 1975. In Nottingham he developed a special interest in vaginal surgery and uro-gynaecology with, more recently endoscopic and minimal access surgery. The new Teaching Units in Nottingham offered many opportunities to hone his already well developed teaching skills at undergraduate, postgraduate and General Practice levels. He became an examiner for the Central Midwives Board, the Professional and Linguistic Assessment Board and the Membership of the Royal College of Obstetricians and Gynaecologists.

Joining the Nottingham Medico-Chirurgical Society at an early stage John Bruce became Secretary in the late 1980 and its President in 1997/98. A generous host, he was much supported during his Presidency by his wife Bryana, a Senior Partner in General Practice in the Town.

But what of the man himself? Professionally John Bruce was committed to his speciality and his adopted city. No doctor is without fault and it has to be said that John was not the most punctual of men - even his addiction to fast cars did not always ensure that he arrived everywhere on time. Even late though, he was always good value! He loved his sport, following rugby football, skiing in the winter and playing golf at Hollinwell and Beeston Fields. Fellow golfers report that he arrives at the first tee still only half dressed but then goes on to win! Certainly a man for all seasons.

Dr David A.N Hoyte
MB ChB MD FRCGP
President of the Nottingham
Medico-Chirurgical Society (1998 - 1999)

Dr David Hoyte, who was the Society's President during the 1998/9 session, pursued two different and contrasting careers; both distinguished. His first was as an academic anatomist, initially in Manchester and later in Jamaica, whereas his second, equally challenging, was as a general practitioner in the Leicestershire villages of Kegworth and Gotham.

David Hoyte was born in Vieux Port, St Lucia, West Indies, the second son of Dr R A Hoyte MB. ChB. (Edin), originally of Trinidad and later of Ghana, West Africa. He was educated at Farnworth Grammar School and entered Manchester Medical School graduating MB. ChB. (Hons) in 1946. During his undergraduate career he was Vice-President of the Medical Students' Representative Association.

After Resident Posts in Stockport, he served with the R.A.M.C. in Egypt and Cyprus, latterly being attached to 40th Commando Company, Royal Marines. On completing National Service, he joined the Territorial Army becoming a Major with a Lancashire Field Ambulance.

In 1952 he embarked on an academic career in anatomy at the University of Manchester becoming in turn, demonstrator and then Lecturer at the Medical School. During his time at Manchester he gained his Doctorate in Medicine, winning the Gold Medal. A move to the West Indies followed in 1960, firstly as Senior Lecturer and then as Professor of Anatomy in Jamaica. During this time he was Chairman of the University Admissions Group, Pre-clinical Vice-Dean and University Public Orator. During the tenure of a Rockefeller Fellowship he was Visiting Professor at Ann Arbour, the University of Manitoba and the University of Helsinki.

With a return to the UK in 1974 came a sea change in David Hoyte's career. He became a principal in General Practice in Kegworth and Gotham and Part-time Senior Lecturer in Human Morphology in the University of Nottingham .He became Member of the Royal College of General Practitioners in 1978 and eventually to the appointment of the Fellowship of the Royal College of general Practitioners.

David Hoyte's Presidential Address to the Society dealt, perhaps not surprisingly, with the history and development of the University of the West Indies in which he had played no small part. His fascinating and wide-ranging career enabled him to draw in speakers of diverse interests to illuminate fascinating sessions.

Charles Patrick Bates BM BCh (Oxon), FRCS (Eng), DM (Oxon)
President of the Nottingham Medico-Chirurgical Society
(1999 - 2000)

Patrick Bates was the Society's President for the year of the Millennium. He was an internationally known urological surgeon, but he will be remembered within the Society for bringing together, in his presidential Year, a wonderfully talented and entertaining group of guest speakers.

Charles Patrick Bates, always known as Patrick, was born in Hampshire and educated at St Edwards School, Oxford, New College Oxford and the Middlesex Hospital Medical School where he qualified B.M. BCh. (Oxon). He was appointed Consultant Urological Surgeon to the City Hospital in 1973 after training at Birmingham Accident Hospital, Gloucester Royal Hospital, the Middlesex Hospital and St Peter's Hospital for Stone. He became a Fellow of the Royal College of Surgeons of England in 1965, Hunterian Professor there in 1970, and was awarded a Doctorate in Medicine from Oxford in 1973.

Shortly after arriving in Nottingham, Patrick Bates set about developing and expanding urological services in the City. He was an industrious fundraiser and was able to bring to Nottingham specialised equipment which an impoverished National Health Service could not afford. One of his appeals resulted in the introduction of the lithotriptor, putting Nottingham in the forefront of this type of therapy at that time. An accomplished surgeon in all aspects of urology, he had a particular interest and expertise in the problems of incontinence in women. In later years his opinion was much valued in medico-legal cases.

His Presidency is best remembered for the variety of entertaining speakers he was able to persuade to come to the Society. Those who were present will never forget Kate Adie, the BBC Correspondent, who addressed a lecture theatre so crammed full of members that many had to sit on the steps.

Outside medicine Patrick Bates enjoyed a second life at his home in Burton Joyce where he developed and cultivated a beautiful garden with his wife Jenny whom he met as an undergraduate. Such was his reputation that Christopher Lloyd described him, in the Sunday Times, as one of the best gardeners in the Midlands. He is much in demand to show visitors round the garden and to speak at gardening clubs. He is also an accomplished cabinet maker who makes furniture and grandfather clocks for the family.

James Spowart McCracken MBE.
MBChB. FRCGP. DCH. DObstRCOG.
President of the Nottingham Medico-Chirurgical Society
(2000 - 2001)

James (Jim) McCracken, President in the session 2000/'01, was appointed M.B.E. for Services to General Practice. This was something of an understatement since his work as an innovative general practitioner led him into other specialties – domiciliary midwifery, genetics, infectious disease in children, health care of the elderly and of those with learning disabilities. If that was not enough he was a first class middle distance and marathon runner, a keen fly-fisherman and a flying instructor.

Jim McCracken was born in Glasgow and educated at Dollar Academy where he held the School Mile and Cross-Country records. After National Service from 1949-51 in the Royal Army Medical Corps as a theatre technician he entered Aberdeen University where he won a double blue and was elected President of the Aberdeen University Athletic Association in 1954/'55. He graduated M.B. Ch.B. in 1957.

After various house appointments at Airthrey Castle Maternity Hospital, Stirling and the City Hospital, Aberdeen he moved to the Hospital for Women in Peel Street, Nottingham. It was a move, which was to lay the foundations for the rest of his professional life.

In 1960 he entered general practice with Dr. Dick Hutchinson in Beeston, Nottingham. However, within three years came a new challenge. Would he consider building practice premises on a new private estate (Rise Park), where no house had yet been built? The challenge proved irresistible; Jim McCracken took the plunge buying three plots of land for a family home, a purpose built surgery with planning permission to extend. The address 'The Surgery, Rise Park' had the intended effect of ensuring no competition from colleagues! At that time in the sixties, such a move was an ambitious one, not without risk. Nevertheless, the risk was taken and Jim, his wife Anne whom he had met when she was working as a radiographer at the Women's Hospital and their young family, were well on their way. Eventually, Anne too was to be awarded an MBE, for Services to Health, in the same honours list as Jim, in 1995.

But for Jim, the challenge of building a new practice from scratch was not enough. His had to be a practice with optional extras! It was the first in Nottingham to offer routine cervical cytology checks and from its onset full obstetric care was provided. Prior to a new maternity unit being opened at the City Hospital in 1975, Jim had delivered 500 babies in their own homes. On its opening, the practice was given full access to the new maternity unit and regularly continued to undertake what became known as 'home deliveries in hospital'.

From the early days of the Nottingham Medical School, Jim McCracken was one of the founding members of the University's Department of General Practice, being a part-time lecturer from 1974 until he retired in 1996. He had already published original research in the B.M.J. and in the Lancet with papers on the Rubella syndrome and the 'Cri du Chat' syndrome. He subsequently published others on various topics including respiratory disease, contraception and family planning. Shortly before he retired, he edited a two-volume book on 'Sport, Exercise and Medicine.'

Outside medicine, Jim McCracken was a man for all seasons. He learned to fly, amassing 1500 hours, a thousand of those as an instructor; he had his own glider and undertook seven parachute jumps. After the death of one of his sons in tragic circumstances shortly before his 21st. birthday, Jim found solace in the loneliness of the long distance runner returning to training, which he had eschewed on leaving university thirty years previously. He ran his last full marathon in 3hrs. 18mins. 20secs when he was nearly 58 years old.

So to his Presidential Year. Jim took as his theme for the year the words of the prophet Joel, quoted by St. Peter in the Acts of the Apostles, "...your young men shall see visions and your old men shall dream dreams". The programme was designed to explore just such visions and dreams and proved, if attendance was anything to go by, one of the most popular and stimulating in recent memory.

Amongst Jim's innovations was a Champagne Reception prior to his Presidential Address, when members of the Society and their guests were enabled to view the Society's own rare book collection, normally held in the Hallward Library on the University Campus. In his address, Jim invited his audience to join him on a 'Two hundred year journey from smallpox to AIDS'. The Summer Ball, which was based on the theme of a Grand Highland Ball was held at the University's Conference Centre and attracted nearly 500 guests. Nevertheless the innovation, by which Jim would best like to be remembered, was inviting Professor Jim Lowe to register a domain name - medchi.org.uk – for the Society and to initiate the development of its own web site.

A man of fun and charisma, Dr. Jim McCracken brought to bear on the Society his immense energy, which made his term of office a year to remember and cherish.

Kevin Patrick Gibbin
MB BChir (Cantab) FRCS (Eng)
President of the Nottingham
Medico-Chirurgical Society (2001 - 2002)

A gregarious, bon-viveur with a formidable local and national reputation as an E.N.T. surgeon, Kevin Gibbin became President of the Society for the 2001/2 session.

Kevin Gibbin was educated at The King's School, Peterborough (where John Dexter, brother of Colin Dexter of Morse fame, taught him!) He went on to Downing College Cambridge in 1962 and coxed the 1st May Boat and later the Goldie Crew in 1964. He undertook his clinical studies at St Mary's Hospital, London and qualified MB. BChir. (Cantab) in 1968.

After house appointments at St Mary's he laid the foundations to his surgical career by becoming a Demonstrator in Anatomy at Cambridge University from 1969 to 1970 and then trained formally in otorhinolaryngology at Addenbrooke's Hospital, the University Hospital of Wales and The Royal Gwent Hospital, Newport from 1971 to 1978.

He was appointed Consultant to University Hospital, Queens Medical Centre, Nottingham in 1978. His major interests are in all aspects of otological surgery including cochlear implantation and bone anchored hearing aids, with special emphasis on the management of deaf children. In the last 15 years he has co-ordinated the cochlear implantation programme at the Queens Medical Centre and was clinical director of the Department of Otorhinolaryngology and Head and Neck Surgery from 1996 -2001.

A prolific author and writer, Kevin Gibbin has published (and continues to publish) regularly in books and journals on cochlear implantation, paediatric airway problems and aspects of Ear Nose and Throat (ENT) for medical students. He is much in demand at local, national and international meetings being President of the Midland Institute of Otolaryngology from 1999 - 2001, President of the British Association for Paediatric Otolaringology from 1998 - 2000 and President Elect of the Section of Otology of the Royal Society of Medicine for 2004.

It is always said that if you want a job doing well, you ask a busy person. This proved a useful principle when Council invited Kevin to become President of the Nottingham Medico Chirurgical Society for the session 2001/2. He had been a regular attender at meetings over the years and was very well known. He had served as secretary several years earlier.

A man of many interests outside medicine, Kevin packed into his life multiple enthusiasms from flying, fast cars and fine wines though he is careful to ensure that they do not mix! In addition to a vintage Bentley, his garage bulged with cars for every occasion. He owned a part-share in a plane and not infrequently flies. ies i.e. to Brittany for Sunday lunch, using his plane also for long-distance national travel to meetings. A member of the British Medical Pilots Association, he is President Elect for 2003 - 05.

APPENDICES
CHRONOLOGICAL LIST
OF
PRESIDENTIAL ADDRESSES
FROM
1885 to 1977

Date	President	Subject
October 17th, 1885	Dr. T. Burnie	"On the Third Stage of Labour."
November 5th, 1886	Dr. H. R. Hatherley	"The present position and future prospects of the healing art."
November 4th, 1887	Dr. W. B. Ransom	" Cold as a cause of disease."
November 2nd, 1888	Dr. H. Handford	"Vomiting as a symptom."
November 2nd, 1889	Dr. J. White	"Heredity in disease."
November 5th, 1890	Dr. Haydon White	"Detail in treatment."
November 4th, 1891	Mr. A. R. Anderson	"Some subjects of surgical interest."
November 2nd, 1892	Mr. R. C. Chicken	"The treatment of hernia."
November 1st, 1893	Dr. W. Hunter	"The comfort of the patient."
November 7th, 1894	Dr. J. S. Tew	"On some of the legal responsibilities of medical men."
November 6th, 1895	Dr. F. R. Mutch	"The present position & future outlook of the General Practitioner."
November 4th, 1896	Dr. W. B. Ransom	"Immunity to disease."
November 3rd, 1897	Dr. C. H. Cattle	"Medicine during the past 25 years."
November 2nd, 1898	Mr. T. D. Pryce	"Limitations in medicine."
November 1st, 1899	Dr. H. Mitchie	"Puerperal sepsis."
November 7th, 1900	Dr. C. B. Wray.	"Modern sanitation."
November 7th, 1901	Mr. E. C. Kingdon	"The temples and ritual of Asculapius."
November 5th, 1902	Mr. J. Mackie	"Modern science and medical practice."
November 4th, 1903	Dr. T. Burnie	"Forty years of private practice."
November 2nd, 1904	Dr. H. J. Neilson	"The need for statutory vacination."
November 1st, 1905	Mr. T. J. Dabell	"Physical Deterioration."
November 7th, 1906	Dr. E. Powell.*	"The prevention of insanity."
November 6th, 1907	Dr. L. W. Marshall.*	"Childrens work in medicine."
November 11th, 1908	Dr. P. Boobbyer.*	"The birth and death rates of Nott'm. during the past 25 years as compared with other towns."
November 17th, 1909	Mr. A. Fulton	"Medical ethics."
November 2nd, 1910	Mr. W. M. Willis.*	"The significance of the rigid abdomen."
No records available, 1911	Dr. F. H. Jacob	*No records available.*
November 3rd, 1912	Mr. W. G. Laws.*	"Man in the making."
November 5th, 1913	Mr. R. G. Hogarth*	"Some medical men.*
1914 to 1919	Dr. W. R. Smith	*No records available:- W.W.1.*

No records available. 1919 Dr. W. T. Rowe		*No records available.*
November 4th, 1920	Dr. J. F. Blurton	"The report of the Consultative Council and our attitude towards it."
November 9th, 1921	Miss S. Grey	"Menorrhagia in young girls."
No records available, 1922 Dr. Thompson Henderson		*No records available.*
" " "	*1923* Dr. F. H. Houfton	" " "
" " "	1924 Dr. W. Stafford	" " "
December 2nd, 1925	Mr. H. Bell Tawes	"Some Emergencies of E.N.T. work met within General Practice.
January 20th, 1927	Dr. J. C. Buckley*	"Diagnosis and treatment of syphilis."
March 14th, 1928	Dr. F. H. Jacob	"One hundred years ago."
January 16th, 1929	Mr. A. R. Tweedie	"The function of the ciliated mucus Epithelium."
February 26th, 1930	Mr. G. A. Robinson	"Gynaecology of General Practice."
October 22nd, 1930	Dr. Wilkie Scott	"Some problems in diagnosis."
October 21st, 1931	Mr. H. C. Allen	"Diseases of the Thyroid Gland."
December 7th, 1932	Dr. A. C. Reid	"Some practicle considerations in glaucoma and ulcers of the cornia."
January 1st, 1934	Dr. G. O. Gauld	"Country Practice in Yorkshire."
December 12th, 1934	Mr. A. M. Webber	"History of Society during the past quarter of a century."
December 11th, 1935	Dr. B. R. B. Trueman	"Some of the Commoner Disorders of Infancy and Childhood."
December 16th, 1936	Mr. W. F. Neil	"New Zealand."
January 19th, 1938	Dr. W. B. Blandy	"Medicine, Past and Future."
January 11th, 1939	Dr. H. Smith Wallace	"Dermatology."

Sessions 1939 to 1946
President Mr. F. Crooks

October 10th, 1945	Mr. F. Crooks	"Some reflections on the progress of medicine."
October 16th, 1946	Dr. A. A. E. Newth.*	"The handicapped child."
October 1st, 1947	Mr. J. Battersby.*	"Heredity."
October 10th, 1948	Dr. J. Llewellyn Davis	"Urological Reflections."
October 5th, 1949	Dr. I. R. Spark.*	"Practice and all that."
October 4th, 1950	Dr. N. P. R. Galloway.*	"The social history of the doctor in Great Britain."
October 3rd, 1951	Dr. J. L. T. Knox.*	"Devils, Drugs & Doctors."
October 1st, 1952	Mr. F. C. Hunt.*	"The progress of surgery during the last thirty years."
October 7th, 1953	Dr. H. A. Summers.*	"Industrial Rehabilitation.."
October 6th, 1954	Mr. S. A. S. Malkin.*	"Osteo-arthritis of the Hip."
October 5th, 1955	Dr. A. Gordon.*	"The Influence of Disease on the destiny of Nations, Indiviuals and Places."
October 31st, 1956	Dr. P. H. O'Donovan.*	"1856-A Centenary Year."

October 4th, 1957	Dr. R. H. Vartan.^	"Progress."
October 1st, 1958	Dr. W. S. Whimster.^	"Some Pains and Pareses in the arm."
October 14th, 1959	Mr. H. J. Malkin.^	"The Healing Art."
October 5th, 1960	Dr. G. Gordon Napier	"Cornial Grafting."
October 4th, 1961	Dr. J. D. Proctor	"Bitter Sweet, or Medicine as before."
October 3rd, 1962	Mr. E. J. Gilroy-Glass.^	"Cancer of the Larynx."
October 9th, 1963	Mr. J. B. Cochrane	"As it was in the beginning."
October 7th, 1964	Dr. A. C. Gladstone	"Medical Photography."
October 10th, 1965	Mr. J. P. Campbell	"The Crooked shall be made Straight."
October 5th, 1966	Dr. P. Bradbury	"Aviation Medicine."
October 4th, 1967	Mr. P. Cowell Barkla	"History of Naval Medicine."
October 2nd, 1968	Dr. E. L. Lowenthal	"A few thoughts about the G.P., Present and Future."
October 1st, 1969	Dr. J. C. Buckley	"Looking Back."
October 7th, 1970	Dr. R. J. Twort	"Its my Heart Doctor."
October 6th, 1971	Mr. I. A. M. Macleod	"My Pleasure."
October 4th, 1972	Dr. K. S. MacDonald Smith	"Memories and Vagaries."
October 3rd, 1973	Dr. E. B. Z. Masterman	"From Barber to Surgeon."
October 2nd, 1974	Dr. J. M. Macfie	"They never tell you anything in Hospital."
October 1st, 1975	Dr. W. K. S. Moore	"Is it safe?"
October 6th, 1976	Dr. A. Murphy	"The Yellow Paint."
October 5th, 1977	Mr. W. M. Gray	"Water Under the Bridge."

Texts of Presidential Addresses

PRESIDENTIAL ADDRESS

By

Mr. E. POWELL

Delivered on 7th November 1906

"Prevention of Insanity"

At a meeting of this society held on November 7th Mr. E. Powell, the President, gave an address on the Prevention of Insanity. He said that the ratio of certified cases to the general population had risen steadily from 1 in 536 fifty years ago to 1 in 319 ten years ago, and even to 1 in 283 at the beginning of the present year. The explanation lay partly in a diminished death-rate and partly in an increasing accumulation of incurable cases in asylums. Many of such cases could quite well have remained at home under ordinary rural conditions but the continuous growth of urban areas drove them into asylums. Such increase was almost wholly confined to the pauper classes. Dealing with preventable cases, he said that the most important of all was heredity predisposition, which could be clearly traced in at least 22 per cent of the cases admitted. The second most important cause was the abuse of alcohol. Amongst women the amount of insanity due to drink was steadily increasing and in towns like Nottingham, where female labour was largely employed, the percentage was higher than elsewhere. Stimulants must be prescribed to neurotic subjects only with the greatest caution. The third most important preventable cause was syphilis, which played such a leading part in the production of general paralysis. As compared with 30 years ago the cases admitted to asylums today numbered fewer acute maniacs but a larger proportion of melancholic and senile cases. Adolescent insanity was increasing in connection with overstrain. It was, therefore, to be regretted that the usual educational curriculum was so little elastic with respect to the special needs of any children who were slightly defective, especially when so much compulsion was applied to education. In the insanity of middle aged men business worries bore an important part and premonitory symptoms, such as loss of sleep and appetite, general irritability, and a tendency to worry over trifles, should never be neglected.

PRESIDENTIAL ADDRESS

By

Dr. L. W. MARSHALL

Delivered November 6th 1907

"Children's Work in Medicine"

A meeting of this society was held on November 6th, 1907 when Dr. L. W. Marshall read his presidential address on "Children's Work in Medicine."

After a brief historical survey he pointed out that children's ailments need be made no speciality in the "popular and evil sense of the word." The word did not deal with an organ but with the entire organism at its most interesting period of development. Arguing from this fact and the universal lament of the student that the medical schools did not provide at all adequately for his instruction in this topic, so that he was left to search for knowledge "on his own" after qualifying. Dr. Marshall urged strongly that attendance on the practice of a children's hospital should be compulsory for every student and that children's diseases should be taught in every medical school by some one who by his earnestness and enthusiasm was fitted for the task - not by one who was asked to sandwich it in between other subjects which were to him of more interest and with which he was more at home. The student should begin his clinical work in the children's ward, for there was no better training-ground for adult work, and the man who had children's work at his fingers' ends started with the best possible equipment for the difficulties of general medicine and general practice. It must not be assumed that children were miniature men and women; their ailments had been well called "the grammar of disease" and should be studied first, for child-life was exempt from none of the diseases of adult life, though it did modify them in proportion to the stage of development reached.

To view life as one great entity of which the infant was the stepping stone was to give to children's work new force, as well as more interest and much pleasure to the worker. The nutrition, feeding, and hygiene of child life were also very important with the object of avoiding disease and acquiring a sound constitution. Possessing no intuitive knowledge the human parent needed guidance as to the care of her offspring and such instruction ought to come from the general practitioner rather than lady visitors who obtained their knowledge only from pamphlets.

Nursery hygiene did not begin and end with feeding and those who had to teach others must themselves have some practical knowledge of the subject. If therefore medical men were to teach others they must first of all be instructed efficiently themselves. In all things they must seek to follow Nature rather than forestall her and education in the technical sense should not begin before the seventh year.

The commoner neuroses of childhood were attributable more to errors in rearing than to heredity, and teething had primarily very little to do with convulsions. The malnutrition often spoken of contemptuously as "only rickets" was, directly and indirectly, responsible for more deaths than any other cause and hence should claim their serious attention. The widespread existence of this scourge might well be attributable in part to their own apathy and indifference in the study of infant life and ite requirements.

PRESIDENTIAL ADDRESS

By

Dr. P. BOOBBYER

Delivered 11th November, 1908

"The Birth Rates and Death Rates of Nottingham during the past 25 years as compared with other towns."

At a meeting of the Nottingham Medico-Chirurgical Society on the 11th November, 1908 the President, Dr. Philip Boobbyer gave his introductory address on the birth rates and death rates of Nottingham during the past twenty five years as compared with other towns.

Taking the birth rate first, this showed a fall of 30 per cent in the last twenty five years; indeed, a decrease of some sort was to be found in almost all the civilised cities of the world, with certain exceptions such as those of Ireland, Spain, and other parts of Austria and Russia. The probable explanation of the exception in these cases was the local maintenance of the old fashioned religious beliefs regarding the subject of marriage and its objects. Writers were not wanting to point to the probable outcome of this tendency, which was in the direction of the extinction of the families of the ruling and professional classes in favour of a reckless and thriftless proletariat.

Turning now to death rates, in the matter of both the general death rate from all causes and that from principal epidemic diseases, Nottingham showed a pretty steady improvement, like most other large towns, but after making due allowance for exceptional epidemics of measles, whooping cough, and diarrhoea, it seemed clear that progress in the right direction had latterly not been quite so rapid here as in the case of some other similar towns. This was especially true of the death rate from enteric fever, in which other towns, by radical forms in the matter of scavenging or refuse and sewage disposal, had outdistanced Nottingham.

During the year 1907, as the result of severe epidemics of measles, whooping cough, and autumnal diarrhoea, all occurring in the same year, the infant mortality for Nottingham had headed that of all other big towns. He pointed out that the local death rate from phthisis was actually less than that for London. As the result of twenty four years of public health work in the county and city of Nottingham, further defects of sanitation would have to be faced and made good, in particular the demolition or improvement of slum areas, as well as the substitution of water carriage system for the present system of dry pail closets.

PRESIDENTIAL ADDRESS

By

Mr. W. MORLEY WILLIS

Delivered 2nd November 1910

"Abdominal Rigidity"

Mr. W. Morley Willis, in a presidential address on the significance of the rigid abdomen, stated that the condition was always an early phenomenon in inflammatory lesions within the peritoneal cavity, and occasionally remained the sole objective symptom until the condition had so far advanced that operative interference was likely to prove unsuccessful. Abdominal rigidity, therefore, in itself justified an exploratory operation. As an instance in point he quoted a case in which a boy, aged 16, had been seized with acute abdominal pain four hours previous to his being seen by Mr. Willis, but only objective symptom was abdominal rigidity. Nevertheless, section was at once performed, and a perforation of the duodenum discovered. In another case in which operation was performed on the strength of abdominal rigidity, the cause proved to be a perforated gastric ulcer. Abdominal rigidity might occur in some pleural conditions, but in these cases temperature was unusually high, and respiration rapid and generally catchy. As a surgical axiom it might be laid down that the necessity for operation was urgent in exact proportion to the intensity of the abdominal rigidity.

In the discussion which followed, cases were quoted in which abdominal rigidity had been absent, although the conditions were urgent and others in which abdominal rigidity had been present, but recovery had occurred without surgical interference.

PRESIDENTIAL ADDRESS

By

Mr. W. G. LAWS - 6th November 1912·&
Mr. R. G. HOGARTH - 5th November 1913.

I.   At a meeting on November 6th 1912, Mr. W. G. Laws, in a presidential address on "Man in the Making," cited instances to show how deep and persistent were the traces of the race history in the structure of the individual, and then proceeded to outline what was known of the more important of the races of prehistoric man, their physical characteristics, and the condition under which they lived, illustrating his remarks by diagrams and specimens of implements of various period.

II.   At a meeting on November 5th, Mr. R. G. Hogarth, in a presidential address, gave an account of some medical men who had practised in Nottinghamshire in early days. One of them was John Arden, who practised at Newark from 1349 to 1370, and eventually became the King's surgeon. He was renowned for his treatment of fistula in ano. Another was John Jones, of Aspley Hall, who in the sixteenth century drew attention to the value of Buxton water. Robert Thornton and Charles Deering were other renowned doctors, though their fame rested more on their work as historians than as medical men. Nottingham boasted of another physician appointed to royalty - Dr. Taylor, who was physician to George II. The foundation stone of Nottingham General Hospital was laid by John Smelley in 1781. It was opened in 1782 with 44 beds.

PRESIDENTIAL ADDRESS

By

Dr. J. C. BUCKLEY

"The Early Diagnosis and Treatment of Syphilis"

At a meeting of the Nottingham Medico-Chirurgical Society, on January 20th, 1927, Dr. J. C. Buckley gave his presidential address on the early diagnosis and treatment of syphilis. Dr. Buckley commented on the importance of early diagnosis and treatment of a disease so prevalent and so disabling, since the most severe results could be avoided. He laid stress on the necessity for the examination of any suspicious sore for the spirochete and gave details as to the technique of the examination by dark ground illumination, mentioning that this should precede the application of any antiseptic to the sore. By this examination a positive diagnosis could be made before the Wassermann reaction became positive. He dealt briefly with the other tests for syphilis, and then detailed the routine treatment as administered at the Nottingham Venereal Diseases Clinic. The drugs in use were (1) novarsenobillon for intravenous, and (2) bismostal for intra muscular injection. The technique of the intravenous injection was described, and the complications of the treatment were detailed, the chief being local sloughing from faulty injections, dermatitis, and jaundice. In dealing with jaundice, he mentioned that since the van den Bergh reaction had been extensively used at the Nottingham Venereal Diseases Clinic the incidence of jaundice had been reduced by 50 per cent.

PRESIDENTIAL ADDRESS

By

Dr. A. A. E. NEWTH

Delivered 16th October 1946

"The Handicapped Child"

Dr. Newth outlined the various methods designed to deal with handicapped school children: these included the Blind and Partly Sighted Child, The Deaf, The Delicate Child (these included the child with Rheumatic Disease) the Physically Handicapped Child, (these particularly referred to the Orthopaedic cases who were in Hospital for a long time and required to be educated on that account) The Diabetic Child, The Epileptic, The Educationally Subnormal Child (and here he mentioned that intelligence tests were of value in spite of the tendency to decry them) The Ineducable Children, Maladjusted Children, and finally, those with speech defects.

PRESIDENTIAL ADDRESS

By

Dr. JOHN BATTERSBY

Delivered 1st October 1947

"Heredity"

Dr. J. Battersby gave an account of some of the biological experiments and observations upon which our present knowledge of the mechanics of heredity is based. He described the classical experiments of Mendal with the edible pea, upon which he based his theory of inheritance. He noted that observations on the structure and behaviour of chromosomes led to the theory of the gene as that part of the germ cell responsible for the transmission of Mendelian characteristics. He described mutations as the cause of suddenly acquired new characteristics and the prime cause of new varieties. Haemophilia was cited as an example of an heredity disease due to harmful, recessive, sex linked mutation. These studies show that what is handed from one generation to the next are the genes in the germ cell and not the complete character, but these determine all one's basic mental and physical characteristics; and so heredity plays a preponderant part in shaping a man's actions and reactions, his health and happiness. The importance is shown in the study of identical twins. Acquired characteristics are not transmitted.

In conclusion, the President noted several ways in which a knowledge of heredity might be useful in medical practice, as for example, in controlling the transmission of heredity malformations or diseases due to a single dominant or a single recessive gene; in the treatment of haemorrhagic disease of the new born by knowledge of the Rhesus factor; while a knowledge of the heredity background of a family might be invaluable in interpreting a patients disease.

PRESIDENTIAL ADDRESS

by

Dr. N. P. GALLOWAY

Delivered October 4th, 1950

Dr. Galloway outlined the social history of the doctor in Great Britain, dealing mainly with the questions of his appearance, mode of transport, social status, and the limitation of his scientific knowledge. He also gave a picture of the earliest hospitals known here and traced their deterioration and recovery during the 19th century. The address was illustrated by slides which showed the evolution of the doctor's attire from the scholar's cap and gown to the fashionable top hat and frock coat of the late Victorians.

Reference was made to the curious prescriptions dispensed and believed in for hundreds of years, and a brief account of the Plague of London reminded the audience of the insanitary conditions of homes and public in the time of Samuel Pepys. Quotations from contemporary literature reinforced the general argument.

In spite of the lack of a scientific basis for medical practice before the 19th century, a few physicians maintained a proud professional tradition in every age. Dr. Galloway concluded with a tribute to the General Practitioner as an essential personality in any medical service, and expressed the hope that this personality would never be submerged under the pressure of new and overwhelming duties.

PRESIDENTIAL ADDRESS

by

Dr. J. T. L. KNOX

Delivered October 3rd 1951.

The President traced man's age-long struggle against disease from primitive man down through the ages. He pointed out that the methods used in the treatment of disease seemed at first sight to be numerous; they were really variations of three basic measures - faith healing, hygiene therapy, and the use of drugs. Faith healing predominated in the lowest grade of civilization and hygiene therapy in the highest. He described the early Christian concept of disease as being the possession of the individual by a demon, which required exorcism before a cure could be effected. He mentioned the King's touch as a means of curing illness, and the faith people had in holy relics.

As medicaments, practically everything which could be taken internally has been used in the treatment of disease. It was not until the 19th century that the aspect of surgical practice was dramatically changed by the discovery of anaesthetics. He paid tribute to the work of Simpson, Pasteur, Lister, Koch, and others.

The revolution in nursing, which led to such improvement in the training and character of the nurses, has done so much to forward the art of healing. He concluded with a plea that if we are to promote the health of mankind, we must seek to encourage not only medical science but knowledge as a whole.

RESIDENTIAL ADDRESS

by

MR. F. C. HUNT

Delivered October 1st 1952

The President described, from his experience, the Progress of Surgery during the last thirty years; this had taken two main directions.

The first and most outstanding line of progress had been to make surgery safer. Examples of this were the much greater safety of surgical operations upon diabetics following the discovery and use of insulin, and in toxic goitre with the pre-operative use of iodine and the thiouracil group of drugs. Next, the solution of the problem of surgical shock with the ready availability of blood plasma substitutes, had removed one of the principal causes of mortality in severe accidents, major operations, and extensive burns. Then, the research into the fluid and electrolyte balance of the body had been of life-saving importance in the treatment of conditions of dehydration and excessive chloride loss, while in acute intestinal obstruction the development of the technique of continuous suction had been of similar value. Mr. Hunt then referred to some of the revolutionary effects of the use of the chemotherapeutic and antibiotic drugs when used prophylactically in traumatic surgery and in the treatment of bone and urinary infections.

The second line of progress, largely made possible by the first, had been the renewed surgical attack upon disease in the last remaining recesses of the human body. This was illustrated by the recent phenomenal development of cerebal surgery; the more extensive modern abdominal operations of radical total gastrectomy, pancreatectomy and portal shunt operations; and the amazing and rapid advance in chest surgery. In the latter, the President sketched the progress of pulmonary surgery; the more recent surgical attack upon the congenital and acquired lesions of the heart and large intra-thoracic blood vessels; and described some of the modern operations for excision of carcinoma of the oesophagus.

In speaking of the future, Mr. Hunt thought that while, with the possible discovery of a biomedical cure for cancer, the whole of excisional cancer surgery might disappear, cardiac surgery was still in its infancy, and there would be continuous progress in traumatic, plastic, and reconstructional surgery.

PRESIDENTIAL ADDRESS

by

Dr. H. A. SUMMERS

Delivered 7th October 1953

Dr. Summers, in his Presidential Address, dealt first with the syllabus for 1953-54 and pointed out the departure from precedent in that three laymen had been invited to address the Society.

He then proceeded to his main theme which was an outline of the work of an Industrial Rehabilitation Unit, and enumerated the aims of rehabilitation. He gave an account of the day-to-day work of various members of the staff, and described the facilities available for the use of each rehabilitee and the methods employed for assessment of capability. The essential differences between toning up and assessment in a Rehabilitation Unit and training in a Training Centre were emphasised. He said that rehabilitation should begin from the moment of injury or of the diagnosis of disease and that it was a logical continuation of the work of the healing. It should therefore be better understood and more often utilised by both the profession and the employer. The members were invited to visit the Long Eaton Unit to judge for themselves.

PRESIDENTIAL ADDRESS

by

Mr. S. A. S. MALKIN
C.B.E., F.R.C.S.

'OSTEO-ARTHRITIS OF THE HIP'

Delivered 6th October 1954.

The President first referred to the functions of the Society. He said that its purpose was two-fold to help its members to keep in touch with the work of eminent specialists and to meet one another. It was a common ground for members of all branches of the profession living in and around Nottingham. This was particularly important at the present time when there were influences at work tending to divide medical men into sections with sometimes emphasis on the different and conflicting interests. He thought it would be advisable to revive the clinical meetings so giving members an opportunity to read short papers and demonstrate cases.

He said that we had a great deal for which to thank our predecessors. They had each year arranged lectures and had maintained the Society's rooms which were so well situated but which were becoming rather small for the purpose.

After these preliminary remarks, the President stated that the subject of his address was osteo-arthritis of the hip and that he proposed to speak about the prevention and treatment of this painful disabling condition. He discussed the pathology and then mentioned congenital dislocations of the hip, Perthes disease and the slipped upper femoral epiphysis which occurred in children and which, if not noticed in their early stages and treated adequately, were likely to lead to arthritis of the hip in later life.

He then spoke of arthroplasty of the hip and referred particularly to the Smith-Peterson operation in which a metal cup is used to separate the head of the femur from the acetabulum and the Judet operation in which a plastic prosthesis is used to replace the head of the femur. He gave the

331

results of 650 cases treated at five different centres. These were obtained from a survey undertaken for the British Orthopaedic Association by Mrs. Shepherd, F.R.C.S. She found that many of the cup arthroplasty and Judet operations had produced a result which was good or excellent. Some of the others which could not be classified as good or excellent, had still proved of great benefit to the patient.

The President then mentioned another method of treatment, a much less ambitious procedure, a trans-trochanteric osteotomy to correct the deformity of the hip might be a cause of the pain and that to correct this, in his experience, often gave very satisfactory results. He spoke of arthrodesis of the hip and excision of the head and neck of the femur which was some-times very valuable in cases of ankylosing spondilitis.

In conclusion, he said there was no reason to adopt a defeatest attitude towards arthritis of the hip as it should be possible in the majority of cases to give relief, if not complete freedom from pain and the ability to walk. Judgement was required in deciding which of the various procedures available was the best to meet the needs of each individual patient.

PRESIDENTIAL ADDRESS

by

Dr. ARTHUR GORDON
M.R.C.S., L.R.C.P.

'THE INFLUENCE OF DISEASE ON THE DESTINY OF NATIONS, INDIVIDUALS AND PLACES'

Delivered Wednesday, 5th October, 1955

Disease has played a dominant role in the destiny of the human race. It has destroyed old races *(e.g.,* the Mayas*)*. It has defeated armies *(*Napoleon's Russian invasion*)*, paralysed trade and altered the economic life of nations *(viz.,* England after the plague*)*, has wiped out old castes. It has profoundly affected the lives of great leaders who have left their impress on history *(e.g.,* Percles, Lenin*)*. Its influence on the minds of great thinkers has changed the course of human thought *(e.g.,* Neitzche*)*. Places have been affected, and monuments put up *(e.g.,* the Church of Santa Maria della salute at Venice*)*. It has changed the ownership of countries *(e.g.,* Panama Canal*)*. Some of the diseases have been conquered, others remain to succumb to our increasing knowledge.

PRESIDENTIAL ADDRESS

Dr. P. H. O'DONOVAN

'Centenary Year, 1956'

Delivered 31st October, 1956.

Exactly 100 years ago there died in Nottingham Dr. J. C. Williams. He was born in the city and spent practically the whole of his professional life there. He is famous for having first recognized the un-importance of the system of palpitation. During his lifetime revolutionary changes took place in the medical and social life of the country. At the beginning of the century great wealth was in the hands of the few; the working class lived under squalid conditions. Nevertheless, quietly, scientists and humane doctors were working and carrying out important researches. The names and works of such physicians as Richard Bright, Thomas Hodgkin, and Thomas Addison are well-known. Perhaps less well-known are the names of those pioneers, John Ferrier, Thomas Percival and Sir Edwin Chadwick. During this first half of the 19th century there took place in Nottingham the Luddite Riots when the stocking frame weaving machines were smashed in factories by unemployed and desperate workmen. There occurred also the Reform Riots of 1831 when Nottingham saw its Castle set on fire by the mob.

With regard to the state generally of the hospitals up and down the country, that can at once be judged by the letters written home from soldiers wounded in the Crimea War. The standard of medical services there before Florence Nightingale began her stupendous work is notorious. After she arrived the soldiers wrote home that they were more comfortable under her care at Scutari than they would have been in hospitals at home. With regard to the General Hospital, Nottingham, at that time on one occasion it is reported that the smell of pigs coming from the styes outside the windows was unbearable; the remedy was not to remove the pigs but to block up the windows.

In 'Martin Chuzzelwhit,' Charles Dickens describes the woman who cared for the sick in hospital when he portrayed those revolting characters Sarah Gamp and Betsy Prig, liars, drunkards, and persons completely devoid of human tenderness. And what sort of characters were the doctors? The ignorant sychophant is described in Henry Fieldings novel 'Tom Jones,' in Thackeray's 'Pendennis,' and in the various novels of Jane Austen. The medical student and his life in hospital are vividly portrayed in the character of Bob Sawyer of 'Pickwick Papers.'

However, the Apothecaries Act of 1815 began the discipline and reform of the medical profession and no longer could doctors practice without a diploma. Courses of study were prescribed and medical examinations acquired a reality.

PRESIDENTIAL ADDRESS

by

Dr. R. H. VARTAN

Delivered Wednesday, 2nd October, 1957

Ladies and Gentlemen,

This is the beginning of a new session and my first duty is to thank you for the honour you have done me in electing me to this high office; secondly, to congratulate you on your fortitude in turning out to listen to me tonight.

You have all received your programme for the session and I hope you will agree that we have managed to arrange an interesting and varied series of lectures by many well-known authorities in their own particular branch and I hope that you will enjoy them all.

Progress?

I don't know how many hundred million of years life has existed on this earth, but I do know that all through those millions of centuries the one unchangeable rule of existence had been 'Adapt or perish.' We have seen some striking examples of this in recent years. Rabbits in this country have had to adapt themselves to myxomatosis. Germs have had to adapt themselves to penicillin. And another lowly form of life, medical practitioners, have had to adapt themselves to the National Health Service.

There are some who think that the National Health Service has been just as deadly for doctors as the big-head disease was for rabbits - though the outstanding symptom has not been the same. Certainly I think we shall all give most careful thought to our position today, and to our future prospects in the healing art to which we all have devoted our lives, and such talents as we may possess. That is why I propose, tonight, to try to paint for you three pictures; one of the early development of the doctor-patient relationship; one of things as they were in 1948; and one of things as they might well become if present tendencies and present modes of thought really take hold of the medical profession. I am not doing a 'Fat Boy in Pickwick' act. I do not want to make your flesh creep. But I do want to stimulate a little thought on a problem which is really serious, and compound, and may well become comminuted and gangrenous as well. The fracture has occurred in the doctor-patient relationship.

The first doctor may have been something like the present-day medicine man of African tribes or he may have been a priest-physician in one of the temples of Egypt. In any case is does not matter; for the first true doctor (medicine being the science as well as the art) was certainly a Greek. The Greeks, as you doubtless know, had temples to Asclepious, the God of medicine. He was the son of Apollo and the nymph Coronis. The centaur Cheiron taught him the art of healing. At length, Zeus, who being afraid that he might render all men immortal, slew him with a thunderbolt! Undoubtedly, the first doctor to be struck off the register! Sick people just went to these temples and slept in them, leaving it to the god to cure them in their sleep. Perhaps there was a little prompting from the priests, but in any case we probably have there the true explanation of the old age to which most of the famous Greeks seem to have lived.

This Olympian age of medicine, however, came to an end with the first great doctor, Hippocrates, who convinced his fellow countrymen that illness was not sent by the gods to punish slights or wrong doing, but that it was quite natural, and the sort of thing that everybody had to expect. We know very little about Hippocrates himself, but he was probably born in Cos, and in that island off the western coast of Asia Minor, there arose a school of medicine which based its theory and its practice on what Hippocrates taught. So I am going to draw my first picture - rather fanciful, perhaps, but true in essentials - of the healing art as it was practised in Cos.

It was a new school. The old-fashioned ideas were kept alive in the opposition establishment over the way - on the mainland peninsula of Cnidus to be exact. There the physicians were content to classify diseases and to regard every patient as just another case of some illness or other. If the patient did not fit in with the normal set-up for that illness he was just being awkward. What they dealt with were diseases, not human beings, and there was, of course, a tendency for them to invent new diseases to fit

336

any unusual case that came along. The doctors of Cnidus were systema-
tists with orderly scientific minds and a delight in classification, and I
don't suppose they had strong objection to filling in forms.

In Cos, however, the doctors were trained to treat each case on its own
merits and to deal with people who were ill, not with illness that had found
a temporary home in the bodies of certain people. The Hippocratic method
was to observe closely every detail and then to decide what might best be
done in each individual case - even if it was only to prescribe a light diet
and rest - whereas the doctors of Cnidus would say: "This is another case
of so-and-so, and so-and-so must always be treated in such-and-such a
way."

You will gather that the school of Cos believed in a physician getting to
know his patients. And indeed it is that the doctors of Cos were very much
like the family physician thirty or forty years ago in this country. They
knew all that was worth knowing about their patients, and this included a
vast amount of non-medical, but nevertheless extremely valuable knowledge about their mental states and their possible worries. All through the
fifth and fourth centuries B.C. there was constant warfare between the
schools of Cos and Cnidus, between those who treated their patients sym-
pathetically, and those who treated them symptomatically. Fortunately, the
final result was a victory for Cos, and for some three or four centuries
medicine was allowed to grow freely without any philosophical fetters.

Unfortunately, the free spirit of enquiry always aroused intense opposition sooner or later in the ancient world - as indeed it still does - and in the
time of Galen, or just afterwards, the iron hand of authority came down on
medicine, not to be lifted until the Renaissance. Then it was again realised, as Sydenham put it, that in medicine 'every philosophical hypothesis
must be put aside' and the 'manifest and natural phenomena, however
minute, should be noted with the utmost exactness.'

Medicine was freed from authoritarian handcuffs in the 17th century but it
also suffered a serious blow from the philosophers. It is only recently that
the serious blow has been realised. Descartes laid it down that man consisted of a material body which worked like any other machine and of a
spiritual mind which had quite a different mode of existence. So there was

an end to the connection between priest and physician which had been so close in the temples of Egypt and Greece, and also in the monasteries of the Middle Ages. The priest was given the care of souls and monasteries of the Middle Ages. The priest was given the care of souls and the physician the care of bodies, and both professions were expected to stay strictly on their own side of the fence, or at least to make any trespassing quite unofficial.

Yet, in spite of the comparative neglect of the mental side of healing, the position of the G.P. some nine or ten years ago was not so very different from that of the school of Cos. Naturally, he knew a little more, but in his relationship to his patients he had the true Hippocratic approach, and also the Hippocratic conscientiousness. The specialist and the hospital doctor had to belong to the school of Cnidus, and deal with cases of this and that as they came in, but most of the general practitioners still preserved some of the virtues of the old family doctor.

It is true that modern progress in medicine had gravely undermined the status of the family doctor even before the National Health Service began. He could not keep abreast of progress in every field and he could not install all the new gadgets which proved so useful, so that more and more of his serious cases had to be passed on to other hands. But he did try to preserve the doctor-patient relationship in its best and truest form. And that is something well worth preserving, even at a high cost in other things. I might also add, without meaning any disrespect, that it is worth preserving even if it means a little trespassing, when so requested, into the territory of the priest.

The relationship between patient and doctor before the passing of the National Health Services Act was unique. The patient came to the doctor with some physical symptoms of illness, but the doctor knew that he had his mental or emotional lesions as well. And the efficacy of the doctor's treatment depended almost entirely, not on the medicines or treatment he prescribed, but on the trust and confidence which the patient had in him. In other words, the doctor treated his patient as an individual, different from every other patient on his list, and he always tried to find out as much as possible about him, so that he could treat, not just a single limb or organ, but the whole man. He had every opportunity, of course, of building up his knowledge about each patient; he had visited him in his home and probably seen other members of the family; he had a good deal of the atmosphere of that home. He may have known the patient for years or perhaps known his father and mother. He certainly knew enough about the patient to treat him as an individual and not another case of soansoitis. And he took a personal pride in treating his personal patients.

But now in many cases what a change there has been! I am not blaming the National Health Service Act for all the deterioration in the doctor-patient relationship for, as I said before, the immense progress in recent years has meant intense specialisation, and if any patient is to have the benefit of the latest research in every branch of medicine he has to become a unit in some sort of centre like the famous Mayo Clinic in Rochester, U.S.A.

Here is Kenneth Walker's description of the 'service' of the Mayo Clinic:

"From the moment of his entry there the patient is, so to speak, caught up on a delivery belt and weighed, measured, photographed, X-rayed and electro-cardiographed. His blood and all his secretions and excretions are submitted to every conceivable form of analysis. During his passage through the numerous departments of the clinic the dossier which accompanies him becomes fuller and fuller of graphs, reports and notes. In short, the Mayo Clinic is a typical product of twentieth-century America, and is an institution in which the art of healing has been raised to the highest degree of efficiency. But when all of these expert examinations and recordings have been completed, it may well happen that little more is known about the patient and his illness than when he entered the clinic's doors. The patient has been so completely dismembered during his passage through the works that nobody is able to see him as a whole man again. The analysis is so thorough that even the extremely efficient directors of the clinic are unable to put together the pieces. As a human being he has all but disappeared and been replaced by a collection of scientific and medical data.

I suppose that something like that will happen when we get our new health centres as outlined in the 1948 Act - though whether any of us here will live to see them built is anybody's guess and apparently nobody's business. Meanwhile, and leaving aside for the present all need for specialist treatment, the doctor-patient relationship has been sadly undermined by the nationalisation of the Health Service.

The State has become between doctor and patient. The State employs the doctor and expects him to consider the State's interests as well as those of the patient. He has to spend a lot of time filling up forms of one sort or another. He has little time to practice his art or to apply his scientific skills properly. He can only deal with the simple cases himself, and direct the others to some hospital or specialist for further treatment or examination.

As for the patient, he may, in some cases, retain the old attitude of friendly confidence in his doctor and, realising how busy he is, he may not call on his services until the need is pressing. But in other cases - in far too many cases - the patient is now an unpleasant person who has paid to have medical attention when he or she is ill, and who means to have that attention, even if he or she has to make or fake the illness. The patient now comes to the surgery, not to seek help and comfort, but to demand his legal rights and to get a certificate which will enable him to draw his benefit. We can hardly blame the doctor if he gives him his legal rights and nothing more, and gets rid of him as quickly as possible.

But this natural impulse strikes at the root of the fine traditions of the medical profession. It is symptomatic of the irritations which have been aroused in the profession by the National Health Service. We have all experienced most of them in some degree or other. We all feel the need for more time to keep abreast of modern progress and we all deplore the waste of time we spend in filling up forms and dealing with people who are not really in need of medical attention - though they might well be in dire need of psychotherapy. And speaking of psychotherapy we all feel that, whereas the general practitioner has an ever greater need for psychological understanding of his patients in the modern world, the very last thing to foster and encourage this understanding is the present set-up of the state medical service.

There are other things in the service which might be improved: notably the inability of doctors to keep in touch with their patients when these have been sent to hospital. Then there is the tendency of big organisations to try to set up their own little machines with the big State machine. A certain nationalised industry, for example, which has a strong desire to be self-sufficient, even to the extent of providing its own coal, set up a sort of super ambulance room under the control of a nurse or ambulance man. These people are enthusiastic enough, and they may even have some knowledge of what they are doing, but they are civil servants now, and you know what that means - pass the baby! So the result of these ambulance rooms, set up with the best intentions, and in the hope of *saving* the doctor some work, is that they serve as collecting stations for a host of trivial cases: trivial cases which are magnificently bandaged in the most elaborate and up-to-date manner; several forms are filled in in triplicate and the patient sent home by specially-charted ambulance with a note or verbal message demanding an immediate visit from the doctor. Send for the doctor *at once* and see that he comes *at once*. In the old days these would have been dealt with on the spot with a drop of iodine or a bit of sticking plaster.

In the old days, indeed, *mirabile dictu* the patient might well have dealt with the matter himself and bathed and bandaged the finger when he got home. But the National Health Service as part of the Welfare State, does not encourage people to think for themselves. It tells them all about their rights, but it never thinks of telling them about their duties, or about their moral obligations if they intend to enjoy those rights. Dr Frangcon Roberts diagnosed this difficulty very neatly a few years ago when he said:

> "A free and comprehensive health service is a noble ideal, but one which the country cannot under existing conditions attain. When the people realize that the benefits which can be derived from the Service depended primarily upon national productions, and that these benefits are adversely affected by all inflationary tendencies - restrictive practices, strikes, lock-outs, go-slow tactics - then only will they be worthy of the fruits of their inspiration. Unless our capacity to induce changes in our environment is accompanied by an equal capacity to adapt ourselves to changes, and unless our conquest of nature is matched by an equal conquest of ourselves, we

shall lose those characteristics of our national life which we hold dear, and the Welfare State will end in Totalitarian State."

Dr. Roberts was thinking of the great mass of the people when he talked about the conquest of ourselves, and about adapting ourselves to changes, but I am going to apply the words to us doctors. For, believe me, unless we do something about it, we shall find the medical profession rapidly being paralysed and losing all its vitality, in the grip of the Welfare State.

It is my firm belief that the basis or king-pin of the fight against disease in this country or in any country is the general practitioner. It is to him that people go at the beginning of their illness; it is on his knowledge and wide experience that they rely for a diagnosis of what is wrong. And it is also my firm belief that the family doctor type of general practitioner is the best possible type. But there no longer seems to be any place for him in the modern world. He is just a sort of casualty clearing station, passing on those wounded in the battle of life to other centres further removed from the actual turmoil. Even the patients themselves often demand all manner of specialist or laboratory attention. They have heard about some new-fangled idea on the radio, or read about in the popular press, and because they pay a few shillings a week for a comprehensive insurance against all possible ills they expect the latest and most expensive treatment as a matter of their rights. And if by any accident or piece of ill-luck anything goes wrong while they are 'on the panel,' you may be sure that they will claim a fantastic compensation, and, with the aid of the State once again, in the shape of the poor man's lawyer, will initiate some most expensive and irritating litigation.

That being so, the family doctor must devise his own protective mechanism in the new and uncomfortable conditions in which he has to live and practice his art. And that brings me to the third of my pictures - a nightmare portrait of things as they might be if the medical profession follows the generally accepted present day tendencies and methods of self-protection.

It will of course, have to develop its trade unions. Not one union, but many. For we could not possibly have a single trade union for both doctors and surgeons. Nor would it really be correct for graduates of one medical school to belong to the same union as those from another. Gentlemen from Edinburgh, for example, could not be expected to belong to the same union as fellows from London, and gentlemen from London would be equally averse to being mixed up with these fellows from Dublin. Then again it would be necessary for each kind of specialist to belong to his own special union. The E.N.T. brigade would be one of the first, but the numbers would rapidly multiply, until we had such things as fantastic counterparts of the A.S.L.E.F. in the association of specialists in the lancing of esoteric furnacles, and of the transport and General Workers Union in the Terminators of Gravid wombs or uteri.

Already the trade-union spirit, or technique as I prefer to regard it, is strongly entrenched in the hospitals among the lay staff, and it is only a matter of time before the virus spreads to the doctors, especially since the younger doctor spends some of his most impressionable years in the hospital.

So here is my 1965 dream-picture of a young doctor just qualified and taking over the panel patients and the practice which his father has built up. The father has left the country on a long visit to a married daughter in New Zealand from which, fortunately for him and his old-fashioned ideals of public service, he will never return alive.

Monday morning surgery is at 9 a.m. and there are already a few patients queuing up outside in the rain as the hour strikes. Dr. Tud (trade union doctor) is very conscientious and he goes and opens the door of the waiting room for them to sit in. "Silly of you to come before time," he says. "You will only catch cold standing in the rain. And your wet clothes will spoil my furniture."

After this gracious and gratuitous advice, he retires into the surgery where he clocks in by opening his case book, and time keeping it 9 a.m. Then he puts the kettle on and makes a cup of tea for himself and his *very* attractive and *moderately* efficient secretary.

At 9.20 he opens the door and announces that he is ready to receive the first patient. It is a man, so the first question he asks is: "What is your union?"

343

"I don't belong to a union."

"You don't belong to a union? What do you do for a living?"

"I'm a Clerk."

"Well, what's wrong with you?"

"I've a pain here" (touching epigastrium). "Makes me feel sick sometimes."

"Comes on before meals, I suppose?"

"Yes, a long time before sometimes."

Here Dr. Tud places a thermometer in the patient's mouth and feels his pulse. No fever is apparent. He pushes back his chair and stands up.

"Sorry I can't treat you. You've got a bad duodenal, and duodenals are caused by worry. You'll have to go and see a psychotherapist. Here's the address."

"But I'm in pain, doctor. Can't you give me something to stop it?"

"Sorry. I could, of course, but that would be interfering with Dr. Flanagan's work. He's you're man and you're his pigeon. My union won't let me. And you ought to join a union yourself, you know. That's the best advice I can give you. Take some of the worries off your shoulders." And then, with a faint touch of compassion for a man almost at the end of his tether, he adds: "Look, its a long way to Dr. Allen's and his surgery might be over by the time you get there. Here's a couple of tablets to suck on the way. But don't tell him I gave you them."

The second patient comes in. It is a woman. Complains of dysmenorrhoea. Dr. Tud scribbles down 'Prescription No. 13' and says: "Take this to the chemist's around the corner. That'll put you right. Good morning." Total time occupied with this case is 15.7 seconds, helping to bring the average time of each case down to the statutory one as laid down by the Executive Body.

The third patient is a hefty fellow looking very fit. But one of his eyes is rather red and inflamed.

"Boilermakers' Union," he says before the doctor can utter a word. Evidently there is some sort of freemasonry among the union members. Dr. Tud smiles. "And what can I do for you, *mate?*"

"Well, its me eye, doc. Think I must have got a bit of steel in it at work. It was a bit sore yesterday and when I was having a couple of pints last night one of my pals said I ought to have it seen to and quick. He'd been off for a month, he said, and it all started with an eye no worse than mine. And it does feel bad this morning."

Dr. Tud makes a careful examination but can see nothing wrong embedded in the cornea. There is some conjunctivitis which might be due to dust or drink. He looks grave, and after writing out 'Prescription No. 19' and adding 'One eyeshield,' he says: "You did right to come and see me. You can't be too careful with your eyes. I'll sign you off work for a few days. Take this prescription to the chemist round the corner and bathe your eye every two or three hours. Wear the shield if you go out and come and see me again about the end of the week. I may have to send you to an eye specialist if it does not get any better, *mate.*"
One or two more patients come in and then the clock strikes ten. Dr. Tud clocks out by time stamping his case book again. But he continues with the surgery. He believes in looking after his patients, especially the union members.

And besides, he is now on time-and-a-half.

The next patient is a young mother with her son. The young lad has been complaining of earache. That is easily dealt with. It just means prescribing No. 23 on Dr. Tud's list of 24 which are all he uses, and which are now 'official,' not only at the chemist's round the corner but all over the country. Anything outside this list has to be prescribed by a specialist. Then Dr. Tud looks at the mother, and another touch of the unfashionable humanitarian feeling shakes him. After all, his father was a real family doctor. "And how are you feeling, yourself?" he asks.

"I'm all right" is the answer - given a thought too quickly. Dr Tud is no fool. He can see the signs of mental and physical strain written all over her face. She needs help for mind and body far more desperately than her son. But Dr. Tud is a busy man. And he is also a trade unionist. He does not go looking for unpaid overtime work. So he compromises with his conscience by saying: "Well, you look a bit run down. Let me write you out a prescription for a tonic. Or would you like to go to Dr. Nervo for an examination?

"Not Dr. Nervo," says the woman. "He asks too many awkward questions and I don't like *strange* men asking me questions." She looks pathetically at Dr. Tud, but his moment of human weakness has passed and does not accept the unspoken offer. He hurriedly writes 'Prescription No. 1' (Mist. Bromoval) and sends her off to the chemist around the corner.

Dr. Tud's surgeries on the following days are very simular, but by Thursday afternoon he feels that he has done enough and earned enough for one week, so he fastens a printed notice to the outer door: 'No Surgery till Monday morning' and goes off for a weekend's golf at Woodhall Spa. Woodhall Spa sounds better if he has to explain his absence, but that is very unlikely. It might lead to a strike.

At Woodhall he meets several medicos from neighbouring counties, and one of them says to him: "I say, Tud, do you ever see anything of old Dr. V. these days? He used to enjoy a game of golf as well as anybody, but I never see him nowadays. What's happened to him?"

Dr. Tud glances round and then buttonholes his questioner and leads him into a quiet corner. "I'm afraid V's in a bad way," he says in a low voice. "You know how old-fashioned he is and there are ugly rumours going about. He never seems to have time for golf now and do you know why? He works too long hours. Real blackleg I hear. I don't know for certain, mind you, but I hear that he was busy in his surgery until ten o'clock one night last week patching up a couple of road accident cases, and neither of them on his panel."

"How disgusting," says the other. "Why did he not send for the ambulance?"

"He did ring up, of course, but they had all been rather busy that day and the only driver in had to have his statutory rest before he could go out again. So V. got fed up with the delay and stitched them up himself."

"He ought to be reported."

"Yes, and he ought to be watched, too. He's a positive menace to medical progress and to our standard of living."

At this point I woke up, as you can well imagine.

You might think my glimpse of the future rather far-fetched, but it does bring out the danger of the present situation and its logical sequelae. Cnidus is all right, and the specialists who treat illnesses can survive and flourish in the Welfare State. But Cos is sinking between totalitarian sea, and the general practitioners who have to study the whole person and diagnose all his complaints find themselves cold-shouldered and trodden in the mire by consultants. Yet it is the G.P. who has to accept the responsibility of sending the patient to the right specialist, and in psychosomatic cases that is not always easy. Illness today can usually be traced to mental as well as physical causes, and if specialists are to be called in there may be need for more than one of them. Then we must have to decide the vital question of which one is to be allowed to start work first. The psychiatrists, with unusual humility, always prefer that the possibility of physical lesions should be explored first of all, and the G.P. generally follows this plan. After all, it is so much easier to put an acceptable label on a physical lesion and so satisfy the patient that his case is understood. But it is not always advisable. It is a pity that we have not got adequate labels yet for some of the psychological devils that get inside us. And it is a pity, too, that most patients are rather proud of having some physical ailment to talk about, but scared stiff of being suspected of having anything wrong with them mentally.

The old family doctor could deal with the difficulty because he knew the patient so well, and because the patient trusted him, and felt that he was on his side. A psychological examination could be carried out without the patient being aware of the fact; in his view the doctor was just being polite and friendly, and hidden worries could be brought out to the surface without upsetting the patient or spoiling the friendly relationship. I do not mean to suggest that any deep examination could be carried out, but the family doctor could often learn to bolster up his physical remedies with some sound psychological advice, and so give his drugs a much better chance of doing their stuff.

Now what is the prognosis? I have diagnosed this compound fracture in the doctor-patient relationship. There are three main causes: the National Health Service, the immense amount of specialist progress made in medicine in the past fifty years, and the modern realisation of the big part played in the majority of illnesses by the mental factor. All three factors have contributed to the weakening of the old fashioned relationship, but in one of them I see the main hope for the future so far as the general practitioner is concerned. That is the mental factor, the rise of psychosomatic medicine.

I think it is absolutely essential for the health of the people to maintain the old family doctor relationship as the basis of the National Health structure. That can only be done by limiting the number of patients on each panel, and by paying the doctor a more reasonable capitation fee. At present, there is usually plenty of money for specialist gadgets and new medicines and drugs, but less money for the G.P. That is wrong. If the G.P's were better paid for smaller panels they would be able to take far better care of their patients, and a lot of the consultations and special treatments would be unnecessary. After all, a National Health Service is supposed to preserve the health of the people, and it is on the prevention of disease, or on the treatment of disease in its early and vulnerable stages that we should concentrate our forces. As it is we let the enemy gain a foothold without opposition and then have to bring out all our heavy artillery to dislodge him.

I have given you my nightmare version of what the G.P. might develop into if he succumbs to the prevalent social diseases of our time. But in my present position of family doctor, if I may so term it, to all the doctors in the district, I feel that I ought to give you some reassurance and hope as well. I found this myself in the Utopian picture painted by Dr. Balint in a recent book in which he recorded the results of the research done at the Tavistock Clinic on the psychological implications of general medical practice. *(The Doctor, the Patient, and His Illness:* Pitman Medical, 1957.) I ought perhaps to tell you that Dr. Balint is a psychiatrist, and that the mental side of illness - of every illness - looms very large in his eyes. He says that "every illness is also the 'vehicle' of a plea for love and attention," that the patient develops an illness in order to be able to complain, and that the personality of the patient decides what he can complain about. He also points out that the tool or instrument in psychotherapy, the counterpart to the surgeon's knife, is the doctor himself, and that it is the doctor's business to see that he is in good repair and in serviceable condition. In his final chapter, Dr. Balint declares that "the more one learns of the problem of general practice, the more impressed one becomes with the immense need for psychotherapy." Therefore, in his Utopia the general practitioner has had some basic training in the art not psychiatry or deep analysis, but in what might be called 'minor psychotherapy.' Economic limitations and professional jealousies have also been eliminated, and the doctor is able to respond freely to the patient's 'offers' or suggestions of what might be wrong.

In this Utopia the G.P. *is* the king pin of the State medical service. He deals with the human problem and calls in the help of the hospital specialists only to help with the scientific problems. The specialist will not be a 'super mentor,' but general practitioner's expert assistant. The G.P. will "no longer be able to disappear behind the strong and impenetrable facade of a bored overworked, but not very responsible prescriber of drugs and writer of innumerable letters, certificates, and requests for examinations; instead he will have to shoulder the privilege of undivided responsibility for people's health and well-being, and partly also for future happiness."

He will have learnt that the 'clinical illness' so well understood and treated in hospitals are only episodes in a long history, and it will be his duty to keep a watch on his patient even while the hospital treatment is in progress. For he will know that in many cases (here I quote): "any such episode represents only one of the several 'illnesses' that a patient 'offers or proposes' to his doctor. The way the doctor 'responds' to these 'offers' has signal consequences for the patient's future. Much more is meant by this than the possibility of overworking an organic process, the frightening bogy that our present training system has so successfully implanted in every doctor's mind."

Yes, the Utopian General Practitioner is in full charge of his patient, and he has the time to follow the medical history of every one of his patients in health or illness. Indeed, he will find that his patients coming to him in the very early stages of any illness, before it has become 'organised.' He will know when to treat the clinical illness, and when to concentrate more on the underlying mental conflict.

Obviously, if we are going to progress, the G.P. is going to have to shoulder an immense amount of responsibility. But he will also feel free once more, and be able to take that pride in his work which was ours before the National Health Service organised us into scribblers of prescriptions and certificates. And I am sure that you will agree with me that the burden of extra responsibility will be gladly shouldered if we can get back to our former status, and make the school of Cos at least the equal of Cnidus . . . I wonder?

PRESIDENTIAL ADDRESS

by

Dr. W. S. WHIMSTER
M.D., M.R.C.P.

'SOME PAINS AND PARESES OF THE ARM'

Delivered Wednesday, October 1st, 1958.

Ladies and Gentlemen,

I must begin by expressing to you my humble thanks for having elected me your President for this Session. I can but give my assurance that I will spare no effort to maintain the high traditions of our ancient society.

I calculate that I have listened to over twenty Presidential Addresses in this room, though never arranged this way round. They have ranged from professional through historical and reminiscent, to almost futurist. One of the most memorable was the first I heard. It was given by Dr. Wilkie Scott in 1930, and was a clinical talk on Congenital Hypertrophic Pyloric Stenosis. I, too, am attempting no evocation of the past, and no flight into the future. Mine is a clinical talk, on some of the pains and pareses which afflict the arm.

To compass the subject in full would be quite impossible in any reasonable time. It would involve the consideration of every structure, bone, muscle, joint, nerve and blood vessel which enters into the anatomy of the arm, whether directly or by reference. I have therefore selected certain more or less common conditions - mainly, as you no doubt expect, from the field of Neurology.

Firstly, since the basis of diagnosis in such cases must be anatomical, a word about anatomy.

Most of you will remember that the arm is supplied by a fifth, sixth, seventh and eighth cervical roots and the first thoracic. These form the Brachial Plexus which runs across the Thoracic Inlet between the clavicle and the first rib where it is associated with the subclavian artery. As the plexus passes behind the clavicle, it consists of an upper part to become the median nerve, a lower part to become the ulnar, and the posterior which becomes the radial nerve.

The charts demonstrate the dermatone supplied by each root and the area of supply of the three nerves.

On the muscular side, it will suffice, I think, to remember that the radial nerve supplies the triceps and the diriflexors of the wrist; the median, the biceps and the outer flexors of the wrist with two of the small muscles of the hand; and the ulnar supplies the inner flexors of the wrist and most of the small muscles of the hand.

So much for anatomy.

Among the very serious but very trying pains which humanity is called upon to bear, is that group of discomforts in the arm and hand called variously Branchial Neuritis, Acroparaesthesiae and many other names. Over the past ten years the origins of most of these diseases have been elucidated.

One of the most fruitful of recent conceptions has been that of Cervical Spondylosis. It has been known for a long time that intervertebral disc degeneration and osteophytic could occur in the spinal column. Only over the past fifteen years or so has it been realised that in the cervical region could this produce marked neurological symptoms. Here, I am afraid, we must have some anatomy. As the spinal cord passes down from the foramen magnum to the thoracic region, it has anteriorly the anterior common ligament, and then vertebral bodies with their discs. The cervical nerves come off at right angles and immediately enter the intervertabral formina. If the disc degenerates, osteophytic formation will occur at any levels from C5 to T1, and in any or all of three directions. If the main protrusion is backward, the spinal cord may be impinged upon and paraplegia result. This is not, however, germane to our present argument. If the protrusion is lateral, it may obstruct the foramina, and nerve root pressure and irritation occur. vascular disturbance and oedema are important factors in the symptoms, and these fluctuations account for the variability of the symptoms in the arms. Motor and/or sensory roots may be involved and some or all of the cervical roots on either or both sides. Naturally the patients are elderly. Apart from cases following injury, or with congenital anomaly, I have seen one under fifty, and mostly they are over fifty-five. It afflicts both sexes. The pain is present day and night, and may so interfere with sleep as to cause loss of weight and severe depression. The diagnosis has to be made from local lesions in the neck and spinal cord, such as tumours of cord, vertebrae or meninges. One such which Mr. Birkett operated on recently for me certainly had spondylosis, but she also had secondary carcinoma of the meninges. Malignant glands in the neck are not uncommon, especially from bronchial neoplasma. Most rarely inflammatory lesions such as tuberculosis of a vertebra may mimic the symptoms. X-rays, careful assessment of the anatomical distribution and examination of the spinal fluid occasionally will avoid gross errors.

The second site at which arm pain originates is in the brachial plexus as it crosses between the clavicle and the first rib. The varieties of mechanism causing these symptoms are numerous. I have seen a list of fifteen anatomical variations responsible. The most obvious in the presence of a cervical rib allowing kinking of the plexus on its passage into the arm. Sometimes in these cases the subclavian may be involved and vascular insufficiency be the presenting symptom.

In the great majority, however, the lesion is not as gross as this, and I think we may leave the precise anomaly to the anatomists and concentrate on the clinical side. The vast majority of the sufferers are women. Most commonly the complaints begin following debility and fatigue, especially at the menopause. Whatever the precise anatomy, the immediate cause is the drooping sagging of the shoulder due to muscular hypotonia. Many of you will have observed the great increase in this type of complaint during the weary days of the war when the carrying of heavy shopping bags and the performance of unaccustomed work put an increased strain on the women at home. The pain in these cases is due to irritation of the lower cord of the plexus, and is felt on the ulnar side of the forearm and hand, with 'spillover' to the whole arm in severe cases. The pain is largely nocturnal causing serious loss of sleep. It is eased by getting up and by various postures of the arm. It is found to be worse after heavy work, such as a wash day.

Diagnosis is fairly easy as a rule. The age is younger than the spondylotics, thirty to fifty years. X-ray may show some anomaly of the thoracic inlet. The ulnar distribution distinguishes the lesion from median nerve compression.

The third group of cases giving similar pains has been shown to be due to pressure on the median nerve in the carpal tunnel. As this slide shows, there is a gap on the volar surface between the radius and ulna through which passes the majority of the flexor tendons to the fingers, and which the only soft structure is the median nerve. Roofing over this tunnel is a tough unyielding fibrous band. If now pressure rises in the carpal tunnel, pain will be felt in the thumb, index and middle fingers supplied by the nerve. The nerve to the palm travels above the fibrous band, and is not involved. Prolonged or severe pressure will produce wasting in the abductor and opponens pollicis well shown by this slide.

As with the other two conditions, pain is largely nocturnal. It is difficult for patients to localise these pains, and 'spill-over' may occur and pain may be felt in the forearm, and even up to the shoulder.

Diagnosis can be difficult. Our patients are rarely trained observer and they may have to be asked to return a week later, having carefully noted the site of the pain. If this is in the median supplied fingers only, it is diagnostic. Wasting confined to the abductor pollicis is also very hopeful. Sometimes one finds an old colles fracture or a ganglion as the cause. One ganglion I saw was tuberculosis. Some of the pain in the hand in rheumatoid arthritis is thought to be of this type.

The range is wide, with a slight preponderance of women at the menopause. Either sex is affected, and not infrequently the pain affects both hands. x-ray is rarely helpful. It does give a very pretty picture of the carpal tunnel. As a rule one is forced back on one's clinical judgement for diagnosis in the milder cases.

The diagnosis of these three types of pain in the hand and arm is of importance since though the underlying causes are not of grave significance, yet the misery produced is great, and the loss of efficiency severe. Each of the three has a treatment which is usually effective, and sometimes curative.

In the Spondylosis, a collar of newspaper may give a miraculous relief. I was asked some years ago to see a man almost suicidal with pain. He was aged about fifty-five. His X-ray showed gross spondylosis. Emergency admission to hospital and the application of a newspaper collar made him comfortable in three days. In more persistent cases we use a plastic collar.(I must note in passing that the results of this treatment in paraplegia are much less satisfactory.) After a period of rest the process seems to settle, and in the majority of cases the collar can be gradually discarded.

Operative fixation of the neck and removal of osteophyte have been tried, but are rather desperate remedies in this type of case.

The treatment of the costo-clavicular group is with shoulder-raising exercises. Bed rest is sometimes necessary. General attention to physical and mental health, and assistance in avoiding the fatigue which is usually the proximate cause, are of course, most helpful. Gradually the tendency seems to improve, and many of the cases recover in a year or two spontaneously. Operation may be necessary for cervical ribs and occasionally for other anatomical anomalies.

The carpal tunnel syndrome usually remits with rest unless there is a gross organic cause. In those cases where pain is persistent, or wasting has occurred, a simple operation for unroofing the carpal tunnel may be performed. The patient only has to stay in hospital for about four days. The results are so good that frequently patients are asking for the other side to be done as well.

I want now to pass on to discuss certain other conditions which we meet less frequently but often enough to justify mention in a review such as this.

The first is called by many names; the one I prefer is Neuralgic Amyotrophy, which indicates two main features: Pain and muscle wasting.

The history of these cases is almost stereotyped. There is fairly acute onset of pain somewhere in the shoulder girdle. It may be widespread or localised. It can be extremely severe. Examination reveals nothing, and I regret to say though I have had the opportunity of making the diagnosis at this stage in three cases, I did not do so. After a week or ten days of this pain, muscle wasting appears, not necessarily in the area which was painful. The wasting may be local to one muscle, or, as in one of my cases, so widespread that the diagnosis of myopathy was considered. As a rule the severe pain abates as the muscular weakness appears, leaving a dull ache which slowly disappears. The muscular wasting gradually recovers over a period of a year or two, in a manner suggestive of the regeneration of nerve. The only associations of this syndrome are Herpes in the brachial area, and post-serum neuritis, for example after A.T.S. It will be remarked that the story closely resembles that of poliomyelitis, and also of shingles itself, but no virus has been isolated so far. Treatment is purely expectant, but on the whole the outlook is good and one can be quite reassuring to the patient once the acutely painful state is past.

The next condition is the frozen shoulder and the shoulder hand syndrome. These can be devastating cases. They may be associated with hemiplegias, injuries, shingles and coronary thrombosis. Some seem to arise without cause. They start with pain over the deltoid insertion, which spreads over the arm and often up to the neck. The patient may or may not notice restriction of movement at the shoulder joint. In the pure frozen shoulder the pain increases and spreads for a few months till it reaches a climax then gradually recedes, leaving ultimately a fairly normal shoulder.

In the more severe shoulder hand syndrome, as the shoulder stiffens the hand begins to look smooth, the small joints stiffen in extension, the thumb becomes immobile. The whole hand and arm is very painful and useless. One has to assume some neurogenic factor in these cases, but so far no conception helpful to treatment has emerged. Particularly in cases secondary to permanent lesions such as hemiplegia the condition itself may be permanent. Pain may lessen, but use rarely returns. Local physiotherapy and cervical sympathectomy have been tried but with little success. Prevention should be attempted by passive movement of all weak or paralysed shoulders. We begin this in strokes while the patient is still unconscious. Active and resisted movements in herpes, and passive movement in cases following coronary thrombosis, may help to prevent some of these most crippling disasters.

The radial nerve comes but little into our purview now. Some of you will remember the bad old days when a man might come home drunk on a Saturday night and fall asleep with his arm over the back of his chair, and appear at the Casualty Department next morning with 'Saturday night paralysis.' It is a rare disease now, as is its a mimicker - lead palsy. The only cases seen are directly traumatic, and hardly concern the physician. By courtesy of Dr. O'Donovan, I show a picture of a recent case.

The last group of cases I propose to discuss are the ulnar nerve palsies. I am particularly and personally interested in these since I have a pair of very exposed ulnar nerves, I cannot sit with my chin on my hand in an armchair without keeping my elbows well in to avoid pressure on the nerves. Pressure on the window ledge of my car or even in bed may cause discomfort, numbness and not even temporary weakness. I was once asked to see a patient in a surgical ward who had pain and numbness of both ulnar nerves, due to 'rowing' himself up the bed with his elbows. Most of this sort of thing is trivial, easily diagnosed by the patient, and not brought to the doctor except as a passing comment. Ulnar nerve palsies are very common, and I was surprised on looking up records to find how many appeared in a year. It will be remembered that the ulnar nerve supplies nothing above the wrist crease, so that weakness in the forearm must be produced by a lesion as high as the axilla, as in the cervical rib. Wasting of the hand muscles is so commonly a result of neurological system disease such as Motor Neurone Disease, Cervical Spondylosis or tumour, that one is tempted to forget the more local causes, thus causing 'gloom and despondency.' If however, the wasting is unilateral, and confined to the lower ulnar distribution, a local lesion should be sought. Recently I had such a case due to osteo-arthritis at the elbow. Many others are due to unexplained 'Neuritis' and clear up completely.

Finally, as a curiosity, I report two cases of local pressure on the palmar branch of the ulnar nerve, giving wasting on the radial side of the hand only. Great alarm was caused in each case, with a diagnosis of that inevitably fatal condition, Motor Neurone Disease. One was a man who worked at reamering castings at 'Rolls Royce.' He had to grip a vibrating tool very tightly. The other was a wife of a friend of mine who decided that an overgrown privet hedge had to be cut. The recurring jolting pressure of the shears on her palm caused the trouble. When I saw her she had marked wasting of the first dorsal interosseus. Fortunately, I had seen an article on the subject, and could be reassuring, though not until recovery took place was her rather too-knowledgeable husband reassured.

PRESIDENTIAL ADDRESS

by

H. J. MALKIN, Esq.
M.D., F.R.C.S. (Ed.), F.R.C.O.G.

'THE HEALING ART'
(AN HISTORICAL SURVEY)

Delivered Wednesday, 14th October, 1959.

Ladies and Gentlemen,

That you have made me President of our Society this year is an honour of which I am deeply appreciative and, apart from this evening, I look forward to a programme that I hope will appeal to you. That this is an old and well-known society was brought home to me by the fact that there was no refusal by any invited speaker.

It is, I am afraid, on this occasion of the first meeting that you have to listen to a talk by myself instead of an address, I am proposing to make reference to some personalities who have a bearing on medicine.

In Ariege, in France. there is painted on the wall of a cave, a picture of a very early member of our profession, dressed in animal skins and made to look extremely ferocious. Even today, in the 20th century there are witch doctors who wear quills through their noses to produce the same effect. This fearsome appearance is presumably intended to strike awe into the heart of the patient and doubtless to make up to a large extent for lack of scientific knowledge. Perhaps the black coats and striped trousers used by past, and sometimes present-day, doctors are a symbol of the same idea!

The progress of medicine was roughly in three stages - the Pre-Dark Ages (up to A.D. 200), the Dark Ages (A.D. 200 to 1500), and the Renaissance to the present day (A.D. 1500 onwards).

In the Pre-Dark Ages, the first physician was Imhotep in 2000 B.C., who built the first Pyramid. He is often associated with Aesculapius, who, at the siege of Troy, was so successful in treating the wounded that he was deified. He was said to be the son of Apollo, and born on Mount Olympus, but his medical successes upset Pluto, who complained that Hell was becoming depopulated, and Jupiter, upholding the complaint, killed the offender with a thunderbolt. Hygeia (whose name is familiar today) was the daughter of Aesculapius. He had started the Aesculapian cult for healing, and 300 temples were built in his name and used as hospitals; their sign was the serpent, the touch of whose tongue healed. This is now included in the badges of many organisations, including the Royal College of Obstetricians and Gynaccologists, where it can be seen twined around his staff.

In Greece, at Delphi, the palace of the Oracle, is the Temple of Apollo, and inside one may see the actual spot where the Pythia or Pythoness (a girl or women selected by the priests as the mouthpiece of the Oracle) sat over a crevice which excuded intoxicating fumes. These fumes sent her into a trance during which she made her utterances. These were translated by the priests, who were very much the wise men of the day, and the translations were so carefully worded that the hearers were satisfied and the priests uncommitted! Kings, statesmen and great leaders, besides more ordinary folk, came from far and wide to hear wisdom, and gain advice, both medical and otherwise, from the voice of the Oracle. One such visitor was Croesus, who came especially to ask whether it would be wise to involve himself in a certain war. The Oracle replied that "in the case of such a war, a great nation shall fall." Croesus went off quiet happy with this verdict. There *was* a war - a great nation *did* fall - but it was that of Croesus, and the Oracle had spoken truly!

Also in Greece, at the temple of Epidaurius, a great deal of healing was done, and I am reminded here of the story of Clio. She was a young woman, who having had no children, went to the Temple to ask that this might be remedied. She duly became pregnant, and grew larger and larger, until, after nearly five years had gone by, and she had not yet come into labour, she returned to the Temple to ask why this was so. She was told hat her wish had been to become pregnant, and this was granted, but she had never mentioned anything about being delivered. However, she was them permitted to come into labour and was delivered a son aged about four-and-a-half years, who took her by the hand and led her home!

Even in those days statistics were of some importance, and in order to keep figures of patient survival satisfactory, all the sick who were unlikely to recover were turned out into the hills to die. (On the island of Delos neither births nor deaths were allowed, and all women nearing confinement, and all aged and sick approaching death, were sent away). The Temple at Epidaurus has been destroyed, but the Greek Theatre, with its round orchestra or stage and perfect acoustics, still remains. It seats about 15,000 people at the Festival each year, and from a seat at the top one can distinctly hear the slightest noise - such as someone breathing - down in the orchestra.

The first medical school was at Cos, and there, about 400 years before the birth of Christ, we find Hippocrates - the Father of Medicine. He has been described, and I think very aptly, as a close member, a humane scholar and the first sound clinician. He recognised the difference between acute and chronic illness, and it was he who said "To know is one thing - to believe one knows, another." The Oath which bears his name is, in fact, the background of a good deal of our medical ethics of today.

Another great man to whom I must refer was as interested in healing bodies as in saving souls. Some sixty years after the birth of Christ, Paul of Tarsus, moving from place to place, preached to the people and told them that he knew the name of the Unknown God many of them had been worshipping. In Athens, near the Acropolis, and in view of the ancient Parthenon and the Temple of the Wingless Victory, one can see the spot from which he preached. He preached in Corinth, too. When a prisoner on the way to Rome, and travelling in the same ship as St. Luke, he was shipwrecked and landed on what was afterwards known as St. Paul's Island, where he and St. Luke gained a great reputation for healing, owing to their success in treating the Govenor of the island, who was suffering from enteric fever. Eventually, after continuing the journey through the Straits of Messina and passing between Scylla and Charybdis, Paul reached Rome for his trial. Later, when condemned to death, his judges discovered that although a Jew, he was also a Roman citizen, and therefore his execution must be by beheading and not by crucifixion as in the case of Peter.

The next great character connected with medicine was Soranus (A.D. 60). Born at Ephesus, and later going to Rome, he was the first specialist in obstetrics and gynaecology, and it was he who wrote the textbook *De Morbis Mulierum,* and it was he who taught version for obstructed labour - and that 1,900 years ago.

Galen, who lived about seventy years later, was medical officer to the gladiators. With him there was "No phenomenon without a name, and no problem without a solution." He developed the fire, air, water and earth theory - fire was hot, air was dry, water was wet and earth was cold, and disease, according to him, was due to the balance of these four being disturbed. He was full of dogmas and he wrote prolifically, but all his theory and knowledge was based on animal dissection. (Incidently, 400 years before this, Theophilus, in the name of Alexander the Great, *vivisected* 600 criminals!)

The Dark Age was about to begin and Galen's teaching lasted for nearly 4,000 years - until the Renaissance. This was unfortunate as he was utterly lacking in sound judgement and his teaching lacked it too, and the only real advance from A.D. 130 to 1500 was the building of hospitals. During the Crusades, between 1095 and 1271 (there were eight Crusades during this time) the Knights Hospitallers founded the hospitals in Europe and the Holy Land and cared for sick and wounded Crusaders. It is interesting that the Saracens already *had* hospitals and were considerably more advanced than the Crusaders, and they practised conservative surgery with great success, thereby saving many lives. Earlier (in A.D. 830) the Hotel Dieu had been founded in Paris. This was, it is true, a hospital - a building which could house the sick, but I will quote here an extract which refers to it.

"There were 1,200 beds. In one bed of moderate size lay four, five or six persons besides each other, the feet of one to the head of another; children besides grey-haired old men; indeed men and women intermingled together. In the same bed lay individuals affected with infectious diseases beside others only slightly unwell; on the same couch, body against body, a woman groaned in the pangs of labour, a nursing infant writhed in convulsions, a typhus patient burned in the delirium of fever, a consumptive coughed his hollow cough, and a victim of some disease of the skin tore with his nails his infernally itching integument. The whole building swarmed with vermin, and the air was so vile in the sick wards that attendants entered them with a sponge soaked in vinegar held before their faces. The bodies of the dead usually lay twenty-four hours or longer on the death-bed before they were removed, and during this time the sick were compelled to share the bed with the rigid corpse."

During the Dark Ages medicine and obstetrics were crude in the extreme. Women in labour were bounced up and down to encourage delivery or held head downwards and shaken, or frightened by burning faggots placed beneath them. In an era when superstitious beliefs and practices flourished it was perhaps not surprising that an ailment might be considered to come from an evil spirit within, and there are many pictures of devils being cast out - usually from the patient's mouth.

An event of particular interest took place in 1500. This was the first successful caesarean section in which the mother and baby both lived, and was performed not by a member of the medical profession but by a Swiss peasant on his wife, after the failure of the 'lithotomists'. There were no sutures, and the patient subsequently delivered herself twins, and later of four other children, she herself living to the age of seventy-seven. (Recently, doubts have been raised as to whether this operation had, or had not been on a uterine pregnancy, as a secondary abdominal pregnancy could account for the successful outcome and the subsequent live births.)

The Renaissance, which we have now reached, is the beginning of the third stage of medicine. The first doctor of repute was Ambroise Pare' in 1510, who was a Frenchman, and his contribution to medicine was of enormous value. He re-introduced ligatures to control bleeding, and he revived a similar version for minor degrees of contracted pelvis, a manoeuvre which, in fact, saved the life of his own daughter during her confinement. He also stopped the practice of cauterising the wounds, and the story of this, whilst he was an army surgeon, is well known. During one night he realised that he had forgotten to cauterise one of the wounded he treated the day before. His anxiety about his patient, and one may imagine his amazement when he found that the man with only the simple dressing was a great deal fitter than those who had their wounds cauterised. Pare' was one of the few who had survived the massacre of St. Bartholomew's Eve, because the King of France felt him invaluable, and said "it was not reasonable that I should die."

A compatriot of Pare', a Hugenot too, named William Chamberlen, also escaped the massacre by fleeing with his family to England. The Chamberlen family consisted of five, of which two, both for some reason named Peter, were Doctors. Both were interested in Obstetrics, and Peter the Elder became physician to James 1st of England and his queen, Anne of Denmark. It was probably Peter the Elder, too, who invented the obstetric forceps - a secret which was kept in the Chamberlain family for three generations. One member of the third generation was Hugh, whose claims for the obstetric forceps were very much exaggerated, and on this point the French surgeons, Mauriceau (to whom the family secret had been offered for the equivalent of about £2,000) took him up. Mauriceau had in labour at that time a rachitic dwarf, with the head above the brim. He felt that if *she* could be delivered by Chamberlain, then Chamberlain must have something worthwhile selling. Hugh boasted that fifteen minutes would be enough for his secret to do its work, but after working solidly for three hours, he admitted defeat; the patient died of a ruptured uterus the next day. Mauriceau's especial skill was his excellence at breech deliveries, and his method of dealing with the after-coming head is still practised at present time.

The 17th century saw the beginning of science as we know it, when William Harvey (physician to Charles 1) discovered circulation. Having found that two ounces of blood flowed from the heart with each beat he did some calculations and realised that this added up to nearly six tons a day. Obviously this enormous quantity of blood had to go somewhere, and he came to the conclusion that it circulated back again; in other words, the heart was just a pump.

The first transfusion was from animal to man; man to man came later, but there were a great many fatalities. These were considerably reduced by the discovery by Lansteiner in 1900, of blood groups, and improved on still by the discovery of the Rhesus factor in 1940.

To go back to the personalities of the 17th century, we must remember William Smellie, whose knowledge of the physiology, mechanics and pathology of obstetrics was detailed and accurate. He trained 900 students, each of whom had to pay 6/- for the support of the "Poor labouring women," and from 5/- to 10/- for each case which they personally attended. It is said by some that Smellie was a little slow on the uptake. I would doubt it. On one occasion when he was delivering a patient under the bedclothes (as was the custom in those days) he accidentally divided the cord on the wrong side of the ligature, the result being a fair haemorrhage before the bleeding end could be tied again. He solemnly explained to the midwife that this was his own method of "preventing convulsions"! He was certainly a great obstetrician and a great teacher.

In the 18th century we have William and John Hunter, to whom we owe amongst other things our knowledge of the foetal and placental circulation. William, in contrast to Smellie, with whom he quarrelled, was an advocate of masterly inactivity and enjoyed showing his forceps, rusty with disuse, and remarking that "it is a thousand pities they have been invented, for where they save one they murder twenty." He was *extremely* conservative, and it is likely that his influence on Crofts (who was accoucheur to the Princess Charlotte) may well have been responsible for the decision for non-interference, which was followed by the death of first child, then mother.

Bartholomew Mosse, who founded in Dublin the fifteen-roomed house for "Poor lying-in Women," the beginning of the world famous Rotunda Hospital, was followed by Fielding Ould. He it was who advocated episiotomy for delay due to a rigid perineum, and whose knighthood gave rise to the verse.

> "Sir Fielding Ould is made a Knight,
> He should have been a Lord by right,
> For then each Lady's prayer would be
> O Lord, Good Lord, Deliver me."

In this same century the contagious aspect of infection was recognised first by Burton in 1751, and then by John Leake, and the first treatise was by Alexander Gordon of Aberdeen in 1795. He showed the transmissability of disease and the need to disinfect both doctor and nurse. He had based his theory on seventy-seven cases and, with *no* knowledge of organisms, said that "Every person who comes into contact with a patient with puerperal fever becomes charged with an atmosphere of infection, which can be communicated to every pregnant patient whom he treats."

The 19th century produced men who supplied theories and practices which were of vast importance to the medical profession and to the patient. Charles White of Manchester, who so strongly recommended fresh air and cleanliness in the treatment of illness; Oliver Wendell Holmes, and Ignaz Semmelweiss, the Hungarian who qualified in Vienna and was so struck by the difference in the death-rate in the wards attended by students, and those attended by midwives. In the students' end of his hospital the death-rate was one in eight confinements, and the midwives' end one in twenty-five. The death of his pathologist friend from septicaemia, following a prick with a knife during a post-mortem, caused Semmelweiss to appreciate a possible source of infection, and he surprised and shocked his students by insisting that they wash in a solution of chloride of lime before touching any patient. In three years the death-rate fell to one in eighty. So likely had death following confinement been part of this hospital, that the patients themselves had realised their danger and begged not to be sent into the wards run by students. The whole setting must have been depressing in the extreme. The lay-out was such that, to reach a patient in that part of the building where the death-rate was highest the priests arrayed in their robes, and with an attendant walking before them ringing a bell, had to pass through five wards first, and the constant deaths, necessitating constant processions, must have been disturbing.

A useful discovery by Laennec was the value of the stethoscope to help in diagnosis - and also keep the doctor away from the verminous bodies - the collecting of vermin from their patients was one of the occupational hazards of the doctors of that time.

Dr. Morton of Massachussetts discovered ether in 1846, and the first operation under it in England was at University College Hospital, performed by Liston, when Lister was still a young man. A year later Simpson discovered chloroform, to which a good deal of publicity was given, and interest in it was enthusiastic. At a dinner party Simpson and some of his friends tried out this new anaesthetic, until gradually, one by one, the guests slid to the floor, or slipped under the table, though one young lady, who was also trying out the new discovery, ran around waving her arms and shouting "I'm an Angel - I'm an Angel" before she, too, collapsed.

Joseph Lister's introduction of antiseptics in 1851 almost eliminated death from the compound fracture, and medicine was by now advancing steadily. Germs were demonstrated by Myerhofer, and then, in 1897, came Pasteur, with his demonstration of haemolytic streptococci, and his use of vaccines. Lawson Tait of Birmingham introduced asepsis, Rontgen in 1895 discovered X-Ray and three years later Marie Curie showed us the value of radium.

Nowadays it is difficult to appreciate that there was no real nursing in this country until Florence Nightingale, who had trained as a nurse in Germany, began her care of the sick and wounded during the Crimean War. The hospital where she and her friends carried out their great and valuable work was at one time called Scutari, on the opposite side of the Bosphorus from Constantinople.

Having now come through the ages to the present day I would like to mention two medical centres in Yugo-Slavia which I visited last summer. Zagreb, the capital of Croatia, had in one hospital an exceedingly efficiently run obstetric and gynaecological department, and whilst I was in Zagreb, I visited their gynaecological clinic, and also spent some time watching their operating sessions, and was most impressed, not only by the work, but by the attitude to obstetrics and gynaecology. It was amusing to find in the maternity block, the patients, together with the doctors and nurses, were locked in, because, the Communist country thought it may be, the visitors are extremely difficult to control, and if entry were possible, would come and go at will. Each time one of the staff wished to enter or leave the department he had to wait to be let in or out by someone with a key to the main entrance, and when visiting time *did* come, and the doors were unlocked, it was the *patients* who rushed out to see the visitors.

At Zadar too, a lovely old former Italian town on the coast, I found again an attitude to obstetrics very similar to our own, and the members of the medical profession I had the good fortune to meet were, without exception, extremely interested in our methods in this country. What was disconcerting the doctors while I was there, was that they had just been told that in October *all* private practice would cease. This would mean a drop in income at the top level from about £3,000 a year to just under £1,000. Another point which I thought interesting was their method of dealing with medical cover for villages. Apparently it is quite easy to find doctors for town practices, but the only way of enticing them to the country ones is to pay them at a higher rate, and in fact, allow them to take in several villages, so that their total earnings might well exceed that obtainable in a town by a very considerable amount.

In the Pre-Dark Ages these islands in which we live knew little of medicine. During the dark ages themselves, our people joined other European countries in forgetting and ignoring what had already been discovered by great personalities of the past, and allowing prejudice and superstition to control what little knowledge of medicine was remembered, but since the Renaissance we have all moved ahead, slowly at first, and then more rapidly, until the beginning of the application of science to medicine in the 17th century produced more and more great men, and the 18th and 19th centuries brought discoveries and knowledge to the profession, for much of the time the world owes its gratitude to the British Isles. It is earnestly to be hoped that whatever the geographical, radical and political boundaries and distinctions, the great men of science and medicine will continue to share and improve their knowledge and skill, to the benefit of the whole world; fortunately there is strong evidence that this hope is being fulfilled.

PRESIDENTIAL ADDRESS

By

Mr. E. J. GILROY GLASS

Delivered on 3rd October, 1962.

"Cancer of the Larynx"

Ladies and Gentlemen,

I feel deeply honoured that you should have invited me to be your President for this session of our Society.

Within a few weeks of my coming to Nottingham as a locum House Surgeon in 1925 I had the privilege of assisting the late Alexander Tweedie with the first laryngectomy performed in Nottingham. In those days laryngectomies were few and far between, and we had no idea of the rehabilitation of the laryngectomised patient. Our primary thought was could we save his life. This man, who was a bookmaker, developed of his own initiative such a phenomenal pharyngeal that he returned to the race course and was capable of shouting the odds.

He lived for seven years after his laryngectomy, and died from a second primary in the oesophagus. During those years his voice always fascinated me. From this rose my primary interest in cancer of the larynx, and it is perhaps not inappropriate that this should be the subject of my presidential address tonight.

Cancer of the larynx is not a common disease, but it has a clinical and historical importance which far exceeds its morbidity rate. It is in this situation that we can study malignant disease at a very early stage, can at times watch its development from pre-malignant condition, and can readily watch the progress of cure, in a way that is rarely possible elsewhere in the body. From an historical standpoint it may be that over-caution in the diagnosis was a contradictory factor in the catastrophy of the two world wars.

Laryngeal cancer was first recognised as an entity as far back as 100 A.D. when the condition was described by Auretius, and Galen about a hundred years later described what was obviously a malignant larynx, but it was not until the middle of the last century that anyone had ever seen the living functional larynx. Those who had seen laryngeal cancer had done so in the post-mortem room, except for a few who had attempted exploratory operations.

The credit of first examining the living human larynx goes not to a laryngologist but to a hitherto obscure teacher of singing. In 1848 a half forgotten revolution swept over Europe and drove King Louis Phillipe from the throne of France. Among those who followed the King to this country was a Spanish teacher of singing, Manoel Garcia, and he continued to teach in London. He had always been interested in the production of the registers of the human voice and particularly falsetto. It was realised that these were manifestations of laryngeal function, but at that time nobody had been able to see the larynx and the theories were but conjecture.

Returning to Paris on holiday in 1854, Garcia observed the flashing of the sun on the windows of the Palais Royale, and the idea came to him that if he could direct the sunlight on to his larynx he might achieve his desire of knowing how the larynx functioned.

We have a record of Garcia's own description of his discovery in the Transactions of the International Congress of Medicine in 1881. I quote:- "Preoccupied with the ever recurring wish, so often repressed an unrealisable, suddenly I saw the two mirrors of the laryngoscope in the respective positions, as if actually present before my eyes. I went straight to Charriere, the instrument maker, asked him if he happened to have a small mirror with a long handle. I was informed that he had a little dentist's mirror which had been one of the failures of the London Exhibition in 1851. I bought it for six francs. Having also obtained a hand mirror, I returned home at once very impatient to begin my experiments. I placed against the uvula the little mirror which I had heated in warm water and carefully dried and then, flashing upon its surface with the hand mirror a ray of sunlight, I saw at once, to my great joy, the glottis wide open before me, and so fully exposed that I could perceive a portion of the trachea. When my excitement and subsided, I began to examine what was passing before my eyes, the manner in which the glottis opened and shut, and moved in the act of phonation. It filled me with wonder."

It is not given to everyone to achieve fame in their lifetime, and by what was little more than an accident, but it is pleasant to relate that Garcia, who died in London at the age of 102, lived to be recognised as the father of laryngology. On his hundredth birthday he was awarded the Royal Victorian Order, the Spanish Royal Order of Alfonso, and the German Gold Medal for Science previously awarded on only four occasions. It is recorded that the old man wondered what all the fuss was about. He never meant to become the founder of a new medical speciality, and he protested that the mirror had only cost him six francs.

Garcia's discovery was first put to the clinical use by Turke of Vienna, a neurologist, but, using sunlight, he described it as an impracticable method. Czermack of Budapest improved on the method by using a concave mirror held in his teeth and reflecting artificial light, the forerunner of the forehead mirror of today. Thus laryngoscopy became a practical method.

It was, however, a British Laryngologist who probably did more to develop the speciality than anyone else. While studying in Vienna and Budapest Morell McKenzie saw Turke and Czermack conducting their primitive laryngoscopies and foresaw the possibilities. Returning to London, he set up practice as a laryngologist and established the Throat Hospital in Golden Square, and was later the founder of the Journal of Laryngology. In 1870 he published an epoch-making book: "Growths of the Larynx," with reports and analysis of 100 consecutive cases of his own. When it was remembered that at that time local anaesthetics had not been discovered, one can realise the wonderful technique which this man must have developed, as all his examinations and biopsies were done without anaesthesia of any kind, and by indirect method.

Unfortunately it was this very facility of being able to take biopsies by the indirect method that was to prove his downfall.

In 1887 he was called upon to attend the Crown Prince Frederick, later the German Emperor III who was believed by his German medical advisers to have cancer of the larynx. McKenzie examined him, and, whilst he did not deny that the condition might be cancer, insisted that there must be a positive biopsy before recommending what was then a serious surgical hazard.

Three biopsies were taken and examined by a Berlin pathologist. All were negative. From what we know today, it is likely that the condition at that time was one of these conditions which we now recognise as pre malignant. It was probably Keratosis or at most Carcinoma-in-situ.

In a matter of months the diagnosis was no longer in doubt, but by that time it was too late to do more than a tracheotomy, and the Royal patient died after having reigned for only 99 days.

It is interesting to surmise what might have happened had the diagnosis been made at a time when laryngofissure was possible and had the royal patient survived what was then a hazardous operation. He was known to have very liberal views, and there is no doubt he would have built up a liberal Germany friendly to this country, rather than the reactionary and antagonistic Germany, succeeded. Two world wars with all their evil consequences might never have happened.

After the Emperor's death McKenzie was violently attacked in England and in Germany as having been responsible for his death. The German press accused him of malpractice and bad faith, and even went so far as to suggest that Queen Victoria had influenced him to make a negative diagnosis. McKenzie attempted to defend himself in a book, but his defence was ill natured and possibly ill-timed and met with unfavourable criticism. He was censured by the Royal College of Surgeons and the British Medical Association and was forced to resign from the Royal College of Physicians. So ended in frustration and disappointment a career which began so brilliantly and to which we today owe so much. Not for him the plaudits which went to Manoel Garcia.

Despite, however, the fall of McKenzie, he probably influenced the practice of laryngology more than any other before or since, for his two volume text book "Diseases of the Throat and Nose" published in 1880 and 1884 remain to this day the basis of all laryngological literature in the

English language - a work which Sir St. Clair Thompson referred to as the Laryngologist's Bible.

While the method of indirect laryngoscopy is still the routine diagnostic procedure, it has been superseded as an operative procedure by the method of direct laryngoscopy. In 1896 Killian introduced the first direct laryngoscope with proximal lighting, whilst in America similar instruments with distal lighting were being developed by Chevalier Jackson, who published the first text book of endoscopy in 1907.

It may be of interest to you that one of Sir Morell McKenzie's mirrors is on display in the Ear, Nose and Throat Department of the General Hospital, and one of Chevalier Jackson's oesophagoscopes made in 1907 was in use there within the last ten years and is indeed still in useable condition.

The surgical treatment of laryngeal cancer was attempted before it was possible to examine the larynx. The operations were necessarily of an exploratory nature. The first record we have of such an operation is about a hundred and thirty years ago, but the first successful laryngofissure was in 1833 when Bauers of Louvain cut through the thyroid cartilage of a man aged forty and "repeatedly cauterized the warty growths occupying it." There is no proof that this was cancer but it is recorded that the patient lived for twenty years.

The first laryngofissure for known intrinsic cancer was performed by Gordon Buck in America in 1851. The operation was done without anaesthesia with the patient sitting up, and one cannot but admire the fortitude of the patient, if not the surgeon. She survived for fifteen months.

The first laryngofissure which by modern standards we should regard as a cure was an operation by Cohen in 1867 from which the patient survived for twenty years.

Despite occasional successes the early results from laryngofissure were disheartening, possibly from poor selection of cases, and it was only at the turn of the century that it became a standard operation.

Probably the first successful total laryngectomy was performed by Billroth in 1875 for a sarcoma of the larynx. This man was known to be in good health three years later.

The operative risk in those days was formidable, but there was nothing else to offer and the attempts continued, with increasing success, till in 1899 Gluck was able to report the recovery of twenty three out of twenty six consecutive cases.

By the early part of this century these procedures were beginning to become standard operations, largely due to the pioneering work of Sir St. Clair Thompson and Lionel College whose results are probably unsurpassed even today, and whose book "Cancer of the Larynx" published in 1930 is still a standard text book on the operative treatment of laryngeal cancer.

Barely forty years ago radioactive substances were used for the first time in the struggle against laryngeal cancer, and in 1929 the radium bomb was used for the first time in this country.

In the years immediately preceding the war the operations of laryngofissure and laryngectomy were standard procedures but the operative risk was still high, for we still awaited the advances in anaesthesia and the control of sepsis which have made the operations relatively safe today. Radium was beginning to claim its successes, particularly the implant method of Finzi and Harmer, but irradiation methods still tagged a long way behind and surgery in one of its forms offered far the best hope of cure.

Since the war there have been enormous advances in radiotherapy technique and equipment, and now the possibilities of irradiation have to be considered in virtually every case. Not all cases are, however, suitable. We are really in the years of reappraisal to decide where our best results are to be obtained. It is our custom here that every patient is seen by both a radiotherapist and ourselves before treatment is advised.

The emphasis has subtly changed from cure, if indeed cure be possible, to the best way of rehabilitating the patient; to assessing the best means of curing the patient with the least interference with the resumption of normal or near normal life.

In the classification of carcinoma of the larynx it is customary to divide the larynx into three areas, the true glottis, the region of the vocal cords, the supra-glottis, comprising the ventricle the ventricular bands with the epiglottis, and the sub-glottis, that part below the vocal cords. Though separated by millimetres only the problem in each of these areas is quite distant.

The commonest site of origin of laryngeal cancer is the vocal cord, the true glottis or intrinsic growth. It is difficult to give exact figures as many of the growths have spread beyond the confines of the true glottis when first seen, and determination of the exact site of origin is surmise only. Figures would, however, suggest that something like two out of every three cases begin in the vocal cords.

It is indeed fortunate that this is so, as the intrinsic area is the most hopeful from every point of view. Anatomically it is a closed lymphatic area therefore metastases are late; clinically the dominant symptom occurs early, so that our attention is drawn to the lesion at a very early stage in the disease.

Predominantly it is a disease of males in a ratio of 10-1. Although occasionally seen in the twenties, it is rare before the age of forty. Hoarseness is generally the only symptom, and it is desirable that any patient who has been hoarse for three weeks or over should have a laryngoscopy done. It is because of this characteristic symptom that we frequently see those cases before malignant changes have occurred, whilst still a keratosis, the only equivalent of leukoplakia. Such cases are a problem, a high proportion become malignant without change of symptom; they are not amenable to irradiation, and the majority do not merit surgery. Meticulous observation, possibly for years, is the only safe course. For this reason we now register keratosis as though it were already malignant and conduct the same follow up routine.

So long as a carcinoma is confined to one vocal without fixation it is amenable to almost any form of rational treatment with about a ninety per cent chance of cure. Laryngofissure is possibly a little more certain than irradiation, but it means permanent voice impairment and is in general reserved for the failures of irradiation.

In the sub-glottic group, the outlook is not so hopeful. Growths in this area tend to be radio resistant; there is a tendency towards lymphatic and sub-mucosal spread down the trachea, so that undetected mediastinal glands occur early, and the symptomatology is so slight that we rarely see these patients early. It is only when the growth is so large that it begins to re-strict the airway, or has spread up to involve the vocal cord producing hoarseness, that the patient has any indication that something is amiss; by then it may be too late. In such cases the advice is generally a laryngec-tomy, but infrequently followed by a course of irradiation, but, try as we will, the prognosis is very doubtful.

Nor is the prospect so good in the supra-glottic group, or in those which by spread have become supra-glottic. Here there is an abundant lymph drainage, so that metastasis may occur early, and again the symptoms may be slight. It is not easy to detect these cases by symptoms alone, from Globus Hystericus which is only too frequent these days. There is one symptom which I always regard as ominous - pain in the ear. Pain in the ear associated with Globus symptoms can be functional, but, in my expe-rience, it rarely is.

Any unexplained pain in the ear with normal hearing occurring in the middle or advanced life merits investigation. My patients seem to have no throat symptoms whatever, and we do not infrequently see extensive extrinsic growth where the presenting sign is a metastatic gland.

This group gives us our greatest problem in advising the correct line of treatment. Each patient is an individual problem and there are no hard and fast rules which one can lay down as to which case would be better treated by surgery, or which by irradiation. In general the more extensive the growth the less the prospect for radiotherapy, but again there are advanced cases where surgery is impracticable, where radiotherapy can be of help. Where fixation has occurred, surgery, if practicable is virtually the only hope.

In some centres the view is taken that in supra-glottic cases irradiation should be tried first and laryngectomy reserved for the failures. A survey which Dr. Fraser and I are conducting at this moment does not support this view. Radiotherapy cannot be regarded as a relatively innocuous procedure which can be used with impunity, and if it fails will permit another chance. Second chances may succeed, but they are rarely as good as the first.

Our policy here is that there must be a joint consultation between the radiotherapist and laryngologist and a frank exchange of views. If we deem there too be a reasonable chance of successful curative treatment by radiotherapy, it has preference, but if there be doubt, reasonable doubt, and a better prospect for surgery, we advise operation.

We rarely had reason to regret a primary laryngectomy, but we have on many occasions regretted trying irradiation first when we were in doubt or where the patient, against advice, had insisted on this.

The disability which arises from laryngectomy is surprisingly little when one considers that for a time it involves loss of the power of speech. With careful rehabilitation it is possible to teach the great majority of patients to develop a very useful voice using the muscles of the pharynx and upper oesophagus. The vast majority can return to their former occupations even when this necessitates a lot of talking. To quote one of my own patients: "The only thing I cannot do which I did before is swim. I do not consider that much of a price to pay for my life."

We regard this question of rehabilitation as of the utmost importance. The rehabilitation begins before the operation. Whenever time permits, and it nearly always does, the patient is visited by a laryngectomised patient with a good pharyngeal voice. It is surprising how the morale of the patient will improve after this visit. The visits continue throughout convalescence, and sometimes the relatives are also invited to help to restore their confidence. Such is the temperament of the laryngectomised, that we have no difficulty in getting volunteers for this visiting; we even get competition as to who is to be chosen, and sometimes several will visit.
After the operation there is a period of some week or ten days when feeding is by oesophageal tube. The unirradiated patient can generally swallow within the week, and heals by first intention, but there may be a delay after irradiation. As soon as possible the patient is taught to change his own tracheal tube and generally look after himself. Once he has achieved

for the first time any of the procedures which must become part of his life afterwards, the job is his - we no longer help him. At the earliest opportunity he is taken to a speech therapy class, and encouraged to make noises as best he can. No matter how rude the first attempts may sound they are encouraged, so that he becomes used to this noise and treats it as something to achieve rather than something to hide. Soon the belch becomes a word and he is on his way to speech.

As soon as possible we have him out of hospital, and whenever possible back to his old job. If the will to work is there the vast majority will be able to return to their former employment. Even hard manual work is not precluded. One of our patients returned to the coal face in just over six weeks - though in this case we did not encourage it - he went without our knowledge - and another who has now attended for over seven years tells me his work involves moving some forty tons of clay per day with a shovel, no mean task for a normal person.

In this address I have dipped into the past, and tried to give glimpse of the present; what then of the future? In just over a century we have progressed, at an increasing tempo, from a complete ignorance of laryngeal function and pathology, to a day when we talk, not of cure, but of rehabilitation. Within the period of my membership of this Society, from the first surgical adventure to a routine operation. Are we on the threshold of a new approach to the treatment of cancer? An age when the equipment of the radiotherapist will be relegated to the museum, when the surgeon's art will be no longer required to treat cancer, but only to repair its ravages.

The first light of that dawn is in the sky. Already chemotherapeutic measures are finding a place in the treatment of malignant disease; within recent years biochemists have determined the structure of deoxyribonucleic acid (D.N.A.), irregularities of which would seem to be the origin of malignant changes. These may well be the first steps in the control of this vile and relentless disease.

When the dawn breaks, and I believe it may not be far distant, it may be in the Larynx that we will be able to visualise our first successes, thanks to the ingenuity of an otherwise obscure teacher of singing.

ADDITIONAL INFORMATION

SIR HUMPHRY ROLLESTON, Bt

President of the Royal Society of Medicine
1918 - 1920

Humphry (Davy) Rolleston was born at Oxford on IJune 21st, 1862, the eldest son of George Rolleston, F.R.S., F.R.C.P., Linacre Professor of Physiology at Oxford, and his wife Grace (nee Davy) niece of Sir Humphry Davy, P.R.S., the renowned chemist. (Humphry Rolleston's brother, John Davy Rolleston (born, 1873) was also to become a distinguished physician.)

He was educated at Marlborough and at St. John's College, Cambridge where he was a scholar and took a double first in the Natural Sciences Tripos. He was trained at St. Bartholomew's Hospital, London and became a Physician to St. George's Hospital in 1898, returning in 1919. He succeeded Sir Clifford Allbutt *(1836-1925)* with whom he had collaborated in the monumental *System of Medicine,* as Regius Professor of Physic at Cambridge in 1925.

In addition to other scholarly works, often historical or biographical, and co-editing the classical *System of Medicine*, he was later in life general editor of Butterworth's British *Encyclopaedia of Medicine and Surgery* as well as being editor of *The Practitioner* for sixteen years (1928-1944). He was also editor of the *Practitioner Handbooks*.

He was in the founding of British radiology. He became familiar with X-rays during the Boer war, in which he served as Physician to the Imperial Yeomanry Hospital in Pretoria in 1900. He retained an interest in the method for the rest of his career, becoming President of the Rontgen Society in 1922/23 and inaugural President of the new amalgamated British Institute of Radiology in 1927/28. He was particularly concerned with the harmful effects of X-rays and the necessity of protection.

He was President of the Royal College of Physicians (1922-1926) during his Regius professorship at Cambridge and at the College was Goulstonain, Lumleian, Lloyd-Roberts and Fitzpatrick Lecturer, as well as Harveian Orator. One of the College lectures is now named after him - the Humphry

Davy Rolleston Lecture. He was Physician-in-ordinary to King George V from 1923 to 1932, and Physician Extraordinary from 1932 until the end of the reign. He was made KCB in 1919, a baronet in 1924. He was awarded fourteen honorary doctorates, an unprecedented achievement for that era.

Physically he was tall, thin and handsome, often displaying a wry smile. He was a person of great industry. As an editor he was meticulous and, as a man, humorous and unostentatious. His deep interest in the Royal Society of Medicine prompted [1] Sir John MacAlister to say "He is the only President to my knowledge who has used his official master key. The caretakers have told me how often they have been startled on Sundays and, sometimes late at night, by finding Sir Humphry going his rounds."

He died, aged eighty-two, at Martin's Haslemere, Surrey, his home after leaving Cambridge, on September 23, 1944. (After failing strength for some weeks, he collapsed in his bath and was severely scalded, from which he did not recover.)

Presidents of the Royal Society of Medicine. Pages 265/6/7. J.M.H.Moll.

---

[1] Sir John Young Walker MacAlister (1856-1925), Resident Librarian and Principle Officer of the Royal Society of Medicine. Appointed in 1887.

ROBERT JONES
1858 - 1933

Born 28 June, 1858 at Rhyle, North Wales father journalist. Educated Sydenham College London, and Liverpool School of Medicine. L.R.C.S. Edinburgh 1978; F.R.C.S. Edinburgh 1889; Ch.M. Liverpool 1909; F.R.C.S. England (by Election) 1918. In practice with his uncle H. O. Thomas, 1878. Honorary assistant surgeon, Stanley Hospital, Liverpool 1881. Surgeon to the Manchester Ship Canal, 1888. Honorary Surgeon, Royal Southern Hospital, Liverpool 1889. Surgeon to the Baschurch Home 1903. President of the orthopaedic section, International Congress of Medicine 1913. First world war: Captain in the Royal Army Medical Corps 1914; Inspector of Military orthopaedic centre at Shepherd's Bush, London. Advisor to the Ministry of Pensions. Honorary Surgeon, Shropshire Orthopaedic Hospital, Oswestry; St. Thomas's Hospital, London; Royal National Orthopaedic Hospital, London; and many other hospitals throughout the United Kingdom. President of the British Orthopaedic Association 1920 to 1925, then life president emeritus. Honorary doctorates University of Wales, Harvard, Smith's College (U.S.), Aberdeen, Yale, and McGill Universities. Honorary fellow, Royal College of Surgeons of Ireland and American College of Surgeons. Deputy Lieutenant, County of Lancaster. C.B. 1917; Knight Bachelor 1917; K.B.E. 1919; Baronet 1926. Sir Robert died on 14 January, 1933 aged 74 years.

History of the British Orthopaedic
Association.
By W. Waugh, 1993. Page 46.

GATHORNE ROBERT GIRDLESTONE
1881 - 1950

Born 8 October, 1881 in Oxford; father, Canon of Christchurch, Oxford. Educated at Charterhouse; New College, Oxford; St. Thomas's Hospital Medical School B.A. Oxford 1904; M.R.C.S., L.R.C.P., 1908; M.A., B.M., B.Ch, 1908; F.R.C.S. England 1911; D.M. 1945. General Practice in Oswestry after appointments at St. Thomas's Hospital. First world war: Royal Army Medical Corps; Wingfield Hospital, Oxford 1915 to 1919. Surgeon-in-charge. Wingfield-Morris Orthopaedic Hospital 1919. Consulting orthopaedic surgeon to the Radcliffe Infirmary and other hospitals in the Oxford area. Nuffield Professor of Orthopaedic Surgery, Oxford 1937 to 1940. Second world war, orthopaedic consultant to the Army, Emergency Medical Service, Ministry of Pensions 1940. President, orthopaedic section of the Royal Society of Medicine 1932 to 1933. President of the British Orthopaedic Association 1942 to 1943. Died 30 December, 1950 aged 69 years.

**History of the British Orthopaedic Association.
By W. Waugh, 1993. Page 161.**

HERBERT JOHN SEDDON
1903 - 1977

Born 13 July, 1903 in Derby; father worked for Union Cold Storage Company. Educated at the William Hulme Grammar School, Manchester; Oxford University; and St. Bartholomew's Hospital Medical College. M.R.C.S., L.R.C.P. 1925; M.B., B.S., London 1928 (Gold Medal); F.R.C.S. England 1928; D.M. Oxford 1940 House Surgeon at St. Bartholomew's Hospital. Instructor in Surgery, University of Michigan, Ann Arbor 1930. Resident Surgeon, Royal National Orthopaedic Hospital 1931. Nuffield professor of orthopaedic surgery, Oxford 1940. Clinical Director, Institute of Orthopaedics, London 1948 to 1967. President of the Orthopaedic section, Royal Society of Medicine 1948 to 1949. President of the British Orthopaedic Association 1960 to 1961. Companion of the Most Distinguished Order of St. Michael and St. George 1951; Knight Bachelor 1964; Hon LLD Glasgow 1965. Officer of the Order of the Cedar of Lebanon 1966. Hunterian lecture 1935. Robert Jones lecture 1960. Died 21 December, 1977 aged 74 years.

History of the British Orthopaedic Association.
By W. Waugh, 1993. Page 265.

NORMAN LESLIE CAPENER
1898 - 1975

Born 4th May, 1898 at Hornsey (then in Middlesex); father, engineer. Educated at the City of London School and St. Bartholomew's Hospital Medical College. Commissioned in the Royal Marines and Royal Navy when a student 1917 to 1919. M.R.C.S., L.R.C.P. 1922; F.R.C.S., England 1924. Luther Holden research fellow, demonstrator in anatomy, assistant in the surgical professorial unit at St. Bartholomew's Hospital. Instructor in anatomy at University of Michigan, Ann Arbor 1926; later assistant professor (orthopaedics). Consultant orthopaedic surgeon, Princess Elizabeth Orthopaedic Hospital, Exeter 1931 to 1963; also Mount Gold Orthopaedic Hospital, Plymouth, the Royal Devon and Exeter Hospital and many other general hospitals in the south-west region. Second world war, consultant adviser in orthopaedics, Emergency Medical Service, south-west region. President, orthopaedic section, Royal Society of Medicine 1949 to 1950. President of the British Orthopaedic Association 1958 to 1959. Scientific director and chairman, Medical Commission on Accident Prevention 1964. C.B.E., 1966. Member of the Council of the Royal College of Surgeons of England 1961 to 1973; senior vice-president 1971 to 1973. Hunterian lecture 1941; Gold Medal of the College 1974. Died 30th March, 1975 aged 76 years.

History of the British Orthopaedic Association.
By W. Waugh, 1993. Page 257.

NAUGHTON DUNN
1884 - 1939

Born 22 November, 1884 in Aberdeen; father in boot and shoe business. Educated Aberdeen Grammar School and Aberdeen University. M.B., Ch.B., 1909. Senior House Officer, Scarborough. Resident Surgical Officer, Royal Southern Hospital, Liverpool. Private Assistant to Robert Jones in Liverpool. Assistant demonstrator in anatomy, University of Liverpool. Honorary House Surgeon, Birmingham and District Cripples' Union 1914. First World War: Royal Army Medical Corps 1915; in Mediterranean Expeditionary Force, invalided home; military orthopaedic centre, Shepherd's Bush 1916 to 1918. Director, military orthopaedic services in the Midlands 1918 to 1920. Honorary consulting orthopaedic surgeon to the Royal Orthopaedic and Spinal Hospital, Birmingham 1920, which became the Royal Cripples' Hospital; Shropshire Orthopaedic Hospital, Oswestry; Warwickshire Orthopaedic Hospital, Coleshill. Lecturer in orthopaedic surgery, University of Birmingham 1926. President of the orthopaedic section, Royal Society of Medicine 1928. President of the British Orthopaedic Association 1938 to 1939. Hon L.L.D., University of Aberdeen 1937. Died in hospital in Dolgelly, North Wales. on 18 November, 1939 aged 54 years.

History of the British Orthopaedic Association.
By W. Waugh. 1993. Page 119.

REGINALD CHEYNE ELMSLIE
1878 - 1940

Born 1878 in Bedford, son of Captain J. A. Elmslie R.N.R. Educated at Brighton Grammar School and St. Bartholomew's Hospital Medical College. M.R.C.S., L.R.C.P. 1901; M.B. 1902; M.S., F.R.C.S. England 1904. House Surgeon, demonstrator in pathology and surgical registrar, St. Bartholomew's Hospital 1912 to 1937. Assistant Surgeon to the Metropolitan Hospital. First World war: Captain Royal Army Medical Corps (Territorial) 1914; later, in charge of the military orthopaedic centre, Shepherd's Bush. Consulting Surgeon to the Ministry of Pensions at Queen Mary's Hospital, Roehampton. O.B.E. (military division). Surgeon, Royal National Orthopaedic Association 1930 to 1931. Member of the Council of the Royal College of Surgeons 1933. Died at Tuesley, near Godalming, 24 July, 1940 aged 62 years.

History of the British Orthopaedic Association
By W. Waugh, 1993. Page 87.

CHARLES GLOVER BARKLA

Charles Glover Barkla:- Born 7 June, 1877 in Widnes, Lancashire. Died 23 October, 1944 in Edinburgh.

Charles Glover Barkla was a physicist who was awarded the Nobel Prize for Physics in 1917 for his work on X-ray scattering, which occurs when X-rays pass through a material and are deflected by the atomic electrons. This technique proved to be particularly useful in the study of atomic structures.

Educated at Trinity and King's College Cambridge, he joined the faculty of Liverpool University in 1902, moved to the University of London in 1909, and became professor of Natural Philosophy at the University of Edinburgh in 1913. In 1906 Barkla along with C. A. Sadler used X-ray scattering to determine the number of electrons in the carbon atom. At about the same time he was able to polarize X-rays (select x-ray waves that vibrate in the same plane), thus demonstrating that X-rays are transverse waves and hence like other electromagnetic radiations, such as light.

Copyright 1994-1999 Encyclopaedia Britannica.